The World of Caves

The World of Caves

Anton Lübke

Translated from the German by
Michael Bullock

WEIDENFELD AND NICOLSON
7 CORK STREET LONDON W1

First published in Germany
under the title
GEHEIMNISSE DES UNTERIRDISCHEN
by Kurt Schroeder Verlag, Bonn
English translation © 1958
by George Weidenfeld and Nicolson Ltd.

PRINTED IN GREAT BRITAIN
SET IN 11 POINT BASKERVILLE
BY EBENEZER BAYLIS AND SON LTD
WORCESTER AND LONDON
N.6212

CONTENTS

CONTENTS

LIST OF ILLUSTRATIONS

All the illustrations are grouped after page 144

FOREWORD

✣

S INCE the earliest times, man has felt a tremendous urge to
explore the depths of the earth. He sought in these depths the
abode of mysterious powers, the gods of the underworld.
Later he battled with rocks, darkness and water, to wrest
from the bowels of the earth coal and valuable ores, and
brought them up into the light of day.

But man's interest was not confined to the mines and shafts
he dug himself in his quest for useful minerals and sources of
energy. His curiosity has always been equally aroused by the
clefts and chasms, caves and grottoes produced by the action
of natural forces unaided by human intervention.

It is with these natural cavities of the earth that this book
is principally concerned. The dramatic advances made in
exploring previously unknown caverns and their hidden
chambers and passages in France, Switzerland and Britain,
during 1952, gave an additional impetus to speleology, the
science of caves. Speleology came to the notice of people to
whom the very existence of this mysterious underground
world was virtually unknown, or at most thought of in terms
of the celebrated stalactite caves. But very few people were
acquainted with the fascinating and important discoveries
made by cavers, whose delight it was to risk life and limb
crawling into the clefts and crannies of the earth. The big
drums of publicity were not beaten for their efforts as they
were for the ascent of Mount Everest. The make-up of the
caver has something in common with the dark and silent
world of his activities: he is modest about what he has seen

9

and experienced in the depths of solitary caverns never before visited by humans.

Not until a caver descended fifteen hundred feet into the heart of the Pyrenees and met a dramatic end, while four equally audacious Swiss speleologists were marooned in a cave for ten days about the same time, did the world prick up its ears. If these cave explorations had passed without incident they would probably have been of local interest only, but the tragedies were so sensational that the world press wrote them up.

The journalists covered one aspect of speleology; it is an adventurous, exciting and dangerous sport. This book aims to show that cave exploration is also of scientific and historical interest. It aims, too, to interest the general reader in a subject which, despite its inherent fascination, has attracted only a handful of amateurs and scholars in the past.

The author has personally explored caves in Germany, Holland, Austria, India and China. For information about these caves and about others which he has not actually seen, he has made an intensive study of the published and unpublished material on the subject.

I

THE RIDDLE OF PREHISTORIC MAN

In 1856, a grammar school teacher named Fuhlrott made a strange discovery in a limestone cave of the Neanderthal, near Düsseldorf. The Neander Valley, which was named after Joachim Neander, a former Düsseldorf headmaster and author of sacred songs, would never have achieved the world renown it now enjoys if Dr. Fuhlrott had not found there a remarkable skeleton. This ravine, whose natural charm was destroyed during ensuing decades by extensive lime-quarrying (it was not declared a national nature reserve until 1921), became a nodal point of prehistoric research. In the spoil earth from the quarries Fuhlrott came upon the remains of what appeared to be an antediluvian man, which eventually captured the attention of the whole scientific world. Amongst the skeletal fragments was an abnormally large skull-cap with big eyebrow ridges and a low, receding forehead, which scientists—after similar skulls had come to light elsewhere— came to regard as characteristic of a prehistoric race of Man to which they gave the name *Homo neanderthalensis*.

'It was pure chance that these skeletal remains were preserved. The majority of the bones found in the cave—including the fragment of skull belonging to them, which later became so famous and is now preserved at Bonn—were rescued from the spoil earth piled up at the bottom of the ravine, and only those which came into my hands shortly afterwards were saved from destruction,' wrote Fuhlrott in the report issued at the time. He continues: 'Under these circumstances it is not surprising that, apart from the whole skull-cap and a considerable fragment of the pelvis, the major components of the limbs should have been the only parts of what may have been a perfectly preserved skeleton to be saved, and that the smaller bones—including the bones of the face and the vertebrae—passed unnoticed in their matrix of clay and were thrown away with the spoil earth.'

Since no tools or animal remains were found in direct association with the skeleton in the Neanderthal cave, it could not be assigned to a definite position in the Pleistocene Period. This, together with the fact that no other similar skull was known to have been found at that time, may have been responsible for the initial lack of interest in Fuhlrott's discovery. (In fact, the 'Gibraltar skull', now preserved in the museum of the Royal College of Surgeons, London, was discovered in 1848; but its true significance was not realized until sixty-two years later, when it was recognized as belonging to a member—probably a woman—of the Neanderthal race.)

The size of the Neanderthal skull must immediately have suggested a human origin, and should have been enough to gain it the closest attention from anatomists. But at the time of its discovery the idea of the existence of human life during the period of the supposed Diluvium or Deluge was rejected out of hand, and the concept of human evolution was regarded with profound distrust, indeed repudiated, by biological science.

In 1857, Dr. Fuhlrott delivered a lecture on his finds to the general assembly of the Natural History Society of the Prussian Rhineland and Westphalia. He met with little sympathy from his audience for his view that what he had discovered were the fossil remains of a prehistoric human being. He did not live to see his interpretation vindicated, for throughout his lifetime the doubts of the scientific world regarding the skeleton's Pleistocene date remained unshakable. No lesser authority than the famous anatomist Virchow gave it as his opinion that the skeleton belonged to a man of the present race, whose skeleton had undergone morbid deformation as the result of rickets. But Fuhlrott valued his find so highly that he turned down very favourable offers of purchase from Britain, where Huxley stated the skull to be truly human, but, at the same time, the most ape-like he had ever beheld—a judgment which later discoveries were to confirm. This archaeological treasure was thus preserved for German museums.

OLD BONES AND SCHOLARS

The skeleton from the Neanderthal cave was not the first of its kind. Other skeletons had been found before, which their finders ascribed to a prehistoric race. In 1618, the vicar of Neukirch, Bavaria, discovered in the Steinbach cavern several human skeletons, which the historian Ranke employed for his studies 270 years later; and in the 1770's another clergyman, Parson Esper of Uttersreuth, investigated fossil bones of men and animals found in Bavarian caves and declared them to be relics of a vanished primitive period of man's history. (See the chapter, 'Exploration and Science of Caves: The Classics of Speleology'.) But no skeletal find has stirred the scientific world like that of the Neanderthal skull.

The discovery in the Neanderthal cave spurred the quest for traces of primitive man, stimulated research into the beginnings of the human race, and created the notion of a prehistoric race of cave men. Thenceforth, scholars earnestly strove to solve the problem of whether man might have evolved from a lower being—the ape—by studying the extraordinary skulls and skeletons which came to light at various places. From the finds, they concluded that the

Neanderthal cave man must have been characterized by an almost chinless face, a large nose with a high bridge, very mobile and apparently very short arms, and small, human hands. Some anatomists have interpreted the combination of a long, low brain pan and a skeletal structure suggesting a semi-erect posture of the neck with a broad face, brow ridges and absence of chin as signs of transition from ape to man.

In the decades following the discovery in the Neanderthal cave, numerous skulls and skeletons have come to light all over the world; but in spite of much research, anthropologists have been unable to trace the 'missing link', the intermediate stage that would bridge the gap between ape and man. The following brief list of the more famous finds made, either in caves or in open country, during the last century will illustrate the great interest taken in the subject by the scientific world.

Apart from the Gibraltar skull found in 1848, other skulls of Neanderthaloid type were unearthed at La Naulette (1866) and at Spy, in Belgium (1886). In 1894, the Dutch army doctor Dubois, in the course of systematic digging on the Bengawan river near Trinil on the island of Java, exhumed the remains of semi-human skeletons which had evidently belonged to creatures of erect carriage. Since the skull suggested an ape man, while the thigh bones were human in character, the owner of this skeleton received the name *Pithecanthropus erectus*, the erect ape man. In 1899, a sensational find of various fragments representing perhaps a dozen individuals was made at Krapina in Croatia. The first decade of the twentieth century was marked by a series of remarkable discoveries at La Chapelle-aux-Saints (Corrèze) in 1908, La Ferrassie (Dordogne) in 1909, La Quina (Charente) in 1911, and at Ehringsdorf, near Weimar, in 1914.

The most momentous finds relating to the Neanderthal race were made in the south-west of France, where lime-

stone caves served prehistoric man as living quarters. Lartet
and Christie found several worked flints in a grotto of Le
Moustier in 1863. In 1908, the prehistorian, Otto Hauser
(born at Wadenswil near Zürich in 1874, later lived at
Weimar) unearthed, five feet below the floor of the lowest
cave at Le Moustier, a skeleton similar to that of the Neanderthal man, which was designated *Homo mousteriensis hauseri*,
while at Combe-Capelle (Dordogne) he exhumed another
skeleton known as *Homo aurignacensi hauseri*. (Dr. Otto Hauser
wrote a series of books on his discoveries: *Man 100,000 Years
Ago*, *The Early Evolution of Mankind*, *Primitive Fauna*, *The
Great Aboriginal Race of Central Europe*, *The Earliest History of
the World*.)

The Le Moustier find is described as follows by Sir Arthur
Keith in his book *The Antiquity of Man* (London, 1915).

The skeleton was that of a lad of perhaps sixteen years of age;
his canine teeth and third molars were not fully erupted; the
growth lines of the long bones were unclosed. There could be no
question: he had been deliberately buried. Near his right hand
was a hand-axe of the Acheulean culture, but typical instruments
of the Mousterian period were near by. Charred remains of the
ancient ox—the urus—were noted. The body had been laid on
its right side, with the face turned down, and a pillow of stones
placed under the head.

This skeleton was later sold by Dr. Hauser to the Museum of
Ethnology, Berlin, for the sum of 125,000 francs. After the
destruction of the museum during the Second World War,
the skeleton was buried beneath the debris. The skull was
seized by the Russians and removed to Russia. At the time of
writing, the rest of the skeleton lies unprotected beneath the
rubble.

On August 3rd, 1908, three French priests, the Abbés A.
and J. Bouyssonie and L. Bardon, discovered in a rock cave
at La Chapelle-aux-Saints, a few miles from Le Moustier,
the skeleton of a man of the same type. Together with the

well-preserved skull were the spine, the ribs, the bones of the hands and arms, and part of the leg. The skeleton was con-jectured to be that of a man of fifty to fifty-five years old, who, in the view of the finders, had been interred with some ceremony. 'Typical Mousterian chipped flint "points" and scrapers' were found near by.

In 1909, further Neanderthaloid skeletons were discovered by Professor Capitan and D. Peyrony. These finds are de-scribed as follows by Sir Arthur Keith (*op. cit.*) :

In the autumn of 1909, while Herr Hauser was exposing the Aurignacian man at Combe Capelle, M. Peyrony, the school-master at Les Eyzies, the picturesque cliff village on the Vézère, was uncovering a human skeleton in a stratum of Mousterian age. M. Peyrony had devoted many years to the exploration of the prehistoric sites along the valley of the Vézère, and, at the time of which I write, was exploring the deposits at the foot of a rock-shelter at La Ferrassie, on the western side of the valley, four miles above the point at which Herr Hauser was excavating. M. Peyrony worked in conjunction with Professor Capitan of the Collège de France, Paris. The deposits at the rock-shelter showed the following strata. The upper stratum, four feet in depth, was made up of soil, with blocks of limestone which had fallen from time to time from the face of the sheltering rock. Then followed three strata of Aurignacian age—representing three phases of the culture of that time—forming a thickness of six feet. At a depth of ten feet came the deposit which particularly interests us here—a deposit of the Mousterian Period. It was about twenty inches in thickness, and contained the typical flint instruments and chips of the period, with broken fragments of the bones of reindeer, bison, and horse—remnants of ancient feasts. In the lower part of this stratum a skeleton came to light, lying on its back with the lower limbs strongly bent. There were no evident signs of grave furniture or of deliberate burial, but we may be certain, seeing that a complete skeleton was represented and that the strata had been the site of human habitation, that the body had not been entombed by natural means. Unfortunately, the skull was broken beyond repair, but other parts of the skeleton were fairly complete, every bone being marked by those peculiar characters which denote, as Professor Capitan recognized, the Neanderthal race. In the same stratum, another skeleton showing Neanderthal characters was discovered in the following year, 1910. Thus, almost in the same month, and less than twenty miles apart, two ancient human skeletons were discovered, one at La Ferrassie and one at Combe Capelle. The last named was found in the oldest Aurignacian stratum, and belonged to a man akin to modern races, while the skeleton found at La Ferrassie, in the Mousterian stratum, was of a race or type totally different from any human race now living. They were folded down between untorn and undamaged pages of the records which Nature makes of the earth's history.

The two skeletons from La Ferrassie were presented by Capitan and Peyrony to the Musée de l'Homme in Paris, where they may still be seen in the public rooms of the section devoted to prehistory.

Oliver C. Farrington and Henry Field of the Field Museum of Natural History, Chicago, writing in *Cultura Venezolana* (August, 1930), describe Neanderthal man, on the basis of the skeletons found, as:

. . . of small, squat stature (under five feet), with a large head and short limbs. The concave curvature of the spinal column continues into the neck, so that head and shoulders must have been permanently bent forward. In consequence of the structure of the femur, the knees, too, must have been permanently bent and incapable of being straightened. Heavy, beetling brow ridges were a salient feature; so were a low forehead, a long upper lip, and a receding chin. Like the skull itself, the teeth and jaws were extraordinarily massive. The nostrils were broad and flat. The low forehead diminished the space in which the frontal lobes of the brain could develop, but this constriction was offset by the protruding occipital region at the base of the skull at the back. According to Boule and Anthony, the brain of Neanderthal man presented a number of primitive features. Thus the frontal lobes, the seat of the higher faculties, were not fully developed and did not exceed in volume those of the anthropoid apes. Similarly, the cervical lobes, in which the faculty of speech is held to be lodged, were very under-developed in comparison with modern man. Hands and feet were both large and the big toe was separated from the rest, as in anthropoid apes. In addition, the feet had very small heels compared with those of modern man, the heel bone being relatively undeveloped.

These authors consider that the Neanderthal race became extinct after inhabiting Europe for a period estimated at about a hundred thousand years, and having lived through the Great Ice Age. They conjecture further that they dwelt in caves situated in high ground, though they do not explain how these human beings managed to exist for these hundred thousand years in a wilderness of ice. One is left to suppose that the Neanderthaloids did not show any development during this long period and remained at an extremely primitive level up to the moment when they were replaced by another race, the Aurignacians, who were taller and longer limbed. There is nothing to show how the latter ousted the former, nor where this new race came from. It appears that during the Ice Age there existed somewhere in the world a taller race with a more advanced civilization than that of Ice Age man.

Amongst German finds regarded as almost as sensational as that in the Neanderthal, the most remarkable were the skeletons exposed at the Baden village of Mauer (1907) and at Oberkassel near Bonn (1914).

Late in 1907, Professor Otto Schoetensack extracted from a bed of sand deposited by the River Neckar, close to the village of Mauer, the beautifully-preserved lower jaw of a primitive man. This jaw, which was remarkable for its massiveness and absence of chin, was found at a depth of about eighty feet and was accompanied by the bones of prehistoric fauna. Professor Schoetensack wrote at the time: 'The mandible of *Homo heidelbergensis* reveals to us the appearance of all the forerunners of mankind and the anthropoid apes.' Professor E. Wirth goes even further: 'In fact, we can see in the Heidelberg jaw only an intermediate form between the normal human jaw on the one hand, and that of an ape on the other. The intermediate form is even clearer here than in *Pithecanthropus*.' Professor Wirth was doubtful about the human character of the jaw and proposed that its owner should be assigned not to the genus *Homo*, but to that of *Pithecanthropus* (the fossil anthropoid found in Java by Dubois in 1894). A whole literature sprang up round this Heidelberg jaw, leading in the end to grave doubts as to whether it was really human at all. Professor Weinert of Kiel lays stress on the fact that at the time of the discovery, in 1907, it was designated *Homo* largely on account of its dentition. In view of the fact that no other skull or mandible according with the Mauer jaw has ever been found in Europe, the latter cannot be stated with any certainty to be human. In the absence of any other components that would permit a reconstruction, the most accurate designation is probably *Pithecanthropus heidelbergensis*, as recommended by Professor Weinert.

The skeleton found at Oberkassel, near Bonn, in 1914 was noteworthy for the various carved bone objects associated with it. The site of this find—a stone quarry—is thought to have been the camping and burial place of hunters in a cleft in the rocks, which later became filled in. The skulls of the two Oberkassel skeletons bear no resemblance to those of the Neanderthaloids. Both skulls show a strikingly broad face with a steep facial angle; the nose is depressed at the root and the brain pan has a good profile curve. The prominence given to the brow ridge by the fact that the centre of the face is missing does give the skull-cap a certain apparent likeness to the Neanderthal skull. But the broad face, depressed orbits, narrow nose and the V-shaped lower jaw coupled with a pronounced chin triangle, on the other hand, are the recognized characteristics of the Cro-Magnon race of reindeer hunters.

Scientists, studying the skeletal remains which still continue to come to light from time to time, have never ceased to ask themselves when the Neanderthal race lived and whether it is to be considered human. Neanderthaloid skulls have been found under circumstances which in no way suggest the epoch to which they are normally ascribed. In 1908, the Polish anthropologist K. Stolghwo wrote in the bulletin of the Cracow Academy of Sciences that a skull of Neanderthaloid type had been discovered at Novosiolka (Kiev government) in association with objects (scale-armour and iron weapons) suggesting that it dated from the period of the Migration of the Peoples. Euringer comments in his *Chronologie der biblischen Urgeschichte* (Münster, 1909) that the assignment of the skulls and skeletons found in the Neanderthal, the Shipka cave, at Krapina, Ochos, La Naulette, etc., to *Homo primigenius* would appear to have been 'premature'.

Anthropologists, palaeontologists and other scholars working in related fields seek to reconstruct man's first beginnings by gradually fitting together the evidence of the various individual finds like the pieces in a jigsaw puzzle. The most valuable finds were made during and after the First World War. After the curious skull brought to light in the cave of Le Moustier came the discoveries at Broken Hill in Rhodesia (1921) and at Tabgha in Palestine (1925). In 1921, the remains of forty skeletons, which were assigned to the *Pithecanthropus* group, were found in a cave in the Dragon Mountains near the village of Choukoutien, about twenty miles from Peking. With these bones were found hearths, as well as implements of bone and other materials. They were named *Sinanthropus pekinensis*, but subsequently referred to by some authors as Java Man or *Pithecanthropus*.

During the 'thirties, the ever-increasing number of fossil human remains, particularly from outside Europe, cast more and more light on the past of the human race. Several skeletons were discovered in the South African Transvaal (Sterkfontein, Kromdraai, and Swartkrans) by Broom, amongst which he distinguished two different genera, named by him *Plesianthropus* or *Paranthropus*, meaning 'almost human'. An interesting skeleton was exhumed by Heberer on Mount Carmel in Palestine. This skeleton, like the one unearthed at Oberkassel, shows characteristics both of the Neanderthaloid and modern man, which led Heberer himself to regard it as a hybrid. Finally, a number of fresh discoveries were made in China and Java which aroused the attention of the whole scientific world by their volume.

In 1935 and 1939, the explorer von Königswald came upon three outsize molar teeth in a Chinese pharmacy. Fossil remains of animals are often sold in Chinese chemists' shops as remedies and charms. These teeth so resembled human teeth as to suggest that they came from an ancient race of giants. Naturally, their discoverer could not accept this hypothesis, but ascribed them to a being which he designated *Gigantopithecus*, giant man-ape, although no teeth of this size are known from any species of anthropoid ape, either living or extinct. Professor Weinert of Kiel undertook the task of reconstructing a jaw based on the three huge teeth and the Mauer mandible. But even the Heidelberg jaw, regarded as the largest fossil human jaw ever discovered, proved too small to accommodate these gigantic teeth.

We shall learn more about the facts and significance of these finds later.

The quantity of skeletons and strangely shaped skulls found buried in the open country and, more particularly, in caves gave investigators plenty of room to speculate on their age and origin. Amongst many ancient peoples, interment in caves—symbolizing man's return into the darkness of the underworld—was the usual method of disposing of the dead. This mode of burial was as general among the Incas as in Ancient Rome and Palestine. Ancient cave-tombs have been discovered in North America and at many points in Europe, some of them dating from historically demonstrable agrarian cultures and others suggesting an origin in the Ice Age. The following are a few examples of these finds.

Between 1935 and 1937, sensational discoveries were made on the Hohlestein in the Lonetal, Württemberg. The rocks of the Hohlestein, situated midway between the Bockstein higher up the mountainside and the Vogelherd lower down, contain two large caverns, the Bärenhöhle (Bears' Cave) and the Stadel. Several well-preserved bears' skeletons were un-earthed in the Bärenhöhle, by Oskar Fraas, as long ago as 1862. Until digging was begun in the Stadel in 1937, the cave had been sealed by a wall erected during the Middle Ages. The discovery of two lance heads and a crossbow arrow in the vicinity of the cave led to the conjecture that it was a medieval fortified stronghold. In this cave, in a shallow pit of grey humus, were found the remains of at least thirty-eight human skeletons of all ages, but predominantly of children. From the roof of the skull to the bones of the ex-tremities hardly a bone was undamaged. The osseous frag-ments were intermingled with potsherds and splinters of flint. Above the level of the skeletons was a hearth, which had carbonized some of the bones. Otto Völzing, in his re-port, *Die Grabungen 1937 am Hohlestein im Lonetal* (Stuttgart, 1937), sees evidence of cannibalism in the circumstances of the site. The same conclusion was reached by A. Saád con-cerning a similar find which he made in the Hungarian cave of Istálloköer, where twenty-seven human skeletons accom-panied by fragments of pottery and bone bodkins were found under a hearth. Here, too, the finder believed he had uncovered an instance of Neolithic cannibalism.

This interpretation is not entirely convincing, however. The fact that the Hohlestein cavern was blocked by a wall nearly four feet thick suggests rather that this burial may date from the time of the Plague, and that the corpses were brought to the cave and walled in after an attempt had been made to burn them. The few bone bodkins do not prove a Neolithic origin, for bone bodkins were also used during the Middle Ages, when metal needles were still very costly.

Even more puzzling was a head-interment grave found in the same cave, containing the skulls of a man, a woman and a child lying side by side in what appeared to be a Pleistocene stratum. Assembled round the woman's skull were the teeth of a species of fish, *Rutulis frisii meidingeri*, no longer found in the German reaches of the Danube. The skulls of the man and woman showed injuries apparently caused by blows from a club, while there were clear marks of cutting on the lowest cervical vertebrae, indicating that the heads had been severed from the body. In the opinion of Otto Völzing this was a 'ruddle head-burial' (a form of interment in which the head is completely enveloped in ruddle, or earthy haematite), dating from the end of the Ice Age and roughly contemporaneous with the burial in the Ofnet cave and the Kaufertsberg skull. This site was remarkable for the remains of mammoth and woolly rhinoceros also found there, which were important factors in dating it. We cannot here consider whether this should be taken as proof that these two great Pleistocene beasts inhabited the same region already lived in by men.

One of the most noteworthy finds of human skeletons was made in the Leichenhöhle or Cave of the Corpses, one of the twenty-two caverns in the slopes of the Hönnetal overlooking the River Hönne, opposite Binolen station in South Westphalia. At the top of a thirteen-foot-high vertical cliff is the opening to a narrow cave passage. During the Second World War an amateur speleologist named Schneider, a factory owner from Balve, crawled along this passage and entered a vault, where he found fragments of forty human skeletons. The nature of the iron and bronze ornaments accompanying the bones suggested that the skeletons were mostly of women and children. The cavern appeared from this evidence to be a Bronze Age sepulchre. Unless the passage was once larger, the bodies must either have been dragged along it or else dropped down a shaft which has since been filled in. The ornaments and various other objects brought to light in this cave afforded valuable information concerning the Bronze Age cult of the dead. The jewellery included amber necklaces, some of fine workmanship, more than eighty ear-rings, amber and glass beads, and bronze armbands, brooches and fibulas, richly decorated with the serpentine patterns so popular in the Bronze Age. The presence of potsherds and even organic remains, such as flower seeds and grains of cereals, indicate that the dead were laid to rest with provisions as well as ornaments.

Since the Second World War, momentous discoveries of human skeletons in caves have been made by the French explorer, Professor Marcel Homet, in the course of his arduous expeditions through the Amazon basin in Brazil, where no systematic archaeological exploration has ever been carried out before.

In the rocky districts of Brazilian Guiana, the explorer found strange monuments to a vanished culture in the shape of petroglyphs, tombs and painted caves. After the First World War Friedrich Merz, an explorer of German origin living in Brazil, had reported finding pottery and drawings, particularly on Marajo Island in the Amazon delta, which he held to be of prehistoric or proto-historic date. From an ethnographic and cultural point of view these discoveries seemed to Merz to show considerable resemblance to similar finds made in Europe and especially in North Africa. This hypothesis received strong support from Professor Homet's finds. The principal monument to this ancient culture was the three-faced *Petra Pintada* or Painted Stone, decorated on all three sides. Beneath this rock the explorer discovered a cave thirteen feet wide and a hundred feet long, which proved to be a vast charnel house.

'On studying the relics of the ancient culture of Brazilian Guiana in their entirety,' he writes, 'what strikes us most, apart from the regular use of the round stone (a see-saw block balanced on another rock), is the appearance of a mixture of cultural elements, ranging from inhabited caves to ossuaries with dolmens.'

On the high plateaux of Tamara, Anaro and Grande, Professor Homet found urns with handles and sepulchral caves decorated with drawings in red ochre representing swans. On the Sapo plateau he discovered spacious caverns with double or triple entrances, and the centre of the plateau yielded funerary urns enclosing bones painted red. In the same region, Homet found a cave 100 feet long with a double urn containing the skeleton of a man in a squatting position. This urn also contained two necklaces, one of wild boars' tusks, the other of glass beads similar to those manufactured at Carthage or Venice. In the same area, the explorer also came upon an important cave city with numerous rock-cut chambers containing urns with red-painted squatting skeletons in them. The mode of inhumation and the many forms of rock drawing, of which we shall have more to say in a later chapter, led Homet to the inescapable conclusion that the culture of the prehistoric population of the northern half of the Amazon basin bore a striking and astonishing likeness to that of the Mediterranean zone. The practice of burying the dead in a squatting position lends a certain credibility to his view. Squatting inhumations are met with among many primitive peoples living far from the caves of Northern Brazil. Among the tribes of Malaya (Sakai, Semang, Semai, etc.) the dead are interred in a pit in a squatting position and facing the setting sun. The same method of inhumation is usual among the Eskimoes. It involves tying the body in such a manner that the chin rests on the raised knees.

It is not easy to say whether any direct link exists between the widely scattered points at which this custom was practised. It is true that Stone Age men were also interred in this squatting position.

2

CAVE MEN AND CAVE DWELLINGS

✣

CAVES INHABITED IN
PREHISTORIC AND HISTORIC TIMES

CAVERNS showing clear signs of human habitation at some determinate or indeterminate period of the past exist in many countries and all parts of the world, especially Europe. It is not always possible to be certain whether these caves were the normal abodes of a past age, or whether they were merely used as temporary shelters under conditions of emergency following natural disasters, economic crises or wars.

Germany possesses a number of caves which are considered to have served as dwellings. They include the Hohefels and Bockstein caves in the Franconian Jura, the Ofnethöhle near Nördlingen, the old Neanderthal cave near Düsseldorf, the caves of Baumann and Hermann near Rübeland, the Unicorn Cave at Schwarzfeld, and the Hyaenas' Cave in the Lindental.

The Langenstein cave dwellings in the foothills of the Harz Mountains are famous. Before the Second World War they were turned into a museum. This strange cave village in the heart of Germany was not a refuge for the down-and-out, but a settlement dating from the Thirty Years War. The village, which is not far from Halberstadt, has a whole street without a single house. It runs past a wall of rock pierced by one cave dwelling after another. No doubt they began as natural cavities, and were afterwards enlarged. Inside the caverns are kitchens, bedrooms, living-rooms, larders, stoves, springs and even stone benches. The chimneys pass through the sixteen-foot ceilings of rock, emerging into the open air amidst gardens. In the years before the War, these caves were tenanted by land-owning farmers, who clung to their underground dwellings despite their affluence. Later, they were occupied by wanderers, and their last inhabitant was a disabled soldier who travelled round the district with his barrel organ.

An odd story surrounds the origins of this cave village. It dates from the destruction by the Swedes, after a long siege, of the mountain fortress of Langenstein. The Bishop of Halberstadt, a man of sound commercial instincts, rented out the whole spur of the mountain to his workpeople, so that they could convert its casemates and cavities into dwellings. Many of those who moved in apparently found these quarters so congenial that they continued to live in them when the crisis was past, and similar habitations were hewn out of other mountain spurs in the neighbourhood. The chaos of those years of war, during which so many homes were destroyed, may explain the adoption of caves as living quarters elsewhere as well.

The *souterrains* of Southern Germany and Austria are more or less artificial underground dwellings consisting of long tunnels opening out into wide chambers. They are thought to date from the Middle Ages and resemble the 'earth-houses' of the British Isles, of which something will be said later. The Catacombs cut out of the soft turf of the hills surrounding Rome are a more elaborate version of the same procedure. Replicas of the Catacombs may be seen in the sandstone grottoes of Valkenburg.

Amongst the most remarkable German caves which once served as habitations are the so-called Heidenlöcher or Heathens' Holes near Goldbach, on Lake Constance. The major part of these historically noteworthy and unique caverns fell victim to road building between 1846 and 1848, so that today only seven remain.

Much has been written about these cavities fifty feet above the road in molasse sandstone. It is not known whether they existed in prehistoric times, whether they were ever inhabited for a long period, or whether they were natural caves gradually enlarged. Of recent years the view has gained currency that they were cave temples, in which Roman settlers made sacrifices to the god Mithras (Keller, *Prähistorische Zeitung*, 1915). Another suggestion is that the caverns were used by the first Christians to settle in the Lake Constance region. The finding of a Roman seal pointed to their occupation by the Romans, and since many of the chambers are hewn out of the rock in the shape of Early Roman vaults, it was conjectured that they had also been used during the Merovingian period, in the fifth and sixth centuries. The division of the caves into rooms with holes to let in the light, seating benches, pillars and alcoves, and kitchens with hearths and flues, point unequivocally to their having once been permanent dwellings. From one point of view, these caverns were ideal living quarters: they received light and air from west and south and offered excellent protection from wind and weather.

The Heidenlöcher were celebrated in literature by Josef Viktor von Scheffel. In his novel *Ekkehard*, he makes the deposed Emperor Charles the Fat (died 888) reside in the Heathens' Holes, from which the people expect him one day to emerge and take over the reins of government again, like Charlemagne in the Untersberg, or Frederick Barbarossa in the Kyffhäuser.

In the novel, the Duchess says to Ekkehard:

'Tomorrow you shall go across to the Sipplinger Hof, over there on the Überlinger See, where the rocky cliff falls vertically into the water; there are all sorts of human abodes cut out of the rock in ancient times. If you see the smoke of a hearth-fire rising out of the mountain, go up. There you will find him I mean;

speak with him concerning the Huns.' 'To whom is my lady sending me?' asked Ekkehard eagerly. 'To the Old Man in the Heathen Cave,' replied the lady Hadwif. 'That is the only name he is known by in these parts.'

Recalling medieval rocky fastnesses, one local investigator believes that the Überlinger Heathens' Holes are the remains of a stronghold dating from the eleventh to fourteenth centuries and occupied by the lord of the manor of Goldbach.

From the account given by Gustav Rommel in his monograph on the district, *Goldbach* (Überlingen, 1949), it appears that the Heathens' Holes were occupied by all sorts of people during the seventeenth century. In the course of earlier centuries, they served on several occasions as refuges for the local population in times of war. During the Thirty Years' War, they sheltered all manner of riff-raff, as well as the poor and homeless from Überlingen. In the eighteenth century, all kinds of vagrants moved into the caves and had to be forcibly evicted. Towards the end of the same century, they were occupied by the famous Schinderhannes—a notorious outlaw of the Robin Hood type, immortalized in Carl Zuckmayer's play of the same name, translated into English as *The Devil's on the Prowl*. After this, residence in the caves was forbidden. Those of the caves which still exist are scheduled as historical monuments and are among the most visited sights of the Lake Constance region.

The Duchy of Salzburg is particularly rich in caves. W. von Czoernig lists no fewer than two hundred and fifty-two in his book *Die Höhlen des Salzburger Landes* (1926). By 1951, the number of known caves in Salzburg had risen to five hundred and sixty. The quantity of objects found show that many of these caves must at one time or another have served as habitations or tombs.

In the cave of Elsbethen, some three miles south of Salzburg, earthenware vessels (combed ware) were found at a depth of one to two feet, and Bronze Age pottery a little deeper, as early as 1909. The lowest stratum yielded primitive artifacts. Particularly important finds were made in a cave of the Mühlgrabenfall in Hallein, a rock shelter fifty-four feet wide, forty-five feet high and forty-two feet long. Excavations carried out in 1922 brought to light one hundred and twenty-nine potsherds, fifty fragments of clay weights burnt red in the fire of a type once used on vertical weaving-looms, iron dross, blackened glass flux, and broken animal bones.

The Bronze Age potsherds exposed in the Schatzloch (Treasure Hole) on the Georgenberg near Kuchl, in the Felsdach (Rock Shelter) on the Lueg Pass, and in the Kühloch (Cow Hole) at Zill point to these caves having been used for human habitation.

In the vestibule of the Lambrechtsofen near Weissenbach, through the entrance to which a river flows, a bronze axe was found. Although this cavern is hardly suitable for a permanent abode, its position on an ancient highway makes it likely that it served as a temporary shelter or a military encampment. Finds in the thoroughly dry Küh- or Melcher-lochhöhle near Saalfelden suggest that it was used during the Bronze Age.

In the case of certain caves (Lambrechtsofen and Kühloch at Saalfelden) the finds point only to Bronze Age use, while in others (the Elsbeth cave and the cave on the Hellbrunnerberg in Salzburg) the lower levels have yielded traces of Neolithic (late Stone Age) occupation.

Natural and artificial cave dwellings are to be met with all over the world, for example in the Sudan, on the western shore of Lake Victoria, in the southern Congo basin, and round the Mediterranean basin. The Sudanese earth-houses are constructed with great skill, while the cave dwellings of many primitive tribes—e.g. the Guanches of Malaya, the Veddahs of Ceylon (the last survivors of the aborigines, representing the Yakkos of Sanskrit writings), and the Semais and Semangs—are in natural mountain caverns. Indian yogis frequently dwell in cave-like hollows that have formed spontaneously in the trunks of giant trees, while in Java hermits often make their abode in hewn-out caves.

To what extent caverns served as primeval human habitations in cold or temperate zones cannot be said for certain, despite the wealth of engraved drawings, paintings, primitive sculpture, fragments of bone, and stone tools. Caves which can unquestioningly be regarded as dwellings are mainly found in warmer areas, e.g. France, Spain, Palestine, Southern Russia, Africa and China. Amongst these caves are many which date from historical times; they include both living-caves and rock-cut temples or shrines. Wherever man was presented with a favourable opportunity for making a dwelling out of a cave, he took it; for in a warm climate they afford better protection against changes in the weather than a house standing in the open. Certain countries are well known for their cave cities of the past or present, chief amongst them being France, both north and south, Spain and China.

In France, the greatest concentration of grottoes that served as prehistoric human habitations occurs in the district of Les Eyzies. In some cases they were occupied for tens of thousands of years, and the relics left by their inhabitants —implements of stone, bone and metal, objects of art, and traces of hearths—are distributed through successive strata reaching to a total depth of more than thirty feet.

One of the most spacious and salubrious of all French caves is that of Isturitz in the Basses-Pyrénées, twelve miles east of Cambo.

This cavern was created at some time in the past by a watercourse that flowed in from the south-east and hollowed out a series of passages in the hill in which it is situated.

At present the entrance of the Isturitz cave forms an arch twelve feet high by sixteen feet wide. It opens on to a vast hall 360 feet long and thirty to forty feet wide. This part of the cave is called the Hall of Isturitz. Towards the centre of this hall, a narrow passage gives access on the left to another

hall, the average height of which is little more than six feet
and which runs parallel with the second half of the Hall of
Isturitz. This is the St. Martin Hall. The successful excavations conducted over a number of years by M. and Mme de
Saint-Périer have revealed the extent and richness of the
archaeological strata. These testify to intensive occupation
and occur even in the slightest irregularities of the walls.
Fourteen superimposed archaeological levels have been distinguished, each of them characterized by its own fauna,
industry and art.

Occupation of the cave seems to have been continuous,
with a few short breaks, throughout a whole period of cold,
dry climatic conditions; it came to an end with a rainy
period that lasted until the Bronze Age. During this epoch
it was used as a sepulchre. The cave of Isturitz, which
yielded a great number of remarkable works of art of
the Franco-Cantabrian culture, is one of the finest in
France.

During the Neolithic Period, the majority of natural
caverns in France were abandoned by man, who, in some
cases, dug artificial caves specially planned for human habitation or as sepulchres. There is a striking agglomeration of
such artificial caves in the Marne valley, to which we shall
return later in discussing burial caverns.

Artificial caves were born of man's desire to have healthier
and safer living quarters, more in harmony with his new
mode of life. They enabled him to choose pleasanter sites, and
positions better placed to enable him to obtain the material
necessities of life.

Natural caves, refuges from wind and weather, which
served for so long as dwellings during the Palaeolithic Period
(Old Stone Age), were not entirely abandoned when the
climate changed, however.

When he set up his encampments out in the open, man
exercised his ingenuity to devise other shelters more appropriate to his new needs and better organized. But certain

natural caverns particularly well adapted to habitation continued to serve him for a long time.

The isolation of certain more primitive communities, the desire to escape from the dominant influence of the time, and the necessity of finding a refuge in periods of upheaval, explain how it is that traces of human habitation in caves are found dating from as late as the Middle Ages.

British caves are especially rich in traces of occupation during Romano-British times, when—like the earth-houses, which will be described further on—they served as temporary shelters for refugees. Many of these same caves show signs of far earlier occupations as well in the lower strata of the cave-earth. Those which have yielded stone artifacts are discussed in a later chapter dealing with Stone Age implements from all parts of the world.

In British caves, as elsewhere, many of the bones and artifacts brought to light seem to indicate, by the circumstances and type of the finds, that the cave was used as a sepulchre rather than as a dwelling. The following are some of the caves that show the clearest signs of having served as living quarters for a longer or shorter period.

Heathery Burn Cave, near Stanhope in Co. Durham, discovered in 1861 but since quarried away, was of exceptional importance as the site of a large series of Late Bronze Age objects, which appeared to have belonged to a family residing or sheltering in the cave and included both weapons and ornaments. Amongst the articles were tools that must have belonged to bronze workers. Of even greater interest, perhaps, were cheek-pieces for horse-bridles made of deer-antler, and four bronze nave bands, suggesting the use of a four-wheeled cart. These objects constituted the earliest direct evidence of the use of the horse and of a wheeled vehicle in Britain. In the same stratum as the implements, and accompanied by the broken bones of domestic animals mingled with charcoal, were two human skulls of long-headed type.

Several caves in Lancashire show definite marks of human occupation during the Roman period, and in some cases earlier as well. Kirkhead Cave about two miles west of Grange-over-Sands yielded several bronze weapons and ornaments, amber beads and a coin of Domitian (AD 81–96), together with human and animal remains. Three caves on Warton Crag, near Carnforth, all showed evidence of Romano-British times, while in one of them, known as Dog Holes, were found human remains belonging to no less than fifteen individuals and indicating that the cave had been used as a burial chamber in Late Neolithic or Early Bronze Age times. Another, known as Fairy Hole, contained—along with various implements and the debris of food bones—pottery sherds that included some first-century Samian ware. From the evidence, it is thought to have been occupied by a Romanized Briton early on in the period of Roman domination.

A number of caves in Yorkshire, the chief of which is Victoria Cave, Settle, also yielded Samian ware, Roman coins and a rich variety of ornaments, especially brooches, of excellent workmanship and constituting fine examples of the Romano-Celtic art that flourished in Brigantia—the Pennine region—during the early part of the second century AD. In every case, it appears that the caves were used as shelters by people of some refinement during periods of upheaval.

Similar evidence of occupation during Roman times has been met with in many other English caves. Thus in Derbyshire there are Poole's Cavern, Buxton, Thirst House, a cave in Deep Dale near Buxton, and Harborough Cave near Brassington, all of which were used during the Romano-British period, while the last-named was also occupied during the Prehistoric Iron Age, the Bronze Age, and possibly much earlier. Thor's Fissure, near Wetton, Staffordshire, showed Romano-British occupation in the upper levels, while the lower strata produced Iron Age, Bronze

Age and even Late Palaeolithic objects and human remains.

Two caves of particular interest in the Symonds Yat
region of the Wye Valley, Herefordshire, were investigated
from 1924 to 1928 by the University of Bristol Speleological
Society, first under T. F. Hewer and then under Dr. Herbert
Taylor. One of these, King Arthur's Cave, near Whitchurch,
was first excavated by the Rev. W. S. Symonds in 1871,
when a wealth of animal remains and a few Palaeolithic
flint implements were found, together with some coarse
pottery of Palaeolithic type in the upper layers. The later
examination revealed traces of almost continuous occupation
of all phases, from Upper Aurignacian to Roman.

Merlin's Cave, half a mile below Symonds Yat, opens in a
limestone cliff about a hundred and fifty feet above the
River Wye. Human remains of at least three individuals
were unearthed and a variety of objects, including bone implements, bone pins and pottery of apparently Neolithic
date. Beaker pottery, a bronze razor and other articles indicated that the cave had been used in the Bronze Age, while
evidence of occupation in the Iron Age and Romano-
British period—spindle-whorls, worked bones, and pottery—
was still more numerous and definite. This cave appears to
have been occupied at intervals from the close of the Neolithic period to later Roman times.

Gough's Cavern, in Cheddar Gorge, regarded by Dr.
J. W. Jackson as the most important Upper Palaeolithic
station in Britain and referred to later in connexion with the
flint implements found in its lower levels, also showed clear
evidence of occupation as a Romano-British refuge in its
surface layers, as did Long Hole, about one hundred and
fifty yards above it.

South Wales is fairly rich in sepulchral caves of Upper
Palaeolithic date (including the famous Paviland cave), but
there are fewer showing signs of occupation in Romano-
British times. The best example is Minchin Hole on the

Gower Peninsula, Glamorgan. Excavations here directed
by Mr. E. J. Mason have brought to light a wealth of
Romano-British pottery sherds and coins, and even some
Anglo-Saxon coins.

A number of Scottish caves show evidence both of occupation and of iron working—in the shape of stone furnaces
and iron slag—during the Iron Age. These include a cave on
the south coast of the Isle of Skye close to the chambered
Neolithic cairn of Rudh' an Dunain; the Big Cave, Kintyre,
which tradition says was still used by gipsies for forging iron
a century ago; and Constantine's Cave, Fife. Wemyss Cave,
Fife, yielded a fine example of Early Bronze Age art: a carving on the wall representing a boat with a steersman and
five oarsmen.

Many Irish caves show traces of occupation. R. M. Young,
investigating some caves in the chalk near the Coastguard
Station at Ballintoy, found in one of them the bones of
domestic animals and fish together with glazed and un-
glazed pottery, which led him to infer that it had been used
as a dwelling-place during the reign of Queen Elizabeth I.

From 1933 to 1936, Dr. J. Wilfrid Jackson investigated
several caves on the North Antrim coast between White-
park Bay and Ballintoy, finding much evidence of human
occupation in the Iron Age or Early Christian period. One
of the most interesting of his finds was a female figure of
baked clay described by the finder as reminiscent of a Mother
Goddess and unique for Ireland. These investigations are
reported by Dr. Jackson in the chapter 'Archaeology and
Palaeontology' of *British Caving* (Routledge & Kegan Paul,
London, 1953), which gives an excellent survey of all British
caves in which signs of occupation and prehistoric burial
have been discovered.

Apart from inhabited natural caves, the British Isles also
contain a number of artificial caverns known as 'earth-
houses'. Under the heading Earth-house the Harmsworth
Encyclopaedia (London, 1909) has the following entry:

An archaic subterranean dwelling, of which many specimens exist in the British Isles. Earth-houses are called 'caves' or 'coves' in Ireland, and sometimes in Scotland, where also the term *weem* is used. Generally speaking, earth-houses are long passages or galleries, made by digging a trench to a depth of 8 or 10 feet, with a width seldom exceeding 8 feet, and often much less; the length varies from 10 to 12 feet to 190 feet (as in the specimen at Pitcur, Forfarshire). The sides of the trench are walled with un-hewn, unmortared stones, the walls being generally perpendicular up to a height of 3 or 4 feet. The upper courses successively overlap each other inwards, until, at a height of 5 or 6 feet from the floor, they are united by huge flagstones which span the trench and form the roof. The whole is then covered with soil and turf, on the same level with the circumjacent ground. In some instances, as at Highfield, Salisbury, Wiltshire, the British earth-houses are excavated out of the hard soil or chalk, and had no masonry. This is also the characteristic of certain souterrains in Lower Austria. (See Karner's *Kunstliche Hohlen aus alter Zeit*, 1903.) The dimensions and ground-plan vary considerably. The objects found in these abodes are utensils of flint, stone, bone, iron, bronze and lead, and the bones of animals and birds used as food. Their rude character points to their having been among the earliest structures made by man. Nevertheless, many of them have been occupied, and even constructed, during historic times. One, at Crichton, Midlothian, is largely built from Roman ruins, and must therefore have been made subsequent to the year 80 AD. Samian ware has been found in several English and Scottish earth-houses. Dean Monro, writing in 1549, speaks of the earth-houses of the Hebridean island of N. Uist as then occupied by 'rebels'. Earth-houses almost identical with those of the British Isles form the winter abodes of existing Eskimoes. Kindred structures in Europe, Armenia, and Egypt are described by Tacitus, Xenophon, Strabo and Aristotle.

THE HEATING PROBLEMS OF ICE AGE MAN

The first traces of the use of fire occur in the Chellean epoch of the Palaeolithic Period, when men lived in the open in

sub-tropical France and in Germany, killing the animals of
the primeval forest with their relatively primitive weapons.
At this period, man used fire mainly as a protection against
wild beasts. Some scholars believe that men were compelled
to retire into caves by the glaciers advancing from the
north.

The Hungarian Johann Dancza spent a number of years
prior to the Second World War measuring the temperature
of twenty-five caves in the Bükk Mountains. He ascertained
that with a low outside temperature the ground temperature
in these caverns fell below freezing point. In the Szeleta cave
—the warmest of all—he found 28° F. when the exterior
temperature was 19° F. Since 13° F. below zero must have
been quite common during the Ice Age, the temperature of
caves must have been regularly far below freezing point,
quite apart from the fact that they would have become wet
whenever there was a thaw, and then be frozen to ice again.

Very ancient cinders have been discovered in a number of
natural cavities, e.g. at three points in the Balve cave, in the
Szeleta cave in Hungary, and in the caverns near the Chinese
village of Choukoutien. The hearth in the Szeleta cave was
thirty-six feet long.

With his primitive implements, coal would have been impossible and timber difficult for Ice Age man to come by.
He could not have felled trees and would have had to be content with fallen wood. Even then, he must have found difficulty in chopping it up.

Some scholars are of the opinion that Ice Age man used
the fat of the animals he killed as fuel, just as the Eskimoes of
today employ whale oil to light and heat their igloos. The
three hearths of the Balve cave contained fire-blackened
animal bones. The fact that all these bones were broken in
pieces led the finders to suppose that they were mammoth
bones which had been smashed up so that the marrow-fat
could be used as fuel. But since fragments of bone only one to
two inches long were merely charred and not carbonized,

and since moreover the total volume of bones was not more than one cubic yard, they can hardly be considered 'Neanderthal man's briquettes', as H. Obermeier calls them (*Urgeschichte der Menschheit*, 1931). To heat a cave the size of that at Balve, or even to warm its occupants, during the cold season would have called for very large quantities of mammoth bones and fat.

For physical reasons, the permanent heating of caves by open fires would have been impossible. The fires would have had to be fed day and night, for months on end; and in caves with only one or two openings, they would have produced so much smoke and such a draught that it would have been impossible to remain in the cave for any length of time. The natural draught in ice caves is often so strong that it almost reaches gale force, making it impossible to stay in them for long.

This is not to say that caves could not have served as dwellings, but they would have had to be dry and small in volume.

CITIES OF A THOUSAND CAVES

In many districts of China the surface rock consists of loess, the product of vast accumulations of dust from the Ice Age. Loess is also formed by wind-borne desert sand settling on surfaces that have first been swept by the wind. The sand gathers in hollows and valleys on the margin of deserts and there sets hard. Loess is generally a fine calcareous quartz dust. Unlike clay, it is permeable to water, and in dry periods the ground-water rises up the fine pores of the loess and moistens the upper strata, so that they are fruitful even in times of drought. In Central Europe a carpet of loess stretches from Silesia across Magdeburg and Thuringia to the Lower Rhine; it is also widespread in Southern Germany, Bohemia and Eastern Bavaria. Loess occupies about seven per cent of the land surface of Europe, and something like three and a half per cent of the total land surface of the world.

In China, the southern part of the North Chinese province of Shan-si consists largely of loess-covered plateaux, which are extremely fertile. Loess is easily hewn, and it is a simple matter to cut caves in it which are stronger than houses and afford excellent shelter for man and beast. Since the loess draws up water from below, wells form and keep the cave dwellers supplied with water.

These Chinese did not turn to the loess for living accommodation until floods, improvident felling and neglect of re-afforestation had deprived them of building timber and, incidentally, greatly contributed to their general poverty. Similar circumstances may well have led to the building of the French and Spanish cave cities. With the exception of Manchuria, China is now extremely short of timber. Cave cities hewn out of the loess, many of them on a considerable scale, have been established in comparatively recent times close to the middle reaches of the Hwang-ho. Military and political factors led to the building of the cave city of Yen in Shan-si province by the Communists, from 1920 onwards. Similar considerations were responsible for the construction of another underground city at Chung-king in the 'thirties.

Apart from China, no country possesses more impressive cave settlements than Spain, which also has the most famous painted caves. The Spanish cave cities may have come into being at a time when war had laid waste the neighbourhood, or when a shortage of timber—the greatest source of poverty and want—forced men to utilize natural caverns as habitations.

In a country with hot summers and comparatively mild winters, cave dwelling is in no way injurious to health, especially when the caves are naturally dry and capable of being enlarged without much effort. From these emergency quarters there arose, in the course of time, civilized abodes quite equal in comfort and hygiene to any ordinary house, apart from the fact that they require perpetual artificial lighting. These underground dwellings possess three great advantages over houses: they can be continually enlarged or added to at small cost; they require little furniture; they give their occupants far greater immunity from changes in the outside temperature than a house standing in the open, being cool in summer and relatively warm in winter. The inhabitants of these cave settlements, having experienced the advantages of this type of dwelling, are unwilling to exchange it for more conventional accommodation.

Kurt Hielscher describes these cave settlements with enthusiasm in his book of photographs, *Das unbekannte Spanien* (Berlin, 1921).

Cave Eyries—The Simple Life. Today I determined to wander out into the open country again, towards the distant horizon in the dewy dawn. Chance would be my guide once more. I could have none better. I set off well before daybreak. The palm trees were shaking themselves awake in the light morning breeze, as I approached a strange landscape of rocks in the first light of day. Dark holes in the cliff face stared out towards the east. But the cliffs held life! People came out of the holes to greet the daybreak. One gigantic wall of rock was riddled with nests. Dwelling upon dwelling, the caves rise in hundreds, one above the other, sometimes five storeys high, accessible from outside. If the cliff is too precipitous, the people dig their way up inside and build upper storeys with spy-holes and 'loggias' in the airy heights. To get more easily from one ravine to the next, they have cut tunnels through the soft stone walls. The children hop about in paradisean innocence, just as God made them. But, wanderer, do not imagine you are looking at uncivilized troglodytes like those of the Ice Age; cast your eyes up at the rock face, read and marvel! Visible a great way off, black on a white ground, stand the huge letters: EL RETIRO.

Every Spaniard knows, by name at least, the famous Retiro, Madrid's splendid park. The effect of seeing this word (it means retreat, or refuge), which has become almost a proper name like Sans-Souci, suddenly loom up aloft is nothing short of comical.

The fact is, an enterprising cave-hotel proprietor has smoothed off his rock and converted it into a roof terrace, where people gather for *tertulias* (social gatherings), to play bowls, or for gay dances. Hence the siren call on the cliff for all who pass by. Another rock bears the succinct and significant words DIOS, PAN Y CULTURA (God, bread and culture).

Another trip yielded me an equally great surprise. Before me in the distance, smoke rose out of the ground amidst a fantastic landscape of eroded mountains. Volcanic phenomena here? Out of the question! And as I drew closer, I could see people walking about among the pillars of smoke. Then I realized to my astonishment that the towers shaped like champagne corks, from which the smoke was billowing, were chimneys. What austere, Homeric grandeur! The valleys are the streets, the mountainsides the house fronts, the peaks proud detached houses. Here and there gnarled giant cactuses, their pointed leaves projecting around them like rows of bayonets, make up the front gardens. The people replied in friendly fashion to my greeting, invited me into the cool of a cave, poured me a drink of water, and showed me their meagre household treasures: the bed on the earth, the hearth with the copper kettle, an earthenware jug, an oil lamp, a stool, the picture of a saint. 'Work?' 'A bit. We grow what we need at the back, on the low ground by the river. We bake bricks for the people from the city who live in houses.'—A perfect picture of the 'simple life'.

The two most famous groups of cave dwellings in Spain are those in the province of Almeria and the cave settlement of Sierra de Guadix. The former have been hewn haphazard from the rocks. Many of the entrances have been walled round, others are merely rectangular holes. The cave dwellings of Guadix, an hour by car from Granada, are somewhat more elaborate. Many of the caves have walled structures built in front of them, which stand out against the grey of the mountain rock. This city of caves numbers forty thousand inhabitants, and twenty-five thousand of them live, work and die in the dark caverns where little of the hot Spanish sun ever penetrates.

Approaching Guadix the traveller enters a barren, rocky zone, from the midst of which the settlement rises before him like a phantom. The practised eye will observe at once that the inhabitants of Guadix do not live in caves because they cannot afford houses of stone or wood, but because caves seem to them well-suited to the hot climate of Spain. The temperature of these cave dwellings is moderate throughout the year, they cost little to construct, and at the present time their occupants are less than ever inclined to move into other quarters because they are convinced that this type of habitation offers the best protection against air raids. Most of the inhabitants of Guadix have never known any other abode than their caves, the majority of which have no doors but only curtains of fabric or bast across the entrance. The subterranean dwellings are divided into two to six rooms, according to their occupants' social status. Many of the interiors are lit only by oil lamps, but electric light has been installed in some and burns all day long. The craftsmen spread out their handiwork in front of their caves, oriental fashion.

This settlement of caverns has no streets or pavements in the ordinary sense. The paths run at random from cave to cave, overgrown with grass. No buses and no horses pass along them. Only a few aged little wooden carts with big disk-wheels, drawn by mules, are occasionally to be seen lumbering along these bumpy tracks. In addition to habitations, a church, schools, and recently even a cinema have been hewn out of the rock. On Sundays, when all work comes to a stop and the whole of the town's life runs its course within the caverns, a ghostly silence lies over Guadix. Scarcely a sound emerges from the walls of rock into the outer world, not even when the southern temperament inflamed by fiery wine breaks noisily out in the cave taverns. Guadix is undoubtedly one of the strangest cities in the world. People work hard in every Spanish town, but Guadix is famous throughout the country for the industry of its inhabitants.

Allied to the Spanish cave settlements are the caverns of
the Maya village of Bécal, an ancient Spanish township on
the Yucatan Peninsula of Mexico with some one thousand
five hundred inhabitants. These limestone caves, fifteen or
more feet below the gardens or courtyards of the houses,
have served since time immemorial as workshops. Their
stable, cool temperature and humidity render them particularly suitable for the local industry of straw-hat plaiting.
About eight thousand straw hats are manufactured weekly
in these caves. Of these, seven thousand are of simple, coarse
quality. A further eight hundred are of so-called 'general
quality' and fetch about twenty pesos apiece. In addition,
fine silky straw hats are produced of which highly-skilled
specialists can make only about ten a week, but which fetch as
much as a hundred pesos. The town also maintains a school
where women, children and young people who are particularly skilful with their hands are taught the craft of straw-hat
plaiting, which they will later exercise in the local caves.

THE CAVERNS AND ROCK SHELTERS
OF THE HOLY LAND

For a long time Palestine appeared to everyone's imagination as a patriarchal and idyllic land, remote from the outside world. But the excavations and discoveries of the last
century show the history of Palestine in quite a different
light, proving that many and various cultures mingled on
this soil—Egyptian, Mesopotamian, Anatolian, and European (through the Crusades)—and that the Holy Land has
a turbulent past behind it. But although the country never
failed to adapt its thinking to changing circumstances, it
never lost its faith in the one God, Jahveh, as may be seen
from the writings of the old prophets.

The country's past is revealed not only in its ruins, in old
buildings and walls, but also beneath the earth, in caves,
grave-chambers and grottoes, in which it is relatively richer
than any other country of the world. They have little appeal

to the pilgrim or the tourist, but they exercise a powerful attraction on the archaeologist, because they were often the background to great events and have been the site of momentous archaeological discoveries.

Rock-cut sepulchres are to be met with all over the country; many of them have been preserved and honoured as memorials to great figures of Scripture. Jerusalem is especially rich in underground habitations, caves and grottoes. A subterranean grotto supported by eighty-eight pillars to the east of the El Aksa Mosque, known as Solomon's Stable, was originally created by Herod and subsequently enlarged and restored, first by Justinian and then by the Arabs. At the time of the Crusades, these cellars really were used by the kings and Templars as stables. Jerusalem's underground city also includes the subterranean buildings near St. Stephen's Gate with the reservoir known as the Pool of Bethesda.

Outside the city, close to the Damascus Gate, lies the Cave of Jeremiah. A courtyard planted with trees and a sort of vestibule lead to two caves, one behind the other, the second of which—supported by a pillar—contains the tomb of Sultan Ibrahim and, at the back, the supposed tomb of Jeremiah, who is said to have written his Lamentations here. The western part of the hill above the cave is held by many to be the true Golgotha.

At the foot of the Mount of Olives a number of grottoes lead into the hillside, some of which represent venerable burial places. There is the Tomb of the Virgin, where tradition says the disciples buried the mother of Jesus; the Tomb of Absalom; the Tomb of Jehoshaphat; Jacob's Cave; and the Pyramid of Zechariah. In the north-east and east of the city are to be found the Tombs of the Kings and the Tombs of the Judges, great rock-cut chambers whose origin and significance are uncertain. Very impressive are the Tombs of the Prophets, which are entered through a narrow passage leading into a vaulted rotunda dimly lit from above. From here passages penetrate deeper into the mountain with rows of grave-chambers side by side in their outer walls. Similar rock-cut sepulchres are scattered all over the country.

Apart from these sepulchral caverns, there are in many parts of the land caves which have clearly served as shrines or dwellings. Under the Dome of the Rock, in the old Mohammedan quarter, runs a cave in which many fabulous things are shown—the praying places of David and Solomon and other Old Testament figures, for example, and a round hole in the roof believed by the Mohammedans to have been bored through the stone by Mahomet's head during his ascension.

The Monastery of St. Saba near Mar Saba, founded by St. Euthymius in the fifth century and about two and a half hours' journey from Bethlehem across the Desert of Judah, possesses some remarkable caves. One of them was the abode of St. Saba, who is supposed to have shared it on friendly terms with a lion. The monastery, which exhibits a number of interesting features, is inhabited by Greek monks sent there as a punishment. The inmates, compelled to live in this desolate solitude, pass the time by feeding the brightly-coloured little birds that flutter around the monastery, or enticing and taming the jackals that live in the surrounding caverns.

On the western slopes of the sub-tropical Mount Carmel are to be found numerous caves that have served as dwellings for fugitives and prophets in search of solitude. Pythagoras—the Greek thinker who taught the connexion between number and the structure of the universe, the transmigration of souls, and a theory of music based on the mystery of number—is also said to have resided here. At the time of Tacitus, an altar to the god Carmel stood on the mountain. Vespasian also sacrificed there when he received the prophecy of his emperorship from Rabbi Jochanan ben Zakai. Many of the anchorites of the first Christian centuries occupied these caves. Here the Carmelite Order was founded, an event commemorated by the Carmelite Monastery, beneath whose church is a cavern in which the prophet Elias is supposed to have dwelt. The precincts of the monastery on the mountainside are full of caves that have been occupied by holy hermits. One cave, partly artificially hewn out of the mountain and forty-two feet long, twenty-four feet wide and fifteen feet high, is held in high veneration by Christians, Jews, Moslems and Druses alike. The Jews bring the mentally sick here, that they may be cured by the healing power of the prophet Elias.

Palestine also possesses a cave settlement in Derat on the Hejaz railway. It lies beneath the present town, and streets, dwellings, and a kind of market place are still intact. This underground town, which still serves as a refuge for those in flight from justice or military service, is described in detail in Wetzstein's *Reisebericht über den Hurân und die Trachonen* (Berlin, 1860). Since the entrances are now blocked by rubble, access to the city is very difficult.

It looks as though caves were used as dwellings in Palestine at a very early period. In his book *Requaim* (Paderborn, 1925), a landmark in the prehistory of Palestine, Paul Karge reported traces of Stone Age settlements in the caves of Mugharet Alemire and Ez Zuttiye. In 1925-6, the English worker M. Turville-Petre subjected both caves to closer examination, and came to the conclusion that the former had not been lived in since Stone Age times, whereas the latter must still have been occupied during the Early Bronze Age. In this cave he also found a skull which, with its receding forehead and brow ridges, closely resembled those of the Neanderthaloids. A number of flint artifacts, flint splinters, and bones came to light, which their finder assigned to the Old Stone Age, considering that the tools corresponded to those of the Aurignacian Period in Europe. The principal objects found were long, narrow flint blades, fine scrapers, carefully worked points, triangular arrow-heads and leaf-shaped spear heads. Bone borers, bone polishing tools, perforated bones, and pottery sherds completed the list.

In the years 1928–34, excavations carried out jointly by
the British and American Schools of Prehistoric Research
brought to light further skeletons reminiscent of the Neanderthaloids in the Carmel caves. Digging in the Shubka cave
near Ramleh yielded a long-headed skull of Negroid type,
with a slightly projecting chin, which apparently belonged
to a man of small stature. Scholars conjecture that this race
wiped out the Neanderthaloids during the Middle Stone
Age. In 1935–8, the remains of seven skeletons ascribed to
the Neanderthal race were exposed by the French Institut
de Paléontologie Humaine at Jebel Kafzeh.

In the years 1902–05 and 1907–09, R. A. Saint-
Macalister, and later A. Rowe, carried out excavations at
Gezer which led them to the conclusion that the inhabitants
of Gezer must have withdrawn from the valleys and plains
into the mountains at the end of the New Stone Age, and
occupied the caves in the soft limestone of the Hill of Gezer
and neighbouring hills. They found caves decorated with
animal paintings and geometric drawings, and containing
stone implements which these workers ascribed to the Neolithic Period. The level above this, dating from the Canaanite
period (*circa* 2200 BC), yielded numerous ornaments, amu-
lets and scarabs—all of Egyptian origin—attributed to the
Twelfth Dynasty. In addition, many ancient bronze weapons
were found in the caves, which had apparently served as
burial chambers.

Was it perpetual floods, flight from the destroyed cities, or
the great cataclysm of which accounts have come down to us
that compelled the inhabitants of these caves to become
troglodytes? In his essay 'Wohnung und Wohnorte in der
Prophetenliteratur (Dwellings and Dwelling Places in the
Prophetic Literature)', extracts from which appeared in *Das
Heilige Land in Vergangenheit und Gegenwart* (Palästinahefte des
Vereins vom Heiligen Land, Nos. 40–42), J. Breuer points
out passages in the Prophetic Books in which the prophets
of the Old Covenant refer to caves as dens of robbers, or

shelters in time of war and oppression. In connexion with the judgment to come, the Bible says: 'O ye that dwell in Moab, leave the cities, and dwell in the rock, and be like the dove that maketh her nest in the sides of the hole's mouth.' (*Jeremiah XLVIII*, 28); 'Flee ye, turn back, dwell deep, O inhabitants of Dedan', (*Jeremiah XLIX*, 8); 'Flee, get you far off, dwell deep, O ye inhabitants of Hazor' (*Jeremiah XLIX*, 30). Through the mouth of the prophet Ezekiel, the Lord announces that even the people of Israel who have sought sanctuary on the mountain tops and in caves shall not escape judgment, but shall die of the pestilence (*Ezekiel XXXIII*, 27). At the time of the prophets, therefore, the solid house or the tent must have been the normal dwelling.

The use of caves as sanctuaries in periods of upheaval may explain a discovery made in a subterranean cavity rather more than a mile from the north-west shore of the Dead Sea and about the same distance from Jericho, close to the village of Chirbet Qumram. In the spring of 1947 a herdsman, seeking a goat that had wandered away from the flock, came upon a narrow fissure in the rock. Squeezing himself through, he entered a cavern six feet wide, six feet high, and twenty-four feet along. There he found a number of stone jars containing ancient parchment scrolls wrapped in linen and carefully packed against damp. He brought some of the scrolls out into the daylight, and after many vicissitudes and changes of ownership they came into the hands of archaeologists, who recognized them as the most momentous written documents discovered in our day.

There were seven scrolls altogether: two Isaiah scrolls, a Habakkuk scroll, the statute-book of a Jewish sect, the apocryphal Lamek Apocalypse, a book of ritual, and a scroll with apocryphal psalms or hymns of thanksgiving. In 1949, further important fragments were found, after the cave had been plundered by unknown hands between the two dates.

In 1953, Dr. Willard F. Libby of the University of Chicago burnt thirty grammes of the linen wrappings and examined the resulting radio-active carbon, carbon 14, in one of the world's most sensitive Geiger counters. The test led him to conclude that the flax of which their linen was made grew 1,900 years ago. Presumably the scrolls were hidden for safety at some time of religious or political turmoil.

The same interpretation must be placed on the use of caves as living quarters in Palestine. Scarcely any other eastern city has been the scene of so much fighting and destruction as Jerusalem. This, together with the lack of timber, which precluded the erection of temporary shelters, explains why her inhabitants were so often forced to seek refuge in caverns.

3

CAVERNS AS PLACES OF WORSHIP

ORIENTAL CAVE TEMPLES

THE earliest stone buildings are often to be found in the countries where the forests first ceased to provide building timber. The pyramids and stone tombs of Egypt, the sacred and profane buildings of Greece and Rome, the temples of the gods in India, and the astonishing unmortared buildings of the Incas are highlights of architectural achievement largely inspired by shortage of timber. These mighty structures of stone, which have defied the millennia, occur in all the Eastern centres of civilization. Among the most impressive are the rock-cut temples, which probably began from the nucleus of natural caves that were extended inwards and fronted with a built-up façade.

The finest and best preserved cave temples are in India. The Buddhists chose caverns for their hermitages and places of worship. In the heyday of Indian Buddhism thousands of caves were occupied for religious purposes, and many of them developed into unique works of architecture. Most of these rock-cut temples are in the north-west Deccan; they date from various epochs, but the majority go back to the first millennium AD. The oldest and most celebrated are the work of Buddhists, but these were copied by the Brahmins and Jains.

One of the most magnificent subterranean temples in this

region is undoubtedly that of Ellora, which is divided amongst Buddhists, Brahmins and Jains. The Buddhist caves, dating from AD 350 to 750, are of two main types: the Viharas, monastery or living caves with a public hall for devotions, and the Chaityas, cathedral or assembly caves for divine service and the housing of reliquaries in the form of a stupa or dagoba. Ellora contains eleven Viharas, running from north to south, and one Chaitya. Great halls and verandas supported by numerous pillars, richly decorated with figures representing the Buddhist saints in various incarnations, render this underground temple one of the foremost sights of India.

The Brahmin temple caves at Ellora are thought to date from the seventh to the beginning of the ninth century. They differ from the Buddhist temples both in their ground plan and in the greater profusion of decoration, which portrays the terrifying demonology of the Shiva and Vishnu cult. Above all, the Temple of Kaila in the centre is a marvel of ancient Indian architecture. The Ravana-ka-Khai, or Ravana's Cave, is eighty-six feet long with a vestibule and central hall, and behind this a shrine of sacred relics.

Amongst the temples of Ellora are the five Jain caves, which probably date from the ninth and tenth centuries, but, unlike the older parts of the temple, contain no monastery rooms. The façades, walls and columns are richly carved in the manner characteristic of Jain architecture.

One of the most famous, though not the most important, of India's rock-cut temples is that on the rocky island of Elephanta in Bombay harbour, six miles east of the city of Bombay. The island, which takes its name from a gigantic stone elephant that once stood near the former landing place at the southern extremity, is four to five square miles in extent and completely covered by jungle. The temple is thought to date from the middle of the eighth century and has affinities with the Dumar Lena at Ellora, to which it is artistically superior, though smaller. Decorated with twenty-six pillars, of which some are broken, the temple and its sculptures are hewn out of the natural rock and are about fifteen feet high. The figures on the walls show the god Shiva as the destroyer and re-creator of things. At the northern entrance stands the colossal Trimurti, the trinity of Brahma, Vishnu and Shiva.

Appreciably simpler are the Kanheri caves on Salsette Island, north of the city of Bombay, a Buddhist monastery from the second to ninth century. The hundred or so monks' cells cut out of the natural rock rise up the hill in six tiers.

The extensive cave temples of Ajanta near Jalgaon, in the Khandesh district, are considerably older than those at Ellora. The caves comprise twenty-four Viharas and five Chaityas cut in the cliffs of a ravine. They are of Buddhist origin, the earliest caves dating from the second century BC and the latest from between the fifth and the end of the sixth century AD.

In his introduction to the Unesco publication *Paintings from Ajanta Caves* (Unesco World Art Series, 1954) Madanjeet Singh writes of these caves:

Architecturally, they are said to be rock-cut replicas of the wooden architecture of the day. The Great Chaitya, of which caves Nos. IX and X are examples, seem to have been derived from the aspidal hall of the secular communities which are mentioned in early Buddhist literature. They have a rectangular portico and nave with side aisles in the form of an apse at the end. On the other hand, the living caves or Viharas are cut in the style of four-sided monasteries comprising a simple central hall with cells along three sides, and provided with stone beds.

Of the astonishingly beautiful paintings on the walls of these caves, which date from between the second century BC and the end of the sixth century AD and surpass anything created in Europe during this period, Madanjeet Singh says:

The main theme of the Ajanta paintings centres round the Jataka stories, the legends of Buddha's reincarnations. Human

life, in the crowded drama of love, compassion, happiness, yearn-
ing, death, suffering and sacrifice, is illuminated by a glow of
religious feeling dominated by a sense of the transience of existence
and profound piety. The multitude of variegated Jataka scenes,
of life on earth, of love and of the pomp and pleasures of kings'
courts, merely form the external settings of the great beings, the
Buddhas and Bodhisattvas, who, in their graceful bodies and
significant attitudes, epitomize wisdom and understanding. In the
intermingling of human beings, plants, flowers and animals there
is a feeling of a deep and intimate spiritual kinship among all
forms of life.

If we turn our gaze to another part of the Orient, to Egypt,
we also find numerous tombs and temples hewn out of the
rock. Excavations during the last decade have disclosed
many rock-cut sepulchres at Beni Hasan and Aswan. Among
the most magnificent rock-cut temples created by Rameses II
is that at Abu Simbel in Nubia, which is also one of the most
impressive of all Ancient Egyptian monuments. The temple
was dedicated to Amon-Re of Thebes and Re-Harakhti of
Heliopolis, the two major gods of the Egyptian motherland.
The building faces east and is designed so that the rising sun
can send its rays into the holy of holies.

The huge sandstone cliffs that flank the Nile close to its
banks near the village of Abu Simbel contain two temples
hewn during the reign of Rameses II (1388–1322 BC), the
greatest of the Egyptian Pharaohs—known to the Greeks
as Sesostris—at whose court Moses was brought up. Three
other rock-cut temples in the same stretch of country are also
his work. Of the two at Abu Simbel, the smaller was dedicated to the Pharaoh's first wife, Nefertari, the larger to the
Pharaoh himself.

At the beginning of the century, the temple was still
largely buried in sand. In 1919, Barsanti cleared part of it
and built a protective wall to prevent it from being smothered
afresh. Today it is possible to gain a comprehensive picture
of the might and majesty of this temple cut out of the rock,

even though the exterior is not in a perfect state of preservation. The façade creates a powerful architectural impression.
Before the entrance rise four gigantic enthroned figures of
the Pharaoh, each sixty feet high and carved out of the solid
rock. One of these figures has been partially destroyed by
lightning. The heads of these royal statues wear the double
crown, their hands rest on their knees. Round their necks
hangs a ring bearing the name Rameses II, which may also
be read on the upper arm and between the legs. To left and
right of each figure and between their legs, on a much
smaller scale, are members of the royal family, Nile gods, and
heraldic plants (papyrus and lily), as well as a row of Negro
and Asiatic captives. An interesting feature is the collection
of Greek, Carian and Phoenician inscriptions cut by mer-
cenaries who came to Abu Simbel in the course of military
campaigns.

The bewildering plethora of inscriptions, bas-reliefs and
statues that decorate the exterior and interior of the temple
is a testimony to the high cultural level of the land of the
Pharaohs and to the great power of Rameses II. The multitude of religious symbols—dog-headed apes, scarabs, sun-
god, moon-god, sun-ship and royal serpents—are an outward expression of the importance attached to this temple in
the kingdom of Rameses II.

The interior of the temple, which goes back 200 feet into
the rock, is in an excellent state of preservation. It consists of
four main divisions and a total of fourteen halls. The roof of
the great Hall of Pillars is carried by eight columns, against
which stand colossal statues of the Pharaoh, thirty feet high.
The walls of all the fourteen halls are decorated with
brightly coloured, meticulously executed paintings and innumerable hieroglyphs, which have proved of immense
value to Egyptologists. The murals show the Pharaoh in all
his power and glory, acting as a god among his people, sacrificing to the highest gods, and conquering his enemies. The
brutality and unrestrained despotism of a mighty ruler in the

ancient world here find uniquely grandiose expression. We can see the Pharaoh driving his spear through a prostrate Libyan; his officers counting the severed hands and limbs of captives and leading other prisoners before the Pharaoh; and Rameses burning incense to the god Ptah, storming a Syrian fortress in his war-chariot, and firing arrows at his fleeing foes on the battlements.

The last hall, the Cella or Holy of Holies, is twenty-three feet long and thirteen feet wide; its rear wall is decorated with four seated statues of gods. To create all these chambers, something like a thousand cubic yards of rock must have been hewn out of the cliff.

The smaller of the two rock-cut temples at Abu Simbel was dedicated to the goddess Hathor and to the deified wife of the Pharaoh, Queen Nefertari. The façade, which is carved out of the rock face, is ninety-two feet long and forty feet high. Three thirty-three feet high statues of the Pharaoh and his Queen lean against the front of the temple, accompanied by smaller statues representing their children. The Hall of Pillars is supported by six columns and, as in the larger temple, its walls are decorated with reliefs portraying scenes from the lives of the King and Queen.

The impressive mortuary caves, which are frequent throughout Egypt, bear witness to the high level of culture of the Ancient Egyptians as powerfully, in their own way, as the great rock-cut temples of Abu Simbel.

THE BIRTH OF CHRISTIANITY IN CAVES

It is an interesting fact that the New Testament story of the life of Christ begins and ends with a cave. Christ was born in an underground stable, and interred in a cavern after the Crucifixion.

The jewel and focal point of Bethlehem, the birthplace of Christ, is the venerable St. Mary's Church, also known as the Church of the Nativity. This craggy, fortress-like edifice, surrounded by Roman, Greek and Armenian monasteries, is built over a ramified rocky grotto where, tradition has it, the stall stood in which Mary 'brought forth her first-born son, and wrapped him in swaddling clothes, and laid him in a manger' (*Luke II*, 7). There is no foundation for the legend that Hadrian replaced the first church on this site by a temple of Adonis, and had a temple of Venus built on Golgotha. The truth is that the Emperor Constantine built a basilica here in AD 350 and that Justinian, considering it unworthy of its position, replaced it by a place of worship that surpassed all the churches of Jerusalem in beauty.

This building was many times restored, improved and embellished, and the Latin Church was often denied the right of possession. But throughout the centuries, the Christian denominations have flocked to its cloisters as though to watch over this precious gem. No non-Christian conqueror ever dared to destroy this church, though they often put it to profane uses. Thus the low entrance, through which it is impossible to walk upright, has been attributed to the Mohammedans' habit of using the church as a stable from time to time. In its sublime simplicity this building, which has five naves and a transept that gives it a cruciform ground plan, is an impressive example of a medieval basilica. Of the richly-gilded mosaics installed by the Emperor Manuel Comnenus in 1169, only fragments remain.

The mysterious charm of this place is particularly manifest in the grottoes, the centre of which is the Grotto of the Nativity. Millions of pilgrims from all the Christian countries of the world and at all epochs have made their way to this marble-panelled cave lit by fifteen silver lamps, on the floor of which is a silver star encircled by the words, *Hic de virgine Jesus Christus natus est* (Here Jesus Christ was born of the Virgin).

Other places of hallowed memory, marked by altars, are to be found in the underground galleries branching off the Grotto of the Nativity. One altar is dedicated to St. Jerome, who translated the Vulgate here and is buried at this spot. Passing through the grottoes one comes to St. Catherine's Church, a richly ornamented edifice which was rebuilt and enlarged by the Emperor of Austria in 1881. There are many legends connected with the Grotto of Our Lady, or the Milk Grotto, where, so the story runs, a few drops of milk from Mary's breast fell on the floor and lent their whiteness to the stone. According to pious popular belief, a drink made from the limestone which occurs in this cave stimulates milk secretion not only in women, but also in domestic animals. In years gone by, this stone, which produces a milky fluid when dissolved in water, was an article of commerce in great demand. (The healing properties of a certain type of limestone will be discussed in the section entitled 'The Radio-active Grotto that Cures Rheumatism.')

In a field near Bethlehem, the cavern in which the angel appeared to the shepherds at the time of Christ's birth is still revered. A flight of steps leads down into the interior, which has been transformed into a chapel belonging to the Greeks.

Like the Church of the Nativity in Bethlehem, the Church of the Annunciation at Nazareth possesses a rock grotto with several chapels connected with episodes in the life of Christ and containing sacred relics.

SEPULCHRAL CAVES OF THE MARNE VALLEY

In France, the finest series of artificial caves dug by man for the interment of his dead is to be found in the Marne Valley.

The very great number of stone implements that can be picked up in this region show the extent of its ancient population. These Neolithic people possessed a rudimentary culture; they lived by simple stockbreeding and by fishing in the lake which stood where the Saint-Gond marshes are now.

To make their tools, these primitive men used the flint

they obtained by tunnelling into the Champagne chalk. They sank shafts at various points, and from these their galleries radiated in all directions. They were sometimes so numerous that certain areas are still undermined by the network of subterranean tunnels.

The honour of having explored these mines goes to the Baron de Baye. They are split up into several groups, some of which comprise many dozens of artificial caves.

They were all preceded by a deep cutting, which made access easy and enabled a sufficient thickness of rock to be left above the cavern to ensure a solid roof.

In some cases, as in one adit of the Trou Blériot station, they went down several yards below the surface. These passages were rectangular. The smallest measured six feet by six feet six inches, the largest thirteen feet by twelve. The height of the roof varied between three feet six inches and five feet six inches.

Some of them were shallow, roughly shaped, and closed by a single stone covered over with rubble and earth. From his observations, de Baye concluded that this type of grave was intended to give permanent burial to warriors killed on the field of battle.

Another type of sepulchral cave that can be distinguished in the Marne Valley shows more careful work. The walls are solid and well constructed, the opening carefully trimmed and not flush with the soil, but on a slight incline to prevent water from entering. These caverns were sealed with an enormous slab of stone. They did not contain many bodies, generally two to five and never more than ten. They were always accompanied by important funerary furniture.

In addition to these two types of artificial cave there was a third, consisting of a more elaborate underground dwelling. In these the main cavity, situated at a lower level, is preceded by an antechamber. Sometimes the great hall is divided by a thin partition, designed to support the roof. Several of these halls are equipped with a ventilation shaft.

Occasionally prehistoric man cut shelves in the walls to accommodate his implements of stone and bone.

A highly stylized human figure in low relief is sometimes found in the vestibule of these caves. It is known as the goddess of the dead, and similar effigies have been remarked on some of the dolmens in the same district and on the steles of the French Midi and Italy.

The great anatomist, Broca, who took a profound interest in prehistory and made valuable studies of the trepanned skulls dating from this period, expresses himself as follows concerning these sculptures.

'These crude but unvarying sculptures on the walls of the de Baye ante-chambers, which we have seen *in situ*, prove that Neolithic religion had already attained the level of anthropomorphism.'

These subterranean places dug by man bear witness to a veritable cult of the dead. Sometimes flat stones, often brought from afar, were arranged to form a bed, on which the body was stretched out. The interment must have been accompanied by funeral ceremonies, for the stones bear the traces of a purifying fire.

Artificial sepulchral caverns were also dug in other parts of France, for example in the Gard. One of these, the grotto of Pujault, is composed of three chambers; the smallest of them contains a paving of stone on which the dead reposed.

THE CATACOMBS OF PARIS

The Catacombs of Paris—the principal entrance to which is in the courtyard of the western gate-lodge of the former Enfer Gate, later renamed the Place Denfert in honour of the defender of Belfort—are an immense charnel house established in the old stone quarries, dating from the Gallo-Roman period, that covered the countryside south of Paris.

These quarries were worked for many centuries without method, without supervision, at the whim of entrepreneurs who did not always respect property boundaries, quarrying far into the country and even underneath the town.

The Observatoire, the Luxembourg, the Odéon, the Val de Grâce, the Church of Saint-Sulpice, and parts of the Rue Saint-Jacques, the Rue de la Harpe, the Rue de Tournon and the Rue de Vaugirard were built over these cavities.

The multitude of accidents compelled the government to intervene, and in 1776 a general inspection and the mapping of all undertakings was ordered. This inspection led in the following year to the creation of a company of specialist engineers and a governing body to supervise the quarries.

Dulaure devotes several pages of his *Histoire de Paris* to the Paris Catacombs, and it is from this book that most of the following information is taken.

Following the example of Rome, Naples and other cities, the bones from the disused cemeteries of Paris were transferred to part of the stone quarries no longer being worked. There was good reason for this.

The Cemetery of the Innocents, situated in what is now Les Halles, had been a burial ground for nearly a thousand years. The resulting accumulation of corpses infected the whole neighbourhood, and the government received a continuous spate of complaints.

In 1780, an accident took place in the cellars of the houses of the Rue de la Lingerie through the propinquity of a pit that must have contained more than two thousand bodies. The clamorous protests of the inhabitants of the street, coupled with a statement issued in 1783 by the Sieur Cadet-de-Vaux, Inspector-General of Public Health—in which this savant forcefully drew attention to the dangers of continuing to retain this cemetery in the centre of Paris—finally induced the Conseil d'État to take notice of the matter. It ordered that the site of the cemetery should cease to be used for this purpose and should be converted into a public market. The

Archbishop of Paris gave his consent to this in a decree dated 1787.

The underground stone quarries of the Mont-Souris plain, which at this time were outside Paris, were chosen to receive the bones removed from the cemetery. The Maison de la Tombe-Issoire, at the same spot, was acquired to serve as an entrance to the Catacombs. The subterranean galleries were reinforced, and on April 7th, 1786, the representatives of the Church formally blessed and consecrated this underground cemetery.

In May, 1787, the cemeteries of Saint-Eustache and Saint-Étienne-des-Grés were also closed and the bones from them taken to the Catacombs. Subsequently, during and after the Revolution, the bodies of those killed in the fighting and the bones from the cemeteries of other churches, monasteries and convents of Paris were successively deposited there.

It was Frochot, Prefect of the Seine, who, between 1810 and 1811, organized and arranged this underground cemetery in the form in which it may be seen today. The galleries of the Catacombs are flanked by two rows of human bones, sometimes reaching a height of sixteen feet. From time to time an inscription calls upon the visitor to meditate. The entrance hall contains the words: *Arrête, c'est ici l'empire de la mort* (Halt, this is the empire of death).

In a square formed by these subterranean passages, Dulaure tells us, Héricart de Thury set up a pathology laboratory where all types of bones deformed by disease were methodically classified.

A vast and ancient quarry workshop was chosen to receive the bodies exhumed from the Saint-Laurent Cemetery, which was closed in November, 1804. A monument was set up of which the base pedestal is composed of bones, the mouldings of the largest possible tibias, while at the top is a death's-head.

The Altar of the Obelisks was built in 1810 and masks structural work designed to support the roof of the quarry.

The altar and obelisks are copied from antique models, and the pedestals on either side of the altar are made of bones.

In one gallery may be seen the bones of victims of various bloody scenes which took place in Paris during the Revolution, with brief descriptions of when and where they fell.

'Those from the battles of the Place de Grève, the Hôtel de Brienne and the Rue Meslée with the commander of the watch, August 28th and 29th, 1788.'

'From the battle of M. Reveillon's wall-paper factory, Faubourg, Saint-Antoine, April 28th, 1789.'

'From the battle of the Château des Tuileries, August 10th, 1792.'

'From the days of September 2nd and 3rd, 1792.'

Beneath the stairway that leads down into the 'Catacombes basses' runs an aqueduct built to carry the water from a neighbouring spring to the well of the Tombe-Issoire.

The Catacombs are open to the public. The entrance is at 2, Place Denfert-Rochereau. The visitor passes along some eight hundred yards of underground galleries and emerges in the Rue Dareau.

RUSSIAN CAVE DWELLINGS AND CHURCHES

Russia is very rich in caves of all sorts, including ancient cave dwellings, cave cities and caverns that have been used for religious purposes.

The Crimean Peninsula possesses a great wealth of caves, many of which are in use as habitations or for other purposes. There are some remarkable caves in the nummulitic limestone slopes near Baktchisarai (Tartar garden city), beside the deep ravine of the River Churuk-Ssu. Not far from an ancient mausoleum built in the Moorish style lies a vast cave formerly used for the incarceration of prominent political prisoners. The Russian ambassador Shermetiev was imprisoned here for about twenty years at the end of the seventeenth century.

There are also a number of caves in the Crimea which are noteworthy from a geological viewpoint. The Scylla cliffs by the sea near Balaklava contain a picturesque grotto, as do the limestone beds near Yalta. In the neighbourhood of Alaushka are two notable stalactitic caves, one by the mountain pass of Alakyty, the other close to the village of Tuak. In the Ssudak Valley, an important wheat and fruit centre, is a two and a half mile-long cave used as a wine cellar—the largest wine cellar in the Crimea. At the foot of the mountains north of Ssudak, in the midst of a thick forest, stands the monastery of Kiziltash. Two caverns pierce the rocks encircling the monastery. The city of Kerch is divided in two by the Mount of Mithridates, the ancient Acropolis. In the northern section catacombs have been found containing fresco-like paintings. The majority date from the second and third century B C. Of particular interest is the Kerch catacomb discovered in 1872, with large fresco paintings portraying scenes of war and burial ceremonies.

Near Tuimasa there is a magnificent cavern containing a number of underground lakes which periodically fill up with water and then empty again. The mountains of Kokchetav, the Blue Mountains, in the Kazak republic, are rich in caves, some of which contain lakes with a depth of 500 feet or more. The region round the important watering place of Borovoye is also noted for its picturesque caverns and lakes.

One of the most remarkable sights of the Crimea is the underground settlement of Cherkesskermen. Its ruins consist of caves of varying size with very thin walls and roofs. At the entrance to the cave city stands the 'Great Cave' with a stone cross, round which are grouped benches. This was once a court and council chamber. Not far from Cherkesskermen and five miles from Sebastopol, lies a second cave city which includes the monastery of Inkerman. The Inkerman stone quarries supply Sebastopol and its immediate environment with excellent building stone. The caves, which are thought to date from prehistoric times, have been partially destroyed by the quarrying with the passage of the years. The monastery of Popes Clement and Martin, who were exiled here during the early years of the Christian era, is of outstanding interest. It contains three rock-cut churches side by side, one of which—St. Clement's Church—is amongst the largest in the Crimea. The catacombs are linked together by corridors and steps cut in the rock.

Moving from the picturesque and sunny Crimea to the north, we find many geologically and historically note-worthy caves. Between four famous rapids of the Dnieper lies the picturesque island of Perun, rising 300 feet above the river and shaped like a sheepskin cap. This island is notable for a cave and the so-called Serpent Ravine. Close to Cher-nigov on the rising ground on the right bank of the River Desna stands the monastery of Ilyineko Troizkye, whose cathedral was built in the seventeenth century by the Ger-man architect Sernikov. A new rock-cut church was con-structed on the monastery's land during the twentieth cen-tury. The city of Kiev possesses a remarkable cave monas-tery. Close beside the eleventh-century Ascension Cathedral and the twelfth-century Church of the Redeemer, an opening in the ground leads down into the former subterranean Pecherskaya monastery, a series of cells and corridors dug out of the clay and said to have been founded by St. Anthony and St. Theodosius. Prior to the Tartar invasion under Batu Chan, the monks from the monastery were buried in these caves. Before the rise of the Soviets, the caves were a famous place of pilgrimage. In 1913 the finding of a boy's corpse in another cave in a hillside near Kiev led to a sensational trial for ritual murder.

During the Bolshevik Revolution of 1918–19, many revo-lutionaries hid in the sandstone quarries of Odessa, from which the stone used in building the city had been taken, and here operated their illegal printing presses.

The Soviet Republic of Georgia possesses a curious archaeological monument in the cave city of Uplis Zikhen,

5

situated on the left bank of the Kura not far from Tiflis. Uplis Zikhen, which means Fortress of the Ruler, dates from Georgia's pre-Christian period. At the beginning of the Christian era, the fortress was strengthened by the Georgian Tsar Arshak. The cave city was still inhabited at the time of Genghis Khan's attack on Georgia in the thirteenth century. It consists of several superimposed storeys cut in the high, rocky Kermaik Mountains and linked by steps and alleys. The cave city was extended in the ninth, twelfth and fourteenth centuries. The underground passage leading to the river is particularly remarkable.

Thirteen miles from the small district-capital of Akhalzig, in the same region, lies the magnificent cave city of Bradsiya, consisting of several hundred caverns with underground churches, halls, cells and passages. The date of this cave city's foundation is unknown. It possesses some interesting old frescoes portraying the Georgian Tsar and Tsarina, David and Tamara. The cave city was severely damaged by the Mongols in the fourteenth century and by the Persians in the sixteenth century.

Georgia possesses a number of other noteworthy caves. An underground river flows near the port of Gagry, and there are some natural fissure-caves in the high cliffs of the Pikherov ravine. Not far from Guma, in the neighbourhood of Novyl Afon, is a famous show cave consisting of several domed chambers linked by narrow corridors.

In the region of Erivan, the capital of the Armenian Soviet Republic, in the wild Garni Chei gorge, lies the old monastery of Kegart or Ari Bank, an Armenian cave monastery with several rock-cut churches. The main church dates from the twelfth and thirteenth centuries, but is not situated in a cave.

This list of Russian caves is far from exhaustive. In its vast mountainous regions Russia contains numberless caves, many of which have yet to be explored.

THE GHOST VALLEY OF CAPPADOCIA

Anatolia, the cradle of many ancient cultures, contains, alongside impressive relics and memorials of the past, a vast treasury of curious natural phenomena, and a wealth of caves and rock-cut churches and monasteries belonging to old Cappadocia, which is now part of Turkey.

The visitor to the district of Urgub, fifty-three miles from Kaisarieh, the ancient Caesarea of Cappadocia, feels as though he has been transported to another planet inhabited by ghosts and spirits, or else that his mind is prey to some fantastic dream. Imagine a vast plain from which rise cones, minarets, pyramids and columns of stone, of the most wonderful shapes and radiating all colours of the rainbow in alternating light and shadow. The multitude of rocks of all shapes and sizes is almost beyond belief, defying the power of the eye to register them all. Imagination runs riot and the observer fancies himself amidst a lunar or martian landscape.

This strange land, unique in the whole world, this region of rocks which still breathes the spirit of bygone ages, was once the habitation of cave dwellers and a place of refuge during the early days of Christianity. Here, too, the first artists of iconography gave enthusiastic expression to their vision in unconstrained frescoes.

The 'Wonders of Urgub' were described in the eighteenth century by the French archaeologist Paul Lucas. His account gives utterance to the amazement he felt at the sight of this rocky landscape. At the time, he considered it the ruins of an ancient city. Nobody believed Lucas's report, deeming it to be at least exaggerated, if not completely fictitious. M. Deslunes, former French ambassador to the 'Sublime Porte', confirmed his statements; but no explanation of the nature and origin of these formations was then forthcoming. Today, geologists have solved the mystery. The area, in which pyramids are particularly numerous, is a plateau about twenty miles long between the volcano of Erceyis to the east, Hasadang to the south, the narrow valley of the Kizil Irmak to the north and the salt lake of Kokh Isar in the west.

Another incredible phenomenon rivets the gaze in the Urgub region. Dotted about the zone are long, narrow and very regular natural cuttings, whose smooth walls rise to a height of 300 to 600 feet and are as regular and perpendicular as the walls of some ancient fortress. The true wonder of the region, however, is the plain itself. Here the fissured and fragmented rocks have assumed astonishing shapes: pyramids, cones, needles, caves, towers, turrets and minarets follow one another in indescribable confusion. Standing among them one has the impression of being in the midst of the ruins of a huge city. Everywhere the eye lights upon what seem to be walls, fallen domes and buildings whose vaulted roofs have collapsed. Here nature has dug out a cave in a rock, there one sees a façade with a row of entrances, farther on a few slender turrets and next to them enormous rocks rise skyward from the debris.

The most magnificent sight, however, is presented by the long rows of cones which spread dramatically across the plain. Here the landscape no longer has the appearance of a ruined city, but looks like a military encampment of tents. The size of the cones varies: some are only the height of a man, many of them measure 30 to 100 feet, while others reach the height of a minaret. A number of these cones bear small, flat blocks of stone on their tips that look like hats. A great many of them have been hollowed out, sometimes in three or four storeys. They contain fireplaces, bed niches, larders, wine-jars and living-rooms that afford protection from all the inclemencies of the weather. The cones are dotted at random about the landscape, sometimes in compact groups, sometimes at considerable distances from one another. According to the estimate of the inhabitants, these cones number about three hundred thousand. The rocks are often dazzling white like chalk. But thousands of them, composed of volcanic ejecta, are brilliant yellow, dark blue and, more rarely, pink or multi-coloured.

All the open country round Urgub is covered with vineyards, which stand out in strong contrast to the white landscape. As manure for their vineyards the vine-growers employ the excreta of wild doves, tens of thousands of which nest in the hollows of the cliffs of volcanic ash or tuff. The inhabitants improve the nesting facilities by digging out fresh niches in the rocks.

If one studies the rows of cones stretching across the plain carefully, an invariable rule becomes apparent. The smallest cones stand on the slopes of the ravine, while those in the middle are far taller, so that strata or layers of particular colours run right through groups of cones at the same level. This leads one to conjecture that the whole mass of stone was once a solid block, which was then worn away by erosion, leaving the cones standing.

The little town of Urgub itself is embedded between the vertical sides of colossal massifs of lava, and seems to do without all the amenities normally considered essential to life, such as water and vegetation. But the abundance of easily worked stone for building in this region offsets many other privations. The town includes a large part of a vast necropolis. Not content with building dwellings to suit their needs, the inhabitants also took possession of the old burial caves, which numbered thousands, broke down the old fronts and replaced them with built-up façades, so that part of the dwelling is underground and the rest out in the open. One asks in vain today what people it can have been whose bones moulder in this gigantic city of the dead. Kaisarieh is too far away for the dead to have been brought here from that city. A great number of the tombs and mausoleums have naturally fallen victim to robbers and vandals. Nevertheless, well-preserved tombs are still to be found cut in the white tuff on inaccessible heights, taking the form of caves with side-niches to accommodate the sarcophagus, as in the Roman catacombs.

In a region completely lacking in timber, where volcanoes furnished excellent opportunities for constructing or finding cave dwellings in the easily worked tuffs and agglomerates, the rock provided accommodation for many purposes. In the course of the centuries not only were dwellings for the living and dead cut out of it, but also halls for religious purposes. Thus large numbers of churches, chapels, monasteries and hermitages are to be found in the cliffs and cones of rock. Here the traveller may experience the joys of discovery, for the majority of the caverns have never been explored.

This multitude of cave chambers, intended for such a variety of purposes, can never have been used at the same time by one population. It seems more likely that each generation burrowed into the rock afresh in order to create something new, either out of superstitious dread of the old, or for the pleasure of this easy and cheap form of building. The architectural styles reveal Roman, Graeco-Byzantine, and in some cases even Egyptian influences, demonstrating the confluence of Western and Eastern cultures in this region.

Of the extant frescoes that decorate the cave churches and monasteries almost nothing indicates pre-Christian origin. Most of the subjects are figures from the Old or New Testament and scenes from the life of Christ. How numerous Christian places of worship once were in this land of Islam is shown by the fact that the Geureme Gorge, also called the Valley of Ghosts, contains three hundred and sixty-five chapels. The churches of Geureme also possess the most beautiful and best-preserved frescoes. Many mural paintings and mosaics were destroyed during the dominion of the Isaurian and Amorian Dynasties, because the Mohammedan rulers of this epoch condemned the worship of images of the saints as heathen superstition. During this period artists contented themselves with simple geometrical ornament. The

Mohammedans scratched away the heads of many of the frescoes.

The finest frescoes are incontestably those in the churches of Tokali Kilise and Elmali Kilise. In the former, the events of the New Testament are depicted in chronological order, from the Annunciation to the Ascension of Christ. A particularly striking fresco is that portraying the Last Supper; in the middle of the table lies a large fish, the symbol of Christ.

The Geureme Gorge is known by the local people as the Valley of Ghosts, because they believe that the souls of the monks who lived here wander about in it. This landscape is certainly ghostly enough. What makes it so, however, is not the monks, but the natural architecture of stone, one of the most magnificent and strange geological formations in the world.

SACRED CAVES OF THE INCAS

The almost legendary, highly-civilized Incas practised an elaborate cult of the dead, which was celebrated in caverns.

Kenko in the language of the Incas meant 'the twisted' or 'the tortuous'. It was the name given to a winding groove down which libations flowed into the subterranean clefts. Heinrich Ubbelohde-Doering, curator of the Ethnographic Museum, Munich, describes these *kenko* caves as follows, in his illustrated work, *Auf den Königsstrassen der Inkas*. 'The entrances are set in the overhanging cliffs, whose surfaces have been chiselled smooth. We are standing before a scene from antique tragedy: the entrance to the Underworld, to the dead. Here we are really in the Kingdom of the Dead, in a cavern out of whose walls altar-like plinths and slabs have been hewn, while in the background and on the right have been cut deep alcoves. Away from the walls rises a huge throne and altar, six feet high and divided in three, with a low back-rest carved out of the solid rock. Behind it, a deep fissure opens on to the subterranean world. Here the funeral rites were performed. The monumental block may itself have been a throne of the dead, of mummies, as were other stone seats under the tall sky of Cuzco. The chiselled rocks of the Sacsayhuaman region were sacred shrines enclosing the entries to the Underworld where dwelt the departed ancestors. According to the belief of the mountain people, men came out of the earth and after death they returned into the earth again.'

The *Lacco*, too, led down into the mysterious world of the dead. This was a more isolated and huge mass of rock, reminiscent of Ancient Greek legend. On the rock blossoms the red Inca flower and the road to Chitapampa passes close by the rock. The Lacco is split by a deep fissure. On the left a group of carvings surrounds the entrance to a cave.

Ubbelohde-Doering describes the first cavern as follows:

The entrance to the cave is on the extreme left under a slab of stone wedged into the rock face and hanging over those who go in and out like an enormous thunderbolt. The monolith on the ground seems to have been used at one time to seal the entrance. Stepping into the dim interior, one sees on the left a large chamberlike alcove and further on several shallow bowl-shaped niches in the wall, in which images of saints or gods might stand. Then the cave bends to the left and narrows to a cleft that loses itself in the heart of the mountain.

The rock mass of the Lacco, in which the cave is situated, is noteworthy for a curious set of steps which admit of no ascent, but only of passage to and fro. These steps, which are important for their bearing on ancient Inca ritual, probably represent Life. Halfway up these 'magic steps' is the entrance to a second cave, more richly carved than the first.

'Just inside the entrance, on the right,' runs Ubbelohde-Doering's description of this cave, 'a low, beautifully chiselled stone tablet catches the eye, with a most remarkable border. If the symbolic character of such carvings is manifest anywhere it is here. The semi-circular projection might serve for the laying down of offerings. But the stepped border can hardly be interpreted as anything else than a symbol. If we go a few steps farther in and turn round, we see the mighty entrance pillar carved out of the rock, from which a narrow flight of steps leads into the open. To the right of the steps two young pumas creep up towards the light; opposite them on the smooth rock wall a serpent in relief wriggles up into the cave, into the earth. Whether we should be justified in conjecturing that the young pumas symbolize mankind's coming forth from the bowels of the earth, and the snake its return thither, cannot be decided at present. At the end of the cave, where an almost nocturnal darkness prevails, there rises another altar-like seat about six feet broad and five feet deep. The abandoned throne of the dead stands in solemn, stony calm in the heart of the mountain. Here is the Kingdom of the Underworld, which rose up out of the clefts beside the throne and vanished into them. The hint of some Mystery still clings to these fissures.'

According to the ancient belief, the forefathers exercised a powerful influence on the fortunes of the living. They could bestow blessings, if they were honoured. They could send misfortune, if they were slighted. Honouring the dead was one of the basic preconditions of existence. The sacred rocks of the Sacsayhuaman region, of which these caves are examples, were places at which the ancestors of the clans of chiefs and kings were worshipped. They were venerated at the points from which, according to tribal myth, these clans first issued.

SUBTERRANEAN PICTURE GALLERIES

Amongst the most sensational discoveries ever made in caves were the rock paintings, which have caused a tremendous amount of speculation in scientific circles. Painted caves have been found not only in Europe, but also in Africa, South America and Australia.

Europe has dozens of decorated caves, particularly in France and Spain. The Spanish province of Santander alone contains thirteen: those of Altamira, El Castillo, La Pasiega, Hornos de la Peña, Covalanas, Sotarriza, La Haza, Salitre, La Clotilde, Meaza, Las Aguas, Santian and Pendo. Southern France also possesses a great number of noteworthy painted caves, especially the departments of Dordogne, Lot, Haute-Garonne, Basses-Pyrénées, Hautes-Pyrénées, Ardèche and Gironde.

These Ice Age paintings and drawings represent wild horses, aurochs, mammoth, rhinoceros, cave-bear, bison, deer, reindeer, wild boar, ibex, apes, felines and fish, as well as humans in various forms. Drawings of hands which appear to be imprints are especially numerous.

The most famous painted caves in Spain are those of Altamira, which were stumbled upon by chance. In 1868, a huntsman's dog fell into a cleft from which he could only be released by removing some pieces of rock. This led to the discovery of the cave. In 1875, the cave was more thoroughly explored by Don Marcelino de Sautuola on whose land it was situated. In the course of digging he found animal bones and flints, which he reported to the geologist and prehistorian, Professor Juan Vilanova in Madrid, who advised him to continue his investigations. On one occasion in 1879 he was accompanied into the cave by his five-year-old daughter, who suddenly exclaimed: 'Daddy, look at the painted bulls!' Amazed and scarcely believing his eyes, he, too, now saw that the walls were covered with paintings. Such wonderful paintings in a dark hole under the ground? Why had they been painted here, where no one could see them? Who could the artists have been, since the cave was absolutely unknown and, until now, inaccessible? After hearing of this new find, Professor Vilanova decided to see for himself. The paintings depicted animals that no longer existed in Spain; the artists must therefore either have worked from memory or have lived during the lifetime of the animals. The problem now was to prove that the animals in question had once inhabited this region. Proof of this was forthcoming as the result of systematic digging in the cave itself, where de Sautuola had already found fossil bones which Professor Vilanova was able to identify as the remains of bison, ibex, deer and primitive horse—the same animals which were portrayed in the paintings. Bones with engravings on them were also found. These bones and antlers engraved with designs that were recognizable as mammoths and cave-bears caused a sensation at the Paris Exhibition of 1878. In a paper published in 1880, de Sautuola asserted for the first time that the cave paintings must date from prehistoric times. The author even gave the period to which, according to their subject and style, the pictures belonged.

A great controversy raged round these wall paintings, similar to that which surrounded the Neanderthal skull. Nobody believed in their authenticity. How could paintings have been preserved for thousands of years in the damp, dark cave? A fatal concatenation of unfavourable circumstances increased the confusion. A French painter of de Sautuola's acquaintance had been his guest during a visit to Santander. This was enough to cause malicious people to attribute the cave paintings to this artist, and assert that he had executed them on de Sautuola's orders. In short, the latter was branded a forger. No one believed the paintings to be genuine, and the specialists in this field—amongst them Cartailhac, the president of the French Prehistoric Society, who later reversed his opinion—were the most energetic in contradicting the Madrid scholar. The first prehistorian to pronounce the Altamira paintings authentic was the Frenchman Piette, who did so in 1887 in a polemic against Cartailhac.

In 1895, the prehistorian Rivière, after visiting the Altamira cave, began to explore caverns in the Dordogne, France. Here he discovered similar paintings in the La Mouthe cave. He placed before the Paris Academy of Sciences some fossilized objects of bone and horn found in the cave, which showed engravings of the same animals as those on the walls. On clearing out more of the cave-filling, Rivière uncovered other paintings on the wall at a level below that of the existing floor. Thereupon an exchange of views began in France, which, despite the opposition of the President of the Prehistoric Society, was manifestly favourable to the theory of the two Spaniards. But the latter died too soon to see their theory vindicated. Later investigators, following the discovery of thousands of cave paintings all over the world, came solidly round to their viewpoint.

In 1902, Cartailhac and the Abbé Henri Breuil[1] undertook a detailed study of the Altamira cave and its paintings and engravings, numbering well over a hundred, of which Breuil made masterly copies. With the assistance of Prince Albert of Monaco, who visited the cave in 1904, a magnificent illustrated work was produced, *La Caverne d'Altamira à Santillane, près Santander (Espagne)*. The two French scholars were helped in their work by the Alcalde of Rio, Don Hermilio, who later extended his investigations over the whole province and so discovered further rock paintings in a number of other caves. In 1906, he reported his finds in a pamphlet entitled *Paintings and Engravings in the Prehistoric Caves of the Province of Santander*. After this investigation, the study of prehistoric paintings in Spain was confined to a few scholars, whereas far more attention was paid to the subject in France.

In the eastern part of Spain, Don Juan Cabré discovered cave paintings different in style from those at Altamira. For many years the Altamira cave was neglected. Today, thanks to the intervention of Dr. J. Carvallo, King Alfonso XIII and

---

[1] In 1952, Abbé Breuil published the book, *Four Hundred Centuries of Cave Art* (Montignac). This French priest has devoted the major part of his life to the discovery, preservation and study of the priceless relics found in the darkness of caves. In this comprehensive book of 418 pages and 531 illustrations, he deals with the cave paintings of Altamira, Font-de-Gaume, Les Combarelles, Lascaux, Les Trois-Frères and Niaux and eighty-four lesser caves.

the Duke of Alba, it has been transformed into a well-kept museum open to the public. In 1924, Carvallo published his book, *Prehistoria Universal Especial de España*, with fine polychrome prints of the most important cave and rock paintings.

The Altamira cave is 890 feet long. Before part of the roof collapsed, the antechamber immediately inside the entrance must have presented an overwhelming sight, for the whole hall as far back as the end wall bearing the paintings was visible in its entirety from the entrance. The dark inner chambers are believed to have been temples in which men practised their magical conjurations and invocations before the totemistic paintings made for the purpose. The Great Hall of paintings has been called the 'Sistine Chapel of prehistoric art', for it contains the finest cave pictures anywhere in Europe. The Great Hall is sixty feet long and thirty feet wide; the height ranges between four and nine feet. The size of the paintings varies. The largest picture, in the centre of the rear wall, representing a hind, is seven feet six inches long. The most numerous paintings are those of bison and range from four feet six inches to six feet in length. The animal is portrayed in every position, in flight, walking, prone, or falling. The painter has made skilful use of all the natural irregularities and protuberances of the rock surface in order to give enhanced plastic quality and realism to his creations.

Towards the centre of the ceiling is a bull's head in black, extremely lifelike and expressive. On the left is a running ibex and farther back, on the wall, the figure of a primitive horse, heavily built and short legged. The colours of the great bison near the centre are still bright, causing some people to think it a forgery, or at least that it has been painted over. In addition to the paintings, there are numerous engraved drawings, incised in the rock-wall with a burin. There are many smooth patches, suggesting that either they were once covered by paintings or else that they were prepared for painting. It is thought that there may have been one or more further halls beyond this one, which have been filled in by the collapse of the roof. In the chambers opening out of the Hall of Pictures, clear traces of cave-bear have been found, and also lines on the ceilings apparently made by drawing the fingers along them.

A number of relics and pictures from the past have been found in other Santander caves. Almost indecipherable signs and figures constructed of dotted lines, together with a sarcophagus of stone slabs containing a human skeleton without a skull, were discovered in the Meaza cave in Ruiseñada. Close to the lower jaw lay a small javelin point made from the tine of a stag antler. In the del Pendo cave only a few faint drawings, perhaps representing penguins, were found, but a large number of bones of deer, ibex, horse, rhinoceros and other fauna were unearthed. The finest piece was a sceptre or *bâton de commandement*. In addition, a small female statuette carved from an antler-tine, and an arrowhead of translucent quartz were found. There were also striking pieces of engraved bone and horn. A unique discovery was the elephant (not the mammoth, but an early elephant, probably *Elephas antiquus*), outlined in red pigment with a heart-shaped spot of pigment in the centre, found in the Pindal Cave at Colombres in the Asturias.

There is hardly any attempt to depict the human form in the Spanish caves, which is doubtless to be explained by the purpose of the paintings, which was, through 'sympathetic magic', to obtain power over the creatures portrayed. In the caves of El Castillo, near Puente Visgo, and also at Altamira, hand imprints have been found, some of them covered with symbols. Oddly enough, similar representations of outspread hands have been found in a cave near Port George IV, Australia, where the forefathers of the Worora tribe are buried. Every descendant who visited this place in the olden days left an imprint of his hand on the flat rock to exorcize the spirits. A third type of hand-imprint was discovered in the French caves of Gargas, Bédailhac, Les Trois Frères and Cabreret.

The Gargas cave, which, to judge by the finds made in it, was used for religious purposes, shows about two hundred imprints of *mutilated* hands. This evidence of mutilation casts an interesting light on the practices of the people who used this and other such sacred caves. As Professor W. J. Sollas points out in *Ancient Hunters*, the rite of amputating one or more joints or whole fingers, especially the little finger, is still practised by primitive peoples of today in many parts of the world. It may be done as a cure for sickness, a sign of mourning, as part of an initiation ceremony, or for some other sacrificial purpose. W. J. Burchell reports observing it in South Africa in his book, *Travels in the Interior of Southern Africa* (London, 1824). It is common among the pygmy races of Mkabba on Lake Ngami, where the mutilation is a tribal sign, and also among certain North American Indian tribes. In his *Voyages round the World* (London, 1897), Captain Cook states that the custom is prevalent in the Pacific Islands, and that in Tonga the finger is sacrificed to propitiate the god Atoa. In the Fiji Islands, a hundred fingers must fall when a chief dies. Among the Dravidians of Mysore in India, there is a sect known as the Berula Kodó (i.e. People who Give the Finger). This sect holds a religious festival every few years at which the last two joints of the third and fourth fingers of the right hand of the women are amputated to the accompaniment of an elaborate ritual. G. W. Stow writes in *The Native Races of South Africa* (London, 1905) that the custom of amputating the first joint of the little finger was almost universal among the Bushmen, its purpose being to ensure a long career of feasting after death or a safe passage to the next world. Even in Europe, the practice of sacrificing a hand, though in a slightly less gruesome form, was still extant in the eighteenth century. The 'servitude of the dead hand' continued right up to the French Revolution. After the death of a serf, his right hand was cut off and given to his feudal lord as a sign that his bondman was now free. The same practice was discontinued in the Bishopric of Liége in about 1142.

What connexion is there between the hand-imprints in the caves of France and Spain and those of Australia? Are they mute testimonies to a time when Australia was not yet an island, but joined to South Africa and India? This old continent is known to the zoologist as 'Lemuria', and to the geologist as 'Gondwana'. Did a land bridge once extend from Australia to the east coast of Spain, before the time when the continents were torn apart by the seismic disaster so vividly outlined by Alfred Wegner in his book, *Die Entstehung der Kontinente* (Brunswick, 1929)? Are these hand-imprints wordless witnesses to a time when our earth had a different shape from the one it shows today?

The French caves contain more engravings of human faces than do the Spanish. Some of them are only lightly sketched, others are sharply incised and often curiously distorted, while a third group at first left observers in doubt as to whether they represented men or beasts. These last are pictures of masked and totally disguised men, of the same kind as those found in the cave paintings of South Africa. It is a remarkable fact that the lightly sketched faces have been found in caves from the Pyrenees as far as Russia. Low-reliefs have also been found, e.g. at Laussel in the Dordogne, giving a similar sketchy impression of a human face. The caves of Marsoulas and Les Combarelles contain heavily distorted depictions of the face characterized especially by large, pendulous noses. In the famous and vast Trois-Frères Cavern, near Saint-Girons in the Ariège department of France, Count Begouen discovered the figure of a man painted in red and black, which is thought to represent a wizard. The finder writes of it:

He has gloved his hands in the skin of a lion's paws, with sharp claws; he is hidden behind a mask with the beard of bison, an eagle's beak, the eyes of an owl, a wolf's ears, and a stag's antlers. He has fastened a horse-tail to the base of his spine. Thus he believes he has taken on all the magic power, all the physical qualities of the animals: the bravery of the lion, the sharp sight of the eagle by day and of the owl by night, the hearing of the wolf, the endurance of the bison, the speed of horse and stag.

On the walls around him are a multitude of drawings of lion, tiger, reindeer, bison, bear, and wild ass, some of them wounded—especially the bears, from whose muzzles blood pours—and interspersed among them are arrows and clubs. Cartailhac, Capitan, Breuil and Kühn have given it as their expert opinion that these are chronicles of prehistoric magic rites which were once performed in this cave. These paintings call to mind a similar specimen of prehistoric art, the so-called 'White Lady' of South Africa, of which we shall have more to say later.

Norbert Casteret gives a vivid account of his exciting discoveries in the caves of Montespan in the Pyrenees during the years 1922 and 1923 in his book, *Ten Years under the Earth* (trans. Burrows Massey, London, 1939). He found numerous rock drawings of mammoth, wild horse, bison, deer, wild ass, ibex, chamois, hyaena, etc. But what only one person had ever found before were some thirty clay models of animals about three feet high, as well as several high-reliefs, half destroyed by water seeping through the rock. This cave must also have been a sanctuary, one of those sacred grottoes in which sorcerers practised their magic rites.

In 1932, after a perilous descent into the Labastide caverns in the same region of the Pyrenees in which Édouard Piette excavated the grotto of Lortet in 1873—a district known as the 'land of the forty caves'—Casteret discovered a cavern containing the bones of animals, potsherds, and a few human bones. Pushing on, he entered a smaller chamber, on the ceiling of which he saw the engraving of a lion's head, a frieze of eight or ten horses, from five to six and a half feet long, following or facing one another. All these horses, and

6

many others which he later came upon in other parts of the cave, had common characteristics—'squat body, short, thick head, spiky, upright mane, and extremely long tail'. In addition to other animal engravings and indecipherable lines and symbols, Casteret found the engraving of an unusual human head which he describes thus: 'Seen from the front it looks like a face in a loophole. The perfectly round face is most peculiar: the eyes are deeply-incised circles; the nose is very large, and includes big, dilated nostrils, more animal than human; the mouth is a slash like that of a mask; a pointed beard completes this strange and bestial visage.' Casteret believes that it represents a man in a sorcerer's mask, saying: 'The snout and round eyes recall forcefully the celebrated masked sorcerer of the cavern of the Trois-Frères (Ariège) and the duk-duk masks of New Guinea.'

Casteret found a number of other engravings on the walls and roofs and on blocks of stone in this cave, but only one painting. This, on an enormous rock fallen from the ceiling and almost blocking the main gallery 650 feet from the entrance, was a horse engraved in line and painted in red with black mane and hooves. He also discovered an engraving of a naked, masked man, with body stooped forward, thighs bent, and arms held out in front of him as though dancing.

The Dordogne, and its tributaries, rising in the Massif Centrale, cut through thick masses of limestone before escaping to the plains. In this section their valleys are flanked by precipitous bastions of rock rising aloft, riddled with caves, many of which are still inhabited. In the year 1940, a group of boys were playing in the woods above Montignac, when their little dog slipped into a crevice in the rock. This fissure opened out into a deep cavern, now world-famous as the Lascaux Cave, which proved to be one of the finest of all painted caves. An ante-chamber leads to the main hall, which is oval in shape and measures about a hundred feet in length by thirty feet in breadth.

This cave sets the prehistorian quite new problems; for in

no other painted caves are the representations so animated in their movement and so rich in colour composition as the Lascaux Cave. One painting, about four and a half feet across, portrays the death of a bison hunter. On the left of the painting is the stylized figure of a bird-headed (or bird-masked) man falling over backwards with outstretched arms. Facing him on the right with lowered horns is a massive bison, his belly, from which the bowels sag to the ground, ripped open by a great barbed spear. Below the figure of the falling hunter is a motif not familiar from any other cave painting: a bird perched on top of an upright pole. H. Breuil interprets this enigmatic bird as a totem, supporting his thesis by the bird-head on the human figure, which he construes as a representation of the dead man's soul. 'To judge by its contents,' says Dr. Fritz Wirth, writing in the periodical, *Forschung und Fortschritt*, for December, 1944, 'this picture was not, like most cave representations, intended as hunting magic to ensure success in the chase. It seems much more likely that it served for some expiatory rite designed to propitiate the offended spirit of the beast—after all, man lived in profound dependence on the animal.'

Leo Frobenius points to a similar manifestation among African tribes in his book *Das unbekannte Afrika* (Munich, 1923). He watched the primitive pygmies performing an expiation ceremony, before and after the hunt, in front of an animal drawn in the sand; the same picture served both for the expiatory ritual and for hunting magic. Some scene of this kind is conjured up by the pictures in the cave of Clotilde de Santa Isabella, Spain, where primitive depictions of bovines, some of them pierced by arrows, have been found scratched in the clay floor.

Expiatory magic connected with hunting is still practised by other living peoples. The author was himself able to observe it on the occasion of an elephant hunt near the little village of Ambanpola in Ceylon. During the hunt in the jungle, the Singhalese beaters danced in front of a little altar to the gods while they scattered incense and beat drums. A singer intoned a trance-like refrain that was repeated over and over again. It was the prayer to Jyrensyaka, the god of forests and elephants. The words ran: 'Thou god of elephants and forests who hast come from Madras (a place of pilgrimage for Hindus in Southern India), who didst remain at Kuderamalai (where the hunt started) to give your protection to this herd, thy children, O lead them to us that we may treat them like our own flesh and blood.' (See Anton Lübke, *Indiens zweites Gesicht*, Saarlautern, 1934.)

If we look for cave pictures beyond the confines of Europe, Africa appears as the third great centre of this art, far surpassing Europe in the magnificence of its cave drawings and paintings. It is true that African cave art, like that of Europe, lacks spatial depth, although a certain limited illusion of depth is occasionally evoked in the representation of herds of animals. But the cave art found in Europe is no more than a pale reflection of what has been found by Frobenius, Breuil and others in Africa. Who were the painters who left an undying record of their art in the caverns of the Dark Continent, and what was their purpose in these paintings? Were they the same artists who painted the pictures in the European caves? Many of them, it is said, belonged to the primitive tribes of Bushmen who are generally regarded as having been the aboriginal inhabitants of Africa. The remnants of this dying folk in the Orange Free State studied by the Austrian anthropologist and ethnographer Rudolf Pöck (died 1921) in 1902 and 1909, were largely cave dwellers. They decorated their sandstone caves in the mountains with crude paintings or engravings representing all kinds of animals, and scenes from the everyday life of their people. Africa explorers, who discovered these ancient cave and rock drawings, made great efforts to unveil the mystery of their origin, ascribing them to a period concurrent with the flowering of the cultures of Nineveh and Babylon. Amongst the paintings, however, are many of quite recent origin showing Bantus, Europeans, and wheeled vehicles. To render the task of interpretation even more difficult, many caves and grottoes show a striking amount of over-painting in a wide variety of different styles.

Of all the figures depicted, those of animals are executed in the most masterly fashion, the thin, almost invisible outlines scratched on blocks of iron-stone or hornblende with a burin or graver of quartz reproducing with startling vividness the natural proportions of the buffalo, rhinoceros or elephant. There are no attempts to render background or even shadow to confuse the clear impression. The primitive draughtsman of the past, who occupied these caves, was able —like a child—to do without any adjuncts that would have weakened the clarity of line with its indication of area and space. Many modern artists consider these primitive drawings the finest of all animal art, because they capture the individual quality of the animal. They have nothing in common with the restrained aloofness of the Egyptian painters nor the harshness of the Syrian sculptors. The portrayals are much more lifelike and betray a far deeper understanding of their subjects.

The districts in Africa most celebrated for their cave paintings are the Maanhaar Rand between Krugersdorp and Rustenburg, the regions of Klerksdorp and the Schweizer Reneke in the Western Transvaal, Vryburg in Bechuanaland, Douglas in Griqualand West, Koffie Fontein in the Orange Free State, and Vosburg in Cape Province.

Geologists have been unable to assess the age of these drawings by the weathering and patination of the rocks. Here and there stone implements have been found buried in the caves, which many workers have assigned to the Middle Stone Age. But this is only conjecture. For it must not be forgotten that although the representations in the caves vary from simple outline drawings to coloured pictures full of moving human and animal figures, many types of technique and style were in use in Africa concurrently. In all likelihood, many different tribes occupied the cave-districts with their herds for varying periods and were successively responsible for the drawings and paintings. The variations are so great that, while the oldest may be ascribed to pre-historic artists, the more recent are probably the work not only of the Bushmen but also of the Korannas, Bantus and even Griquas.

The most famous paintings are undoubtedly the work of Bushmen, however, and thousands of these have been found in Rhodesia, all the provinces of the Union of South Africa, and South-West Africa. They occur either on blocks of granite or in the sandstone caves of the mountains and valleys. Many of them are relics of the modern Bushmen, but amongst the paintings are a number from an older period. The modern Bushman painted himself very tall and slim with his characteristic lines accentuated. His animals are also very much elongated, and painted on a ground of flat colour, without polychrome shading such as generally occurs in the archaic pictures of his unknown predecessors.

The pictures are usually painted with red and yellow ochre, a mineral compound of an earthy variety of limonite (hydrated ferric oxide) with clay, which is found in large quantities close to the caves. Walter Battiss tells in No. 41952 of the South African periodical *Lantern* of Bushmen who manufactured pigment from a mixture of haematite (a red mineral made up of ferric oxide with seventy per cent iron, which sometimes occurs in shiny, black masses known as kidney ore) and animal fat, while others in the Eastern Transvaal boiled red ochre with castor oil. Since the pig-ment of the cave paintings contained saltpetre, Professor van Riet-Lowe conjectures that urine was also used. In many cases the white and black pigment has vanished, while in other paintings a white pigment is found that has outlasted all the rest. The cave painters did not confine themselves to these colours, however. They employed a rich and varied palette: white, black, yellow and orange ochre, pink, dark red, ash grey, and chestnut and red browns obtained by heating bones. The use of haematite in these colours suggests that the ancient Bushmen may have employed iron ore for other purposes as well. Perhaps they were able to smelt it and forge tools and weapons. There is no certainty that they employed nothing but implements of stone to trace their drawings on the walls and rock.

On close examination, South African cave art seems to be divided into two phases. Many workers claim to distinguish three, and others as many as eleven, superimposed layers of painting. But it is quite certain that in many cases the oldest and generally faded pictures have been painted over by work in a more recent style representing men and animals in lively movement, and it is this latter that is generally thought of as 'Bushman Art'. In the more archaic style there is far less movement, and the productions of this phase resemble the cave paintings of Spain and France. The later style, on the other hand, is full of violent action. Its subjects are men fighting or hunting animals, dancing in masks, or running, fishing, or indulging in various competitive sports.

These are not the only subjects dealt with, however. Walter Battiss found in the Herschel district a picture of a battle between Bushmen and Bantus, who drove the former out of the region two hundred years ago. Another cave in the same district showed figures wearing animal masks reminiscent of the Ancient Egyptian animal deities. Drums and amphorae in the same painting recall Egyptian rather than Bushman art. Battiss also found pictures containing wild cats, an ant-eater and a jackal. Unfortunately, as Battiss points out, the sandstone in these caves is very much affected by the damp and large numbers of paintings are destroyed by the peeling of the surface. Nothing can be done to check this deterioration.

The most magnificent painting of this latter type—though it is not strictly speaking a cave painting—was discovered in 1910 amidst a stony wilderness on an island in the River

Ugab near the Brandberg in South-West Africa. In 1917, the Dutch surveyor Maak found on this very lively, frieze-like rock painting, amongst exotic human beings and animals, the figure of a white woman whose legs painted in white pigment had been preserved. From this figure the rock painting came to be called 'The White Lady'. The whole composition is extraordinarily full of life, but its details are in great contrast. It is clear that many foreign influences were at work in this painting. The masked and armed figures of men, the various species of animals and the picture's stylistic peculiarities have caused much surmise among scholars. So far no conclusive explanation of the painting has been offered.

One important consideration must be borne in mind in connexion with the provenance of cave paintings and rock drawings. It must not be forgotten that Africa—particularly the Sudan and Central and West Africa—once possessed flourishing Negro kingdoms with a high level of culture. The majority of these cultures fell victim to the greed of Arab slavers and the colonizing activities of antique races. Before European industrial and commercial nations set foot in Africa, Arabs, Medes, Persians, Mongols, Huns, Turks and Berbers harassed the indigenous peoples of Africa and brought about their downfall.

At one time, the Negroid race appears to have been more widely distributed than any other, or at any rate not to have been confined to the Dark Continent. In the earliest days of mankind this race inhabited not only Africa, but also parts of Asia and Europe. The first skeletons indicating the presence of the Negroid race in Europe, which came to be known as 'Grimaldi man', were found in 1872 in a complex of caves (the Grotte des Enfants) on the Mediterranean coast near Mentone on the Franco-Italian frontier. Similar skeletons of Negroid origin were subsequently found all over Western Europe and in the Balkans. In the course of these excavations, female sculptures were brought to light showing a remarkable enlargement of the buttocks such as still characterizes the women of the Hottentots and Bushmen. The Negroid race has left even clearer traces in Asia, particularly in Southern India, Indo-China, South China, Japan and Malaya. Negroid characteristics are unmistakably evident in the Negritos of the Philippines and the Andamans, the Semangs in the Malayan jungle, and the Papuans of western New Guinea. All these peoples are similar in many respects to the Pygmies of Central Africa.

The Negroids of Africa failed to produce any system of writing, but they showed great gifts in the plastic arts. What we know of them has reached us via the Arabs and other neighbouring races. The lack of any script in the ancient Negroid cultures explains the absence of inscriptions from the cave and rock drawings of Africa. But a comparison between the slender, narrow-hipped figures of modern Negro art and those of the cave paintings shows a startling identity. The Negro still carves narrow-hipped, elongated figures in wood which bear a striking resemblance to those depicted in numberless cave paintings. He still paints on hollow ostrich eggs—which he carries on his back as hunting talismans—the same figures that the Bushmen have left behind them in the caves of South Africa.

AUSTRALIAN CAVE ART

No discussion of cave art would be complete without a reference to the cave and rock paintings of the Australian aborigines. Culturally, the aborigines of Australia are still at the Stone Age phase of human development, and their art follows the same lines and fulfils the same functions as the art of prehistoric man. For a people without writing pictorial representation acquires immensely enhanced cultural importance. It becomes the only means of preserving their philosophies, laws and myths, and permeates their whole social existence.

The date of the earliest extant aborigine paintings is unknown, but the art still practised today does not differ essen-
tially from the oldest examples. Several distinct styles may
be distinguished with their homes in different areas of the
continent. Southern and Central Australia are characterized
by a simple and abstract art made up of spirals, concentric
circles, wavy and spiral lines. The word abstract is, however,
something of a misnomer; for these geometrical forms are
not used for their purely aesthetic value, but are symbols
with a known and accepted concrete significance, generally
referring to definite myths or legends of the race.

In the Hawkesbury River basin of New South Wales, the
flat rocks bear huge outline engravings of men, animals,
birds and fish, some of them as much as sixty feet long.
These are the work of artists now dead, and their significance
is no longer known to the living aborigines of the district.

The caves of North-Eastern Australia show large anthro-
pomorphic figures wearing ornaments recalling haloes. These
figures are known as Wandjina and are associated with rain-
making and fertility rituals.

The most interesting and highly developed aboriginal art
is found in Arnhem Land, Northern Australia. This art is of
such ethnological and anthropological significance that
Unesco has devoted the third of its publications in the World
Art Series to the cave and bark paintings of the Arnhem
Land aborigines. These paintings also possess considerable
qualities of pattern and design reminiscent of the work of
certain artists of the modern school.

A brief description of the paintings given by Charles P.
Mountford in his introduction to this publication, *Aboriginal
Paintings—Arnhem Land* (Unesco World Art Series, 1954), will
not be out of place here.

The most decorative and colourful cave paintings have been
found along the western edge of the Arnhem Land plateau.
Recent investigations have shown that they are of two different

types: the static, polychrome, X-ray paintings—some of them produced within the memory of living men—of animals, birds, fish and reptiles, but seldom of human beings, in which the internal as well as the external details are portrayed; and an older, more vital, monochromatic art, consisting almost entirely of single-line drawings of human beings in action—men running, fighting or throwing spears and women carrying their food vessels. These single-line monochromatic drawings have a sense of movement entirely lacking in the polychrome paintings.

The aborigines believe that these drawings—most of them less than half a metre high—are the work, not of their own kind, but of a tall, thin-bodied fairy people known as Mimis, who live in the rocky plateau. No one has seen a Mimi, though they collect food and hunt in the same way as the aborigines, for the Mimis are shy people, particularly keen of hearing, who, at the faintest sound of an intruder, run to a cleft in the rocks of the plateau and blow upon it. The cleft opens, admits the Mimis to their underground home, then closes behind them to keep out all intruders. The belief in the Mimi artists is, it would seem, a rationalization on the part of the aborigines to explain an ancient art form which they themselves do not practise.

The materials and tools with which the artists of Arnhem Land paint on the walls and ceilings of caves—and also on the inside of sheets of bark stripped from a eucalyptus tree—are as simple and primitive as those of the South African Bushmen and our own prehistoric ancestors. To quote Mountford again: 'The colours are black, red, yellow and white pigments ground to a thin paste on a flat stone. The fixative is the sap of a bruised orchid bulb, rubbed directly on the painting surface. The brushes, too, are no more than strips of chewed bark for the broader lines, thin sticks for making dots and a single feather or strand of palm leaf for cross-hatching and finer details.'

Mountford makes the interesting point that the artists work with a sureness which indicates a complete mental image of the finished work before the first stroke is made, so that there is rarely any alteration in the design or correction of the slightest detail. Of the function of the paintings, both on bark and in caves, he says: 'In the initiation rituals, secret designs, painted on sheets of bark, instruct the novitiates in the esoteric myths of the tribe, and, in western Arnhem Land, where some of the cave paintings have magical qualities, the old men can, by chanting the correct incantation at the appropriate season, force the magical power of the painting to increase the supply of food.'

He goes on to point out that many of the paintings have no ceremonial or religious function, but are produced for the pure pleasure of creative effort, in response to the same impulse which governs artists of all epochs all over the world.

Thus the study of this contemporary 'Stone Age' art, where it is still possible to question the artists who produce it as well as their audience, confirms the hypotheses advanced by archaeologists concerning prehistoric art which were derived simply from examination of the objects themselves.

4

THE STONE AGE

✤

THE AWAKENING OF STONE AGE MAN

THE concept of the Stone Age first arose during the nineteenth century. The attention of scientists was drawn to the
prehistoric era and the culture and activities of prehistoric
man by the multitude of finds made in caves. The first discovery that pointed to the existence of a primitive culture
was made by Boucher de Perthes, the chief customs officer
at Abbeville in the north-east of France and an amateur
archaeologist. In 1838, Perthes found in the alluvial deposits of the Somme, together with the bones of prehistoric
animals, curiously shaped flints which he considered to be
implements fabricated by 'antediluvian' man. His celebrated
countryman, G. Cuvier, the outstanding naturalist of the day,
declared his opposition to this view in the famous sentence,
'L'homme fossil n'existe pas.' Like Fuhlrott, who, two
decades later, discovered the Neanderthal skull, Perthes
had to fight for years before he won acceptance for his
opinion. These first flints and skulls came to light too
soon, for the Darwinist theory of evolution had not yet been
developed. Charles Darwin (died in 1882), observing the
marvellous order reigning throughout the animal and vegetable kingdoms, formulated in *The Origin of Species* (1859) the
theory that the higher species were derived from the lower.
At that time, however, he still believed in a Creator, and it

was not until 1871 that he advanced the thesis that man was descended from the beasts, in his book, *The Descent of Man*.

The appearance of this book created an intellectual climate favourable to the view of those who had been led by their archaeological finds to believe that man had developed from a lower animal-like being amongst giant reptiles and prehistoric beasts. De Perthes gained influential support for the extreme antiquity of the objects found in the Somme, in the person of the great British geologist Sir Charles Lyell. Belief in a Stone Age became more and more firmly established when flint implements, particularly so-called hand-axes, were found in other river deposits, e.g., in the Seine and Thames Valleys.

In the course of twenty-five years, no less than twenty thousand hand-axes were found at St. Acheul near Amiens, in the valley of the Somme. At that time, apart from the Thames Valley, practically no hand-axes had been found outside France, only nine having been discovered by H. Obermaier in German caves up to 1914, so that it was still customary to speak of a 'Rhine limit of the hand-axe culture'. A certain number of similar flint hand-axes were later found in the Neanderthal (1927) and other German caves, while in Britain finds of flint implements indicating Old Stone Age occupation have been made in a number of caves, the most noteworthy being Kent's Hole, Torquay; Gough's Cave, Cheddar; Wookey Hole, Somerset; Oldbury Rock Shelter, Kent; the Creswell Caves, on the borders of Derbyshire and Nottinghamshire; and King Arthur's Cave, Whitchurch, in the Wye Valley.

The Stone Age is subdivided into Old (Palaeolithic), Middle (Mesolithic) and New (Neolithic) according to the strata in which human and animal skeletons have been found, and the varying forms of the artifacts. Our modern tools—knives, saws, augers, chisels, axes, hammers, pincers, etc.—are made of metal, mainly iron and steel. But the Iron

Age did not begin in Central Europe until about 800 BC. Before that, men used tools of bronze, an easily smelted alloy of copper and tin. Scholars put the beginning of the Bronze Age at about 2000 BC. China is considered the classical land of the Bronze Age, and it is believed that bronze was employed in that country as early as 3000 BC. Prior to the Bronze Age, men used weapons and tools of stone and bone. Thus the Stone Age ended somewhere between the third and second millennia BC. When it began is shrouded in darkness. Palaeontologists suppose that it covered a vast span of time during which development took place, hence its subdivision into the Old, Middle and New Stone Ages, although there are differences of opinion as to the duration of each of these periods. Some scholars date the Neolithic Age in the north of Europe from about 4000 to 2000 BC and the Mesolithic Age from about 12000 to 4000 BC. The Old Stone Age, or Palaeolithic Period, is further subdivided into Early (or Lower), Middle, and Late (or Upper) Palaeolithic. Here the figures become positively astronomical. F. Wiegers puts the end of the Old Stone Age at 20000 to 25000 BC. Soergel estimates the duration of the whole Ice Age at around 570,000 years, basing this estimate on Köppen and Wegener's calculation of the solar radiation curve. C. Schuchhardt, G. Schwantes and J. Friesen place the end of the Old Stone Age at approximately 12000 BC.

According to the varying types of stone implements found near different villages in France, the Old Stone Age is broken down into phases: the Chellean from Chelles (Seine-et-Marne), now more usually called the Abbevillian: the Acheulean from St. Acheul (Somme); the Mousterian from Le Moustier (Dordogne) with the sub-group Micoquian from La Micoque (Dordogne); the Aurignacian from Aurignac (Haute-Garonne); the Solutrean from Solutré (Saone-et-Loire); and the Magdalenian from La Madeleine (on the River Vézère, Dordogne).

The Middle Stone Age, or Mesolithic Period, which is

subdivided into Capsian, Azilian and Tardenoisian, resembled the Old Stone Age, but marked the appearance of
the first polished and perforated stone implements and the
beginnings of pottery.

With the New Stone Age or Neolithic Period a prodigious
cultural advance took place, bringing agriculture and stockbreeding, the spinning-wheel and the weaver's loom, pottery
and ornamented vessels. The stone implements of this period
were polished and perforated, and generally of fine-grained
igneous rocks, such as basalt and diorite, or of volcanic ash,
(green coloured rock being preferred), since flint is too hard
to pierce. This highly-developed culture is believed to have
carried on trade, in the course of which northern daggers,
axes and spearheads of stone found their way to the south.

THE WORLD-WIDE DISTRIBUTION
OF STONE IMPLEMENTS

Great quantities of Stone Age tools and weapons, which
scholars have designated hand-axes, hand-points, scrapers,
blades, burins, and borers according to the use inferred from
their shape, have also been found in many places outside
France—notably Britain, Germany, Switzerland, Lower
Austria, Moravia, Hungary, Yugoslavia, Belgium and Palestine, as well as on the continents of Australia, America, Asia
and Africa. Many of these implements have been found in
caves, and they were very frequently associated with the
osseous remains of prehistoric animals.

Certain limestone caves in Sauerland, Westphalia—e.g.
the Balve, Feldhof and Volkringhaus caves, and the former
Martin's Cave near Lethmate—proved particularly rich in
such objects. In the Balve cave, fifty thousand artifacts were
found. The majority of these were of siliceous schist, the rest
of siliceous limestone, flint and greywacke. Apart from flint,
all these rocks occur in the immediate neighbourhood of the
cave. The great number of these stone artifacts of all types,

which were mingled with a large quantity of bones of prehistoric animals, led to the supposition that the Balve cave
had served as a 'factory', in which Stone Age man manufactured hunting weapons. Since the Balve cave is regarded as one of the major sites of Stone Age occupation
in Europe, the finds made in it are worth studying more
closely.

Because of its phosphorus content, the earth of the Balve
cave had been dug out year after year by the local peasants
for use as a fertilizer. Hence the greater part of the cave-filling
had been removed. In view of this, and the fact that digging
some decades earlier had revealed nothing of interest beyond
animal skeletons, it was thought unlikely that the interior of
the cave would yield anything else of significance. In 1937,
systematic digging was begun in the area in front of the cave,
and by the end of 1938 no fewer than two thousand artifacts
and eighteen thousand 'intermediate products'—cores, flakes
and unworked stones—had been found. In 1939, despite the
amount of the cave-earth that had been cleared away, excavators discovered three feet below the surface, in a fissure in
the rock ten feet across at the top and running to a point at
its base, a thirteen-foot-deep deposit of greyish black material
containing two hundred and eighty-five 'retouched' stone
implements, fifty-five stone cores and one thousand one hundred 'intermediate products', flakes and fragments, as well as
bone implements and bone charcoal.

At Balve, Professor Riek of Tübingen employed for the
first time in a cave the so-called Hallanser lacquer-film
procedure for the conservation of early palaeontological deposit. The stratum is sprayed with a mixture of acetone and
zapon varnish; this binds the earth, which then receives
several coats of a special lacquer. Once it is dry, the layer of
earth so bound can be peeled off like the plaster from a
wound. In this way, the earth and everything imbedded in it
is preserved in its original stratification, and the palaeontologist can take it home and examine it at leisure.

7

The most important discoveries at Balve were made on the
right-hand side of the cave, sixty-six feet from the entrance.
After removal of a block of stone that had fallen down at
some time or other as a result of weathering, a cohesive grey
deposit was found sixteen inches below the surface, which
proved to contain bones, bone charcoal and stone implements. The block of stone, which had defied efforts to shift it
during earlier excavations, had protected this deposit, so that
its original stratification remained undisturbed. The cleft in
the rock was ten feet across at the front, widening to twenty-
three feet inside the cave. Several weeks' continuous excavation of an area barely eight yards square brought to light
some one thousand one hundred stone implements, 'classic-
ally beautiful flaked points of the Late Mousterian type,
finely worked curved scrapers, magnificent saw-shaped,
round, flat and multiple scrapers, as well as all kinds of
blades,' as the report says. In addition, there were four
thousand six hundred fragments, unworked stones and flakes,
some 'auxiliary implements', hundreds of animal bones, and
a quantity of animal charcoal.

Similar finds were made in other caves and in the open
country in the same area of Germany. In his book, *Die Mittelsteinzeit am Nordrand des Ruhrgebietes* (Leipzig, 1940), Karl
Brand describes the Mesolithic stone implements found in
river banks, sandy soil and small quarries at a large number
of points on the northern edge of the Ruhr. Implements of
bone and horn were also found in this district.

Rhenish caves yielded artifacts associated with the skeletons of prehistoric animals. Digging was begun in the Wild-
scheuer Cave near Steeden an der Lahn in 1874 and continued until after the First World War. Here, in three successive strata, each a little less than two feet deep, hearths
were found which pointed to human occupation. During the
first excavation, Cohausen, curator of the Nassau Provincial
Museum, unearthed three hundred artifacts, besides animal
remains. From 1911–13, the museum director Rademacher

found in the Karstein cave near Eiserfey six hundred and thirty-seven flints, of which four hundred showed signs of use, and some hundred quartz and twenty quartzite implements. Similar finds, though not so extensive, were made during the eighteen-seventies in the Buchenloch near Gerolstein. In autumn 1927, two artifacts were found in the Neander Valley a few yards from the site of the Neanderthal skull—an eight-inch-long quartzite hand-axe and a five-inch quartzite scraper.

An immense number of stone implements have come to light in French caves; in some they can be counted in tens of thousands. This is the case with the cave of Isturitz, the Laugerie-Basse cave in the Dordogne, and those of La Marche in the Vienne and the Placard in Charente, to name only a few.

The last of these is particularly interesting. It contains eight absolutely distinct archaeological levels clearly separated by sterile strata, composed of limestone fragments fallen from the roof.

The total depth of the cave filling is over thirty feet, of which twenty feet are limestone rubble and ten feet deposits due to human occupation. It was among the deposits of this cave that human brain pans were found fashioned by prehistoric man into the form of a cup. One of these strata also contained a complete female skull resting on a slab of stone and richly adorned with a large number of shells. As similar discoveries have been made in many European caves, there are good grounds for thinking that they represent customs peculiar to the peoples of the Reindeer Age. (Upper Palaeolithic Period.)

Stone implements are found in the open all over France: for instance in the abandoned beds of the rivers beside which prehistoric man established his encampments. Swept away by the flow of the water, the implements sank to the bottom and were covered by mud, sand or gravel.

In the gravel-pits of these old river-beds, stone implements may sometimes be found mingled with the bones of the fauna of the period—hippopotamus, rhinoceros, elephant, etc. The remains of these animals have been found, amongst other places, on the banks of the Seine where Paris now stands.

Millions of Palaeolithic stone implements have been obtained from old river beds, and millions of others of more recent epochs have been found at many different points. The Neolithic deposits of the Montmorency forest in particular have yielded hundreds of thousands. The site was well chosen, and especially in the locality known as Montaugland in the Montmorency forest which lay close to a spring in the northwest of the forest; it occupied part of the little plateau of so-called Fontainebleau sandstone. From this sandstone, prehistoric man selected the pieces that were suitable for cutting, worked them on the spot, and left the chips where they fell. These chips accumulated at the most favoured sites and amongst them may be seen numbers of implements broken in the course of manufacture.

British caves have yielded their share of Stone Age implements, not to mention skeletal remains of a wide variety of animals that cast an interesting light on the prehistoric fauna of the British Isles. Particularly noteworthy is Kent's Hole in the Devonian Limestone at Torquay, where implements of the Early Palaeolithic Period were found in the lowest deposit—evidence of what is probably the earliest occupation of a cave by man in Britain. Kent's Hole became famous early in the nineteenth century—when it was investigated by the Rev. MacEnery—as the site of the first discovery of flint implements in any cave, as well as by the discovery of the teeth of the extinct sabre-tooth tiger (*Machairodus*). The importance of this cave is such as to justify detailed consideration of its contents, which are described as follows by J. Wilfrid Jackson in *British Caving*.

The distinctive deposits in the cavern were found to consist of the following, in descending order: I. Black Mould; II. Granular Stalagmite; III. Cave-earth with a dark layer called the 'Black Band' in the upper part; IV. Crystalline Stalagmite; and V. Breccia (rock of angular stones cemented by lime, etc.).

The superficial Black Mould contained sherds of ornamented pottery of Early Iron Age type, some like those from Glastonbury Lake Village, Somerset; many spindle-whorls; some bronze implements; sea shells; flint flakes (about four hundred); an ornamented bone weaving comb; Roman coins; human bones and remains of existing animals. In the Granular Stalagmite below were a few bones and flints, charcoal, fern impressions, and a human palate, which was found by William Pengelly in 1867.

The cave-earth and Black Band, representing the debris of the hearths of the cave-dwellers, contained the remains of extinct and still existing animals, and many implements of flint and bone. Among the bones and teeth of animals were those of cave lion, hyaena, cave bear, mammoth, woolly rhinoceros, reindeer, giant deer, red deer, horse, and many others. In addition there were the jaws of numerous smaller creatures, including many northern and Continental voles, the common lemming, various hare, and pika, representing a typical tundra fauna of the Late Pleistocene Period. The remains of beaver and glutton were also found. The implements from the different horizons found in the cave-earth comprised harpoon-heads of antler, barbed on one or both sides, and of late Magdalenian type; also bone tools, worked flint knives, scrapers and other tools, of Upper Palaeolithic types (Creswellian, Aurignacian, and pro-Solutrean), and a hand-axe of chert and an oval flake tool of flint belonging to the Mousterian industry. A fragment of a human upper jaw with teeth (like that from the Granular Stalagmite) and of Aurignacian date was also found in the cave-earth.

The Crystalline Stalagmite was of great thickness, over ten feet in places, and contained fallen limestone blocks and a few remains of cave bear. In the Breccia below, the remains of animals were almost all of cave bear, and with them occurred several large and roughly made flint implements of Early Palaeolithic type.

Other animal remains recorded from Kent's Hole include those of hippopotamus and straight-tusked elephant.

Many Somerset caves have yielded Stone Age and later implements in association with human and animal remains. One of the most noteworthy is Aveline's Hole in Burrington Combe, where evidence of human occupation in Upper Palaeolithic times was found in the shape of human remains of at least ten individuals together with hundreds of flint implements (gravette points, gravers and borers), beads made from perforated sea shells, and a barbed harpoon-head of deer antler of Magdalenian type. Gough's Cavern, in Cheddar Gorge, became famous in 1903, when human remains were found buried some eight feet down accompanied by flint implements and a so-called antler sceptre. It was excavated again in 1927 and 1928 by R. F. Parry, who found several hundreds of worked flints, a second sceptre, part of an ivory rod, perforated teeth of animals, perforated sea shells, and bone awls, associated with human remains and those of Late Pleistocene animals. In the Hyaena Den at Wookey Hole, about forty stone implements were found near the entrance with charcoal and burnt bones. The implements comprised flakes, scrapers and hand-axes made of flint and chert, and were accompanied by two rude bone arrow-heads.

Goat's Cave, Paviland, on the Gower Peninsula in South Wales, was the finding-place of the famous 'Red Lady of Paviland', which eventually proved to be the skeleton of a Cro-Magnon man. This cave was thoroughly investigated in 1912 by Professor Sollas and the Abbé Breuil, who concluded that it had been the site of prolonged occupation by Aurignacian hunters. It yielded flint implements of several different types. Similar flint implements were found in another Glamorgan cave known as Leather's Hole, near Parkmill.

Several Scottish caves, both on the mainland and the isles, have yielded stone implements, the most important being a series of shallow coastal caves or rock-shelters near Oban. All these caves showed signs of human occupation and indeed afforded the earliest relics of man in Scotland. The evidence is that one of them, MacArthur Cave, was occupied by primitive fisher-folk or strand-loopers when the beach was formed, by a rise in the sea level, in Mesolithic times. The inhabitants, known as Azilians or Obanians, appear from the remains of red deer, roe deer, seal, and shellfish found among the debris of their middens to have lived by hunting and fishing. The artifacts unearthed in this cave by J. Anderson include seven flat harpoons of deer antler, bone pins, flints, and hammer-stones. There were also a great number of round-nosed, chisel-ended implements of leg-bone or stag-antler, which may have been used in the dressing of skins.

Outside Europe, important discoveries of stone implements have been made in the caves of Palestine, Asia, Australia and America.

In 1947, according to the report of the American prehistorian, Ralph S. Solecki, 'seventeen stone implement industries' and an artifact of the type known as the Folsom culture (from the Upper Palaeolithic site at Folsom in New Mexico) were found in the archaeologically unexplored inland region of North-west Alaska on the Utukok river. This provided an incentive for the investigation of the neighbouring region on Rivers Kukpowruk and Kokolik. No evidence of the Folsom culture came to light here, but Solecki reports one hundred and ninety-two sites belonging to other prehistoric cultures, two of which present noteworthy flint industries. The implements are of a very primitive type and their finder considers that they resemble those discovered in the Gobi Desert of Central Asia by N. C. Nelson in 1937. Solecki sees this as evidence of human migration from Asia to North America.

One fact which at first sight appears to cast doubt on the authenticity of the Alaskan finds is their situation on a hill of calcareous sandstone, on which little or no humus had formed. Solecki deals with this difficulty as follows. 'The dry climate of Alaska offers little opportunity for the formation of humus. Moreover, the whole of the so-called "northern glacis" is totally treeless, since it lies beyond the limit of trees. The surface soil remains frozen throughout the year, with the exception of a few months during summer. All these circumstances explain why the artifacts were found either on the surface or at a depth of at most six inches; in many cases they were lying on the bare rock of stony and soil-less areas. The majority of the stone implements have been fabricated from flint nodules, mostly of grey-green and less often of red or black colour, which occur locally in river-beds or adjacent strata.' (Ralph S. Solecki in *Die Umschau*, No. 8, 1950).

NEOLITHIC FLINT MINES IN FRANCE AND BRITAIN

In some places, such as the Montmorency forest, as we have seen, the raw material of primitive man's stone implements lay on the surface of the soil, within easy reach. In certain particularly fortunate localities the abundance and quality of this raw material were such that they became veritable centres of industry.

The most celebrated of these industrial centres was situated in Indre-et-Loire, in France. This was the Grand Pressigny site, which extended over an area eight miles in length. This region produces a quantity of flint of an unusual golden amber colour, which is easy to work and was at that period the object of a brisk trade. Very fine blades of large proportions, some of them more than fourteen inches long, were manufactured from it, and these blades were exported to less favoured regions through the agency of packmen who travelled great distances to exchange their wares. These pedlars sometimes established depots of their goods, leaving them concealed in some spot known only to themselves. The stocks of cut stones still come to light from time to time and are known to prehistorians as 'hoards'. The same practice continued into the Bronze Age, and similar hoards are found along the ancient highways, but this time containing objects of bronze.

The quality of the Grand Pressigny flint really was exceptional. Surface flint, exposed to all the action of the weather, was generally unsuitable for working. Flint that has been frozen splits when struck, and primitive man was unable to obtain from it the splinters and flakes he needed for the manufacture of tools.

Flint preserved in geological strata, which is what miners call 'quarry-fresh', is more easily fashioned.

Prehistoric man was therefore compelled to dig for raw material he could use. He sank shafts, the traces of which may be seen all over France. These shafts were from two to four feet in diameter and went down to the flint strata. They were frequently several yards deep, and one shaft has been found that is more than twenty-six feet deep. From this central shaft horizontal galleries were dug, propped up at intervals by piles of chalk to prevent the roof from caving in.

Collapses took place, however, and the well-known prehistorian Boule relates finding staghorn implements crushed beneath a fall from the roof of the gallery.

The tools used for digging out the flint-nodules were of stone or antler, according to the hardness of the rock to be cut through. As they opened up new pits, the prehistoric miners filled in the old ones with the rubble from the new.

Southern England, and particularly the South Downs in Sussex, was also a leading centre of flint mining and manufacture during the Stone Age. One of the most interesting sites is that associated with the earthworks or camps on the top of the Downs at Cissbury, near Worthing. In 1868, General Pitt-Rivers began an investigation of the circular pits and depressions, about fifty in number, which occupy the same site as the earthworks, and discovered that they were the filled-in mouths of vertical shafts which went down thirty to forty feet in the chalk. Of this discovery Sir Arthur Keith writes in *The Antiquity of Man*: 'The significance of these shafts or mines was also clear; they were sunk to obtain the kind of flint most suitable for working into implements. They were flint mines. The veins of suitable flints were followed by driving horizontal galleries from the vertical shaft.' As in France, the miners left tools behind them, which are now preserved in the filled-up mines. Two skeletons were also found in the Cissbury mines and these are now housed in the University Museum, Oxford.

TECHNICAL ASPECTS OF FLINT

The stone implements found in caves and open country are of siliceous schist, siliceous limestone, greywacke and flint. Flint is the most frequent. It consists of minutely crystalline silica (or quartz, which is silicon oxide) and occurs in irregularly-shaped, rounded nodules, either irregularly distributed, or in regular bands, especially in the chalk of Northern France, Southern England, the Danish islands, the island of Rügen, and incorporated in the diluvial deposits in the north of Germany. For a time flint was used in flintlock rifles, and our ancestors used it for lighting fires. Up to 1850, the manufacture of flints was a flourishing trade and formed part of the armaments industry.

The assumption that primitive man used flint for the manufacture of weapons and tools is supported by the fact that Mexican Indians and the aboriginal inhabitants of Tierra del Fuego used to make arrowheads from flint or obsidian, a vitreous rock which can be worked in a similar way to flint. A variety of tools and weapons were made from similar stones by the Australian and Tasmanian aborigines. Flint is easily worked and does not lose its hardness. Scholars believe that Stone Age man began by striking off a bulbous lump with a flat surface from a nodule of flint with a stone, and completing the work by percussion or pressure.

Flint is a mineral that splinters when struck hard, breaking up into fragments with sharp edges and leaving shell-like surfaces on the core. Like glass, it also cracks under the effect of sudden changes of temperature. Flint gives a more high-pitched ring when cold than when warm. Travellers in the desert have reported that small fragments split off flints that have been exposed to the blazing sun during the day, as they cool down after sunset.

As Karl Brand states in his book, *Die Mittelsteinzeit am Nordrand des Ruhrgebietes*, fragments and splinters of flint showing signs of contact with fire have been found in all cave sites. Many of them were completely annealed and therefore light in colour or criss-crossed with fine cracks due to heat. In particular, if the cores at the various sites are examined, says Brand, they are found to have—at least in part—the lighter coloration due to firing. There must be some reason for this, concludes Brand, and continues:

Flint is much better for working when it is warm; it can then be more easily and more surely split, especially when it is a question of striking flakes from flint. Flint may in many respects be compared to glass. Glass cracks in a similar manner. It is very risky to cut glass when it is cold; in consequence of the high tension engendered by the cold, the sheet of glass rarely cracks along the guiding cut. If the glass is warmed, it cuts much better.

Hauser also sees in the fact that flint is found alongside hearths proof that Stone Age man was in the habit of warming his flints in the fire to render them more tractable.

As hafts for his flint implements primitive man used long bones, bamboos or branches, attaching the flints by means of vegetable fibre, pitch or resin. In the Balve cave, three pieces of worked bones were found beside a damaged mammoth rib a yard long. Some scholars believe that these are the oldest bone tool-handles so far yielded by any indisputably Palaeolithic level in Europe. A similar handle had previously come to light in the calcareous tufa at Weimar. The largest haft discovered at Balve was sawn from the antler of a stag and hollowed out to a depth of just over two inches. The second is made from a reindeer antler, with the thin end sharpened more or less to a point and bearing a notch about half an inch deep. The third haft is the radius of a cave bear, cut on the slant and hollowed out in an oval two and a half inches deep. Professor Andree, of Halle, and Professor Wieger, of Berlin, described these objects as unique and magnificent bone artifacts of Neanderthal man at the Mousterian level of culture.

But primitive or prehistoric man was unquestionably a creature of the forest, and the forest provided him with everything he needed for his existence. Timber was his most important raw material, not only for building his dwellings but also for making fires. We have only to think of bamboo, the universal raw material of tropical man, with the aid of which he can satisfy all his needs. A learned Chinese once counted all the things that could be made of bamboo; he reckoned up one thousand three hundred and eighty-six articles. It may be said with justice that practically everything needed to raise simple agrarian man to a certain level of culture can be made from bamboo. He employs it for building; he makes innumerable different implements from it; he plaits all kinds of things from its fibre; and by rubbing together the wood, which contains silicic acid, he even makes fire. Anthropology is right in speaking of a bamboo or wood culture, a stage in human cultural evolution when man utilized the products of the forest and could only live in well-wooded areas, perishing when the forest was destroyed.

Fire was not the discovery of a particular human race or a particular cultural phase. It existed as long as man existed and as long as the sun sent its rays down on to the earth. Even tundra peoples possessed fire. They saw it when the grass of the steppe caught fire, when lightning set fire to trees or wooden huts, or when fire was kindled by friction.

At an early stage it became one of man's allies in his bitter struggle with the forces of nature and the animal kingdom, a struggle in which flint was also an indispensable aid in many parts of the world.

5

CAVE FAUNA AND FLORA

ANIMAL REMAINS IN CAVES

AMONG the most momentous discoveries in many of the
caves explored during the nineteenth and twentieth centuries
were the bones of animals long since extinct, or existing today in a different form. The older geological writers were
compelled, for religious reasons, to resist the idea that fossils
could be anything other than freaks of nature. At most they
regarded the objects found in caves as relics of the Flood, or
of a cataclysm preceding the Noachian deluge and known as
the 'Diluvium'. But as long ago as the seventeenth century,
there were scholars who considered that these petrifactions
were not freaks of nature, but the remains of organisms. The
issue was raised in 1689 in the fourth volume of Balvasor,
dealing with natural curiosities; and in 1749 a physician at
Holzmaden in Württemberg found the first complete skeleton
of an ichthyosaurus. Little heed was paid to the bones found
in caves; elsewhere the phosphatic humus, in which many
of the skeletons were embedded, was a welcome agricultural
fertilizer, and the bones were generally held to be those of
giants or unicorns. By the end of the eighteenth century,
however, the skeletons unearthed in caves had become an
object of scientific interest. In 1796, the first work on fossil
bones, dealing with those found in caves at Gailenreuth,
appeared in Paris. This was followed by hundreds of books

and innumerable essays on cave fossils in the course of the nineteenth century. Osteology became an active science during the Age of Reason, but to begin with it dealt exclusively with the bones of animals, which were all that had come to light. When Boucher de Perthes, between 1836 and 1863, discovered bones in the gravel pits near Abbeville that pointed to the occupation of the district by prehistoric human beings, osteology extended its field of study to include fossil human skeletons as well.

Among the relics of the great beasts that once lived in northern latitudes, the teeth and bones of the mammoth are frequently met with, both in caves and in open country. Together with the cave bear, the mammoth (*Elephas primigenius*) which is a member of the elephant family, was one of the largest terrestrial animals of prehistoric times. The name was adopted by the great French anatomist Georges Baron de Cuvier, one of the leading experts on extinct fauna, from the Russian word *mammot*, a mole, applied by the Russian peasants to the mammoth skeletons which they unearthed from time to time, in the belief that they were the bones of giant moles. The word means 'an animal that lives under the ground'. Whether the mammoth was a specifically cave-dwelling animal, like the cave bear, is doubtful. Mammoth remains have been found both in caves and in open country.

The size of the mammoth is generally over-estimated; it is sometimes said to have reached a height of twenty feet. In reality it was no larger than the Indian elephant. The biggest mammoth skeleton so far discovered—at Boulon (Ariège) and now in the Foix Museum—is ten feet eight inches tall. Another error made by naturalists until a few years ago, and perpetuated in many reconstructions, was to draw the mammoth with the spine almost horizontal. Actually the spine sloped sharply towards the rump, like a giraffe's, and it would have been impossible to saddle it with a palanquin like the Indian elephant. In other ways, it differed considerably from the modern elephants, particularly as regards its tusks, which were much larger than those of the elephant and spread outwards and upwards in an almost spiral curve. As the well-preserved mammoth corpses found in the Siberian ice show, the mammoth was covered in thick reddish wool and black hair, which formed a mane round the neck reaching down to its knees.

In his book, *Mammutleichen und Urwaldmenschen in Nordost-Sibirien* (Leipzig, 1926), W. W. Pfizenmayer states that it was even possible to analyse the blood of these frozen mammoth bodies, study their cells under the microscope, and examine the contents of their stomachs, which were always found to contain a prodigious quantity of fir shoots. The Eskimoes came upon mammoth bodies in the Greenland ice—long before they had captured the interest of the scientific world—which were so marvellously preserved that they were able to use their fat for fuel, and feed their meat to their dogs. Mammoth steak from these frozen mammoths was served at the final banquet of the members of a scientific congress at St. Petersburg in 1905.

Mammoth remains are not confined to the ice of Siberia and Greenland, however. Mammoth bones and teeth have been found in many caves in England and Wales associated with other cold tundra fauna of the Late Pleistocene Period, such as hyaena, lion, cave and brown bear, wolf, otter, woolly rhinoceros, bison, urus, red deer, giant Irish deer, reindeer and horse. British caves which have yielded mammoth remains include that at Kirkdale in Yorkshire; several caves near Creswell in Derbyshire; King Arthur's Cave near Ross-on-Wye; many caves in the Western Mendips, Somerset, where the wealth of remains suggests that vast herds of mammoth must once have roamed the fertile valleys north of the Mendip Hills. These include Soldier's Hole in the Cheddar Gorge, and the Hyaena Den at Wookey Hole. Mammoth remains have been found in Devon in the famous Kent's Hole at Torquay, Bench Cave, near Brixham, and in

Kent in Boughton Cave, near Maidstone. Welsh sites include the caves of Cae Gwyn and Ffynnon Beuno on the
eastern side of the Vale of Clwyd; several caves in Glamorgan, and the celebrated Goat's Cave on Gower Peninsula,
site of the Cro-Magnon skeleton known as the 'Red Lady of
Paviland', which was itself associated with mammoth remains; Coygan Cave, south-west of Laugharne, Carmar-
then; the cave known as Hoyle's Mouth, near Tenby, Pem-
broke; and two caves on the north coast of Caldy Island off
Tenby coast, where the Rev. G. N. Smith obtained mammoth bones as long ago as 1860.

In Ireland, finds of mammoth bones and teeth have been
concentrated in County Cork, in the south. The most
famous site is actually known as Mammoth Cave. Excavations in this cave, which lies two miles north-west of Doner-
aile, were started in 1904 by R. J. Ussher, who published
reports of his finds of mammoth in its lower deposits in 1905,
1906, and 1908. Remains of mammoth were also obtained
from the Foley Cave in the Awbeg river gorge at Castletown-
roche, in the same county. Some of the British caves listed
above have also yielded warm Early Pleistocene fauna, particularly hippopotamus, extinct straight-tusked elephant,
and slender-nosed rhinoceros.

In Germany, the Balve cave, the site of some of the most
important prehistoric finds in Europe, where some ten
thousand bones had been unearthed by the outbreak of the
Second World War, yielded during the 1937 excavations a
much-weathered mammoth's tusk measuring fifteen feet.
Mammoth molars were found in the Balve cave as far back
as 1844, and the excavators of the time gave the name
'mammoth layer' to the deposit in which these teeth were
unearthed. Before the Second World War, no less than fifty
molars belonging to mammoth of all ages were dug up. Together with those discovered during the nineteenth century
this gives a total of some hundred molars. Taking into
account the fact that a mammoth possessed four molars, it

8

can be seen that these finds represent the teeth of a whole herd of mammoths. The high fat-content of one layer of mould was believed to be derived from the carcasses of mammoths, which had a four-inch-thick layer of fat under their shaggy hide.

The mass of mammoth bones obtained from the Balve cave during the excavations conducted by Virchow in 1844 and 1870, and by von Dechen in 1871, and during those of 1925–6 and the years immediately preceding the Second World War, point unequivocally to the vast cavern having been a refuge for this gigantic beast, or, as some palaeontologists believe, a mammoth hunters' shelter. The vast quantity of stone arti-facts found in the same cave, which have already been re-ferred to, are thought to have been manufactured here and used by the hunters in the pursuit of the monstrous beast. The absence of any remains of mammoth from the rest of the caves of the Hönne Valley lends support to the view that the Balve cave was occupied by mammoth hunters rather than by mammoths.

The remaining bones from the various levels of the Balve cave include those of rhinoceros, cave bear, hyaena, red deer, aurochs, reindeer, beaver, marten, wolf, alpine hare, arctic fox, bison, hippopotamus, and elk.

Apart from Sauerland, the Eifel hills in Rhenish Prussia were one of the richest sources of fossil animal remains in Germany. In the years 1911 and 1913, C. Rademacher un-earthed in the Karstein Cave at Eiserfey a wealth of fossil bones of tremendous importance for the light they cast on Ice Age Germany. These remains, drawn from various levels, included wolf, hyaena, cave bear, grey bear, cave lion, arctic hare, beaver, vole, mammoth, rhinoceros, horse, reindeer, bison, red deer, giant deer, lynx, arctic fox, weasel, marten, hedgehog, badger, brown bear, mole, hamster, various species of mouse, marmot, pig, musk ox, wild horse, marsh ptarmigan and mountain ptarmigan.

To list all the caves from which relics of the great beasts

of the Ice Age have been obtained would be tedious. In all cases a wide variety of different species have been found together. Two caves, one above the other, at Arcy-sur-Cure in the department of Yonne, France—the Reindeer Cave and the Hyaena Cave—yielded from their twenty-six levels mammoth remains accompanied by the remains of reindeer, chamois, arctic fox, red deer, wild ass, hyaena, wild horse, etc. As in the Balve cave, the remains of mammoth were found together with those of other animals at various levels.

Faunal remains have come to light at many points in the open country through Western Germany, which were once depressions and then inundated by floods. Before the last war, Professor Schaafhausen brought to light in a loess pit on the left bank of the Moselle, near Metternich, the bones of elk, reindeer, lion, mammoth, woolly rhinoceros, aurochs, wild horse and red deer.

In 1883, the remains of wild horse, reindeer, aurochs, arctic fox, alpine hare, etc., were found on the Martinsberg-platz, near Andernach, under thirteen feet of pumice-stone between blocks of lava in the loamy surface of the underlying loess. The site of the Mauer jaw also yielded a quantity of bones of mammoth, aurochs, wild pig, elk, red deer, roe deer, lion, wild cat, wild dog, bear, beaver, bison, wild horse, rhinoceros and elephant. In 1911, dredging in the Rhine and excavations at Lock Six of the Rhine-Herne Canal brought up the remains of mammoth, woolly rhinoceros, aurochs, reindeer, giant deer, roe deer, wild horse and wild pig from a depth of about forty feet in the river gravel. These are a few examples of the very numerous finds.

The cave drawings of mammoth discovered in France point to man having existed during the lifetime of this beast. In 1864, Lartet and Christie found in the celebrated rock shelter of La Madeleine a piece of ivory bearing an engraving of an attacking mammoth, whose shape resembled that of Siberian mammoth carcasses. Many similar engravings on bone, ivory and slate came to light subsequently. A

mammoth carved in reindeer antler was found in the rock
shelter of Bruniquel (Tarn-et-Garonne), while the cave of Les
Combarelles and that at Bernifal, near Les Eyzies, contain
wall engravings of mammoths. Shortly after the First World
War, no less than fifty mammoth skeletons were found at
Wisterlitz, in Moravia, mingled with the skeletons of reindeer and horse. Amongst them was the statuette of a mammoth carved out of a mammoth's tooth.

One cannot help being surprised by the fact that, in prehistoric caves from Russia to Spain, remains of bison have
been limited to a few isolated finds. They are extremely
scanty in relation to those of mammoth and bear. Although
complete reconstructions of the two latter creatures may be
seen in many museums, not one possesses a skeleton of *Bos
priscus*, although there is little doubt that this great mammal
also once roamed Europe and Africa in vast herds.

The bison was certainly not a specifically cave-dwelling
animal, and those bones and teeth which have been found in
caverns were probably brought there by beasts of prey or are
the remnants of human meals. Observation of the European
bison, descendant of the prehistoric bison, in the Byaloviska
Forest, Lithuania, has shown its habitat to be cool, shady
woods with thick undergrowth and bogs. It likes to hide in
thickets, and occasionally seeks refuge in caves. We know
that the Teutons were given to hunting this mighty primeval
beast of the forest. Amongst the Romans, the slayer of an
aurochs or urus was held in high esteem and celebrated as a
hero. Even during the Middle Ages, hunters tackled this
proud and valiant creature at close quarters, mounted or on
foot. It must have been easier for prehistoric man to bring
down the bison with his primitive weapons than a mammoth, and its flesh was doubtless more palatable than the
latter's. Like the horse and the reindeer, the bison played an
important part in the life of prehistoric man. This is proved
by the frequent occurrence of bison among the paintings
and engravings in the caves of Altamira, Font-de-Gaume,

Marsoulas, Montespan and Niaux. In these representations the bison are often shown pierced by arrows or spears, or wounded by axes, clubs or stones. The repeated appearance of the bison in these sacred caves shows how large this animal—which must have been one of the essentials of his existence—loomed in the mind of prehistoric man, and what an important part it played in his magical conjurations.

The bison is one of the few Ice Age animals still in existence, in very limited numbers and a hybrid form. The last bison at liberty in Germany was felled by a poacher's bullet in the Tapiau Forest in 1755. Tsar Nicholas II gave special protection to the bison in the Lithuanian forest of Byaloviska. There were still one thousand four hundred bison here in 1850. By 1914, this number was down to seven hundred bulls, cows and calves, and by the end of the First World War, the species seemed to be extinct. But the remnants of a closely-related species, *Bison bonassus caucasicus*, were found still to exist in the Caucasus. Interest was re-aroused in this relic of the European Quaternary era, especially in Germany, where the animal was preserved in a number of national parks and crossed with breeds from outside Europe.

Whether the prehistoric European bison was identical with the urus or aurochs, or whether it was a type of buffalo similar to those found in other countries today is still uncertain. There is also some doubt whether it was really a contemporary in our latitudes of the mammoth and the cave bear. Its modern descendant is a creature of the thick forest and lives on grass, leaves, twigs, buds and bark; the prehistoric bison probably did the same. It is therefore difficult to believe that it belonged to the cold tundra fauna of Late Pleistocene times.

If it can be deduced with almost complete certainty that the bison was a denizen of the thick forest, it remains to be asked from what period the remains of bison found in caverns and river beds date. It is clear from the circumstances of these skeletons that the animals met their end in large groups and at a number of widely separated places. This cannot be coincidence, but strongly suggests some catastrophe that drove the creatures out of their natural habitat and caused them to seek shelter in large caves or deep hollows.

Perhaps the true age of the bison, as of other prehistoric animals, will eventually be revealed with the aid of nuclear physics, by the method already referred to in connexion with the Dead Sea scrolls. By measuring the degree of disintegration of the radio-active carbon present in every dead or living organism it is possible for physicists to estimate with great accuracy the age of mummies, weapons, ancient timber, or the bones of men and animals. When this procedure has been widely employed on the fossil remains in museums some surprises may be in store, and many accepted estimates may have to be drastically reduced.

THE HOME OF THE CAVE BEAR

Skeletons of the prehistoric great cave bear are almost never missing from amongst the faunal remains in European caves. The cave bear seems to have been distributed all over Europe, for its remains have been found in German and British caves as well as in the Pyrenees and the south-east. To judge by the frequency with which its skeleton occurs, the cave bear must have existed in stupendous numbers during the Ice Age. Just as the hyaena of today is allied to the prehistoric cave hyaena, so the modern brown bear (*Ursus aretos*) is descended from the great cave bear (*Ursus spelaeus*). Unlike the brown bear, however, the cave bear was a beast of prey. It is also clear from the skeletons that the cave bear was considerably larger than the brown bear. It was, in fact, a gigantic beast, as large as a bull, but with bones far more ponderous than those of an ox, and huge muscles. Many of the skulls found show canine teeth the size of bananas. When full-grown it reached a length of ten feet and stood five feet at the shoulder. With its long, shaggy hair and five strong, non-retractile claws on each paw it must have presented a truly terrifying sight. Norbert Casteret, who has devoted much study to reconstructing the habits of these formidable beasts from their remains, points out that, secure in their great strength, they had no need to drag their prey into caves like most animals, but devoured it in the open air. This is evident from the fact that no food debris ever accompanies the cave bear skeletons in caves.

One of the most noteworthy bear caverns in Europe is the Karlshöhle at Erpfingen in the Swabian Alps, discovered in 1834 by a school-teacher named Fauth. One particular cavern of the Karlshöhle was given the name 'Bears' Cave' because of the quantity of bears' skeletons obtained from it. This cavern, a continuation of the Karlshöhle, was not discovered until 1949. The old Karlshöhle is a stalactite cave; for many decades it was pillaged both of stalactite formations and of remains of cave bear. The Bears' Cave escaped this fate, so that bear skulls and skeletons may still be seen there *in situ* in great numbers. The Karlshöhle comprises seven great chambers, of which the first is twenty to thirty feet high and thirty to sixty feet wide, while Hall VI, the finest of the lot and containing the greatest number of bear skeletons, is fifty feet high and seventy feet wide. Hall I, which is lit from above by the so-called Fauth's Hole, is notable for the fact that a fifteen-feet-high pile of rubble underneath this hole was found to contain no less than fifty human skeletons, believed to be those of plague victims thrown down the shaft. They are accompanied by the bones of a quantity of domestic animals. It looks as though the shaft had once been used by a knacker. Hall II contains an ancient hearth with wood charcoal and the charred bones of deer and pig, evidence of human occupation at some period.

The Karlshöhle is a good example of a stalactite cave with splendid cascades, curtains, organ pipes, embossments, cones, and lacework, many of them in bright colours. Hall VII is geologically remarkable. In it stands a beetling crag which is not, like the rest of the cave, white Jurassic lime-stone, but thick calcite interspersed with layers of biggish calcite crystals, some of which are transparent or snow-white, while others are clouded and coloured by iron com-pounds.

The Bears' Cave, which opens out of the Karlshöhle and is reached by ascending a slope of flowstone, was the true abode of the cave bear. A large number of bear skeletons lie beneath a covering of flowstone (layers of calcite, which is crystalline calcium carbonate deposited from thin films of saturated calcium carbonate solution, set hard after loss of carbon dioxide and evaporation of water) at the entrance to the cavern. A three-feet-high hollow stalagmite of calcite has formed on one pelvic bone. One of the finest and most im-pressive parts of the cavern is the 'Great Hall', measuring thirty-three feet in height and a hundred in width and filled with stalactites and stalagmites, particularly the latter. A multitude of small straw stalactites cover the ceiling, and at one point a row of longer stalactites betray a crack in the rock through which the water perpetually seeps. The present floor of the cave is covered over with flowstone, in which are em-bedded a large number of bear bones—skulls, jawbones, shoulder blades, spines, three pelvises, and thighbones. The complete skeleton of a bear assembled by Professor von Huene of Tübingen University, from bones found on the spot, stands in the centre of the cavern and adds to its im-pressiveness.

In the niche of the Great Hall, six bears' skulls were found one on top of the other. It is thought that the bears used this cave to hibernate in. This is probably where their young were born, and here they found their last resting-place. Amongst the chambers of the Bears' Cave, in addition to the Great Hall, the 'Great Sinter Dome' is especially remark-able. A fifty-foot vertical shaft leads into this cavern. In the course of the years, the water that poured down this shaft, whirling sand and shingle along with it, has carved corkscrew forms in its walls. Today this chimney issues in the topmost peak of the mountain.

The multitude of stalactite formations and the manifold shapes moulded by the deposition of calcite, coupled with the wealth of cave bear remains, render the Erpfingen Bears' Cave an unparalleled natural monument. It affords a direct and magnificent impression of the abode of the most widely distributed of cave creatures, the cave bear, and of its physical structure. Comparison of the mass-finds of cave bear in the Bears' Cave and other caverns in Europe as far as the Caucasus, and in North Africa, with the finds of other greater or lesser beasts of prey among its contemporaries, strongly suggests that the cave bear—unlike modern beasts of prey or the generally solitary bears of today—was gregarious. It is clear that the cave was a living-place, for among the bones of full-grown bears were many skeletons of half-grown cubs or sucklings. This assumption is confirmed by finds in other caves, for example the Nikolaushöhle at Veringstadt, the cavern of Hohefels near Schelklingen, the Hepenloch at Gutenburg, and the cave at Velburg in the Upper Palatinate. Many caves contained prodigious quantities of bears' bones. The bone- and dung-impregnated cave earth of the Drachenhöhle, or Dragon's Cave, at Mixnitz in Styria, yielded so much high-grade phosphatic fertilizer that sixty goods trains of fifty wagons each were needed to take it away.

Another region once inhabited by the cave bear, and still the haunt of its descendant the brown bear, is the Pyrenees. Every major palaeontological collection in France contains a complete skeleton of the cave bear, from which its great size may be seen. In the caverns of the Pyrenees bear skeletons are found in clay, not, as at Balve, under flowstone. The wide distribution of the finds and the depths to which the animal penetrated indicate that the bears explored every corner of the cave systems. Norbert Casteret reports finding the mark of bears' claws on walls and floors covered with clay or delicate stalagmite deep in the heart of the mountain and even in narrow vertical passages, or chimneys.

'In the caverns of Planque (Haute-Garonne),' writes Casteret, 'two hundred and thirty feet below ground, I found the skeletons of two bears which had fallen into one of the lower pits with vertical walls, and which died of hunger after violently scratching the rock in attempts to climb out.'

Similar clear traces have been found in many Pyrenean caves, including the famous Trois-Frères and the 'oubliettes' of the caverns of Gargas and Montespan. The marks of bears' paws in the clay, which has set hard with the passage of time, have been observed at many points. In the cavern of the Tuc d'Audoubert, which was a favourite resort of the cave bear, Count Begouen discovered what he has christened 'the bears' toboggan slide'—a clay slope plunging into what used to be a small pond, though it is now dry. There is every sign that the bears used to go sliding down this slope and land in the muddy water. The marks of the hair of the bears' fur are still visible in the once plastic clay. Arctic explorers have watched polar bears indulging in this sport, to which seals are also addicted, on slopes of ice. Where opportunity offers, they may be seen amusing themselves in this way in zoos.

Casteret also reports that cave bear found diversion in the bear dance, as the modern bear does today when bored by solitude or captivity. The bear dance consists in a perpetual rocking to and fro with the head swaying in unison. Signs of this dance are visible in the cave of Pène-Blanque (Haute-Garonne), 3,250 feet up in the Massif d'Arbas, in the shape of innumerable overlapping prints of its four paws in the clay, made as it shifted restlessly from side to side for hours on end during its long hibernation.

The number of artistic representations of the cave bear are surprisingly few in relation to its obvious numbers and ubiquity. This is attributed by Casteret to the existence of some magical taboo due to fear of the animal. He believes that 'the few depictions of cave bears which do exist were plainly the work of witch-doctors specially authorized to draw the accursed creature'.

The first representation of a cave bear was discovered by Dr. Garrigou in the Pyrenean Grotte de Massat (Ariège), where a large number of bear skeletons were also found. It is an engraving on a pebble of a bear rising on its hind legs in a menacing attitude, which is enhanced by an expression of ferocity on the face.

Several other portrayals of bears have come to light. The cavern of Marsoulas contains a full-face engraving, and a similar drawing engraved on a reindeer antler was found by the well-known speleologist Édouard Lartet in the Grotte de Massat. It is now in the Toulouse Museum. The cavern of Les Trois Frères, so often referred to already, also contains a drawing of three bears on the rock wall. They have all been disfigured, probably in the course of some obscure magic rite, and one of them is shown with a bison's tail and the spots of a leopard or hyaena.

The cave bear must have been an almost invincible opponent to prehistoric man, with his primitive weapons. When he succeeded in slaying one of these formidable monsters it meant not only a welcome source of meat and clothing, but also the accomplishment of a truly heroic deed. As an aid to the incantations designed to give them power over their adversary, the ancient hunters did not content themselves with engraving the bear on the walls, but also made three-dimensional or high relief representations of him carved in rock or modelled in clay. Thus a small bear's head carved in rock has been found in the grotto of Isturitz (Basses-Pyrénées), while a clay statue of a cave bear has been obtained from the cavern of Montespan. The latter, which is headless and riddled with spear-holes, has evidently been mutilated in the course of prehistoric magic rites.

There remains the question of how the cave bear died out. It is not likely to have been exterminated by prehistoric man with his primitive weapons. Plenty of evidence points to its extinction having been due to degenerative disease. A large number of diseased bones and the remains of strikingly under-sized bears were found in the Drachenhöhle at Mixnitz in Styria. The prehistorian O. Abel concluded from this that the whole species of *Ursus spelaeus* underwent a process of degeneration. '*Ursus spelaeus* seems to have succumbed to a disease, for no migration can be traced,' confirms Norbert Casteret. He surmises that the cave bear fell victim to a wave of extreme cold that swept across his habitat and brought with it degenerative disease and malformation of the bones.

The Museum of Natural History at Toulouse possesses a unique collection of diseased bear bones, in the shape of deformed jaws, joined vertebrae, shoulder blades encrusted with bony tumours, and limb bones distorted by arthritis.

Just when this crippling malady developed and how long it took to wipe out the species cannot be said for certain. It was probably a rapid process which took place when a period of intense cold forced the bears to shelter for long periods in damp caves, where they contracted rheumatism and gout.

The number of caves containing quantities of bear skulls, but no complete bear skeletons, suggests human handiwork. The absence of any trace of man in these caves is not conclusive evidence to the contrary. The drawings and models in the Pyrenean caves demonstrate that man once used the caverns, in which bear remains have been found, for ritual purposes. In many bear caverns the skulls of bears lie side by side on plinths or in niches in the cave walls. This is the case in the Karlshöhle Bears' Cave at Erpfingen, the well-known caverns of the northern Harz Mountains, and elsewhere. In the Drachenloch near Vättis, the Wildmannlisloch on the Selun (Switzerland), and the Petershöhle near Velden in central Franconia bear skulls have even been found packed in a kind of box of stone slabs or piled up in niches in the rock. These are certainly not hunting trophies, which would have been displayed outside the cave. 'They are more likely to be evidence of a fully developed cult of this animal, which was so useful to man, a totemistic cult in which the bear appears both as a creature to be hunted and an object of veneration. Corresponding practices still live today among modern hunting peoples in Northern Asia. It may therefore be assumed that many bear caves were not places to which the bears went to give birth or die, but the sites of a cult that approaches the earliest forms of religious thinking.' (Professor Friedrich Behn in *Die Umschau*, No. 22, 1950.)

We do not have to look as far back as the Ice Age to see the position occupied by the cave bear. The ancient Greeks considered the bear the strongest animal of the forest and held it sacred to the goddess Artemis. In ancient Nordic, Slav and Finnish popular belief the bear was regarded as holy. As a symbol of strength it was sacred to Thor, who himself bore the name of the beast: Björn. It was believed that the strength of the bear could be acquired from bear's blood. In olden days curative powers were attributed to the teeth, fat, gall and claws of bears. In the Middle Ages, bear hunting was still looked upon as a knightly exercise, and the heraldic bears in the arms of the cities of Berlin, Bern and Bernburg no doubt date from that time.

HOW THE CAVE HYAENA LIVED

Most European caves with osseous remains contain the bones of cave hyaena. The hyaena lived in caverns and consumed its prey in them, as quantities of gnawed bones show. The hyaena is highly unpopular with speleologists and palaeontologists in search of the remains of prehistoric men and animals, for it wrought havoc with any carcass it came across. The power of its jaws was such that it cracked and ground large bones that would have defied the lion or tiger. It also swallowed and digested them, and its excrements have accumulated in the hyaena caves in the shape of coprolites, or fossilized dung. The digestive waste remained perfectly preserved until today by virtue of its high lime content, due to the phosphate in the bones.

Complete hyaena skeletons are rare, no doubt because these creatures did not hesitate to devour their own kind, once they were dead. Two virtually complete skeletons were unearthed by Félix Regnault in the Gargas cavern in 1880. One of these is now in the Paris Museum of Natural History, the other in the Natural History Museum in Toulouse.

Depictions of hyaena occur much less frequently than those of other animals in cave paintings and engravings. This is no doubt the outcome of a repulsion which this scavenger, despite its obvious utility, must always have inspired. Amongst the drawings of animals in the cavern of Montespan is a two-inch engraving, the smallest rock engraving known, which is thought to represent the head of a hyaena. The museum at Eyzies (Dordogne) possesses the ivory statuette of a hyaena which was found in the rock shelter of La Madeleine.

Scientists have taken a particular interest in the problem of the relation of modern species of hyaena to their prehistoric ancestor. Research into this question was undertaken shortly before the Second World War by the director of the Vienna Institute of Palaeontology, Professor Kurt Ehrenburg, in conjunction with the Krahuletz Society at Eggenburg, which is responsible for the wealth of finds obtained from the Fuchsluke and Teufelsluke near Roggendorf and now housed in the Krahuletz Museum.

In *Forschung und Fortschritt*, No. 7, 1939, Ehrenberg reports carrying out extensive comparisons between the fossil remains of the cave hyaena and the three modern species of hyaena—*Hyaena striata* (striped hyaena), *H. crocuta* (spotted hyaena) and *H. brunnea* (brown hyaena)—in order to ascertain the common and divergent characteristics. He came to the conclusion that the cave hyaena was undoubtedly the most specialized and involved of all hyaenas, and as such deserved to be assigned to a separate species.

The investigation of the traces left by the cave hyaena undertaken by Dr. Helmut Zapfe of Vienna University, cast an interesting light on this Ice Age scavenger from another angle. In the Teufelsluke, mentioned above, and many other cave sites a quantity of broken bones have been found bearing visible marks of gnawing. The Vienna Institute of Palaeontology conceived an ingenious plan for testing whether these marks could be attributed to hyaena. For a year the spotted hyaenas in the Schönbrunn Zoo, Vienna—which are allied to the cave hyaena—were fed with the bones of cattle, horse and deer, and the way in which each hyaena tackled these bones was carefully observed. A mass of material accumulated to show that all the animals proceeded in a remarkably uniform manner, producing identical marks on the bones and bone splinters. In the case of the large limb-bones the hyaenas regularly began at the joint ends, gnawing them away in order to crush the hollow bone and get at the marrow. It could safely be assumed that the cave hyaena had gone about things in the same fashion.

This assumption was confirmed by examination of material from the Lower Danube loess and the wealth of finds from the Schwedentischhöhle in the Moravian Karst. Dr. Helmut Zapfe points out (*Forschung und Fortschritt*, Nos. 20–21 1931) that bones of the rhinoceros (*Tichorhinus antiquitatis*) from various hyaena dens in the loess round Prague and Kovartsik and in Northern Bohemia, described by Laube, show signs of gnawing by hyaenas. The same is true of the rhinoceros bones from the loess of Brno in Moravia, Czechoslovakia, interpreted by Makowsky as traces of Ice Age man. Zapfe reaches the conclusion that comparison of material from Ice Age hyaena dens with the bones gnawed by hyaenas in the zoo exhibits a perpetual recurrence of shapes which coincide exactly with those of various bones which have hitherto been interpreted as showing the marks of Ice Age man. Great caution must, therefore, be exercised in future before Ice Age bones are designated 'the kitchen refuse of Ice Age man' and regarded as proof of his presence in the caves where they are found.

BATS, REGULAR VISITORS TO CAVES

Amongst the cave fauna which can be found without difficulty are the various species of bat. They occur in caves all over the world, which they use either as permanent dwelling places or for their winter hibernation. There are certain bats which do not enter caves. These include the 'flying fox' or fruit-bat (*Pteropus medius*), a gigantic bat with a wing-span of over three feet which hangs by day in vast swarms from the branches of very tall trees. But European bats seek the dark by day and fly only in the dusk or darkness, guiding themselves by the radar-like impulses of a special organ, which enables them to register the presence of an obstacle yards away by echo-location. Hence they are well able to find their way through the pitchy obscurity of a cavern.

The number of different varieties of bat that make their habitation in caves is quite surprising. For example, no less than nine species have been observed in the Siebengebirge, Rhenish Prussia. Cave bats constitute an interesting subject of study for bio-speleologists, who have been at great pains to learn their habits, particularly as European bats perform excellent service in destroying insect pests. For this reason research on bats was very actively pursued in Germany before the Second World War, and today a bat-research institute exists once more at Frankfurt-am-Main. On farms in Upper Bavaria, for example, it proved possible to eliminate the troublesome swarms of flies, and so appreciably increase the milk-yield of the cattle, by settling swallows and bats in the area. Thus bat-research and bat-protection are economically valuable.

The mouse-ear and horseshoe bats inhabiting the caves of Lower Austria were studied there after the Second World War, with remarkable results. An essential part of this study was ringing bats in a similar manner to that employed with birds. Austrian speleologists showed particular enthusiasm for this branch of their science. With their assistance, no less than three thousand cave bats were ringed in Lower Austria between 1945 and 1950.

From his observations of the greater horseshoe bat in Brandenburg, Eisentraut established that, for reasons unknown, the losses among females exceeded those among males. Thus, in one control winter, the males were found to outnumber the females in the proportion of 58:42. Banding the greater mouse-ear bat in Lower Austria also showed a general preponderance of males over females. But it is worth noting that in caves with a small bat population the figures are reversed, the females preponderating.

In Britain, studies of cave-dwelling bats have been made during the past few years in the caves of Devon, Somerset, Derbyshire and Denbighshire. Six species of bat have been found in British caves: the greater and lesser horseshoe bat, the long-eared bat, Natterer's bat, Daubenton's bat (very rare), and the whiskered bat. Ringing, which was begun in the U.S.A. by such workers as Mohr and Griffin as long ago as 1934, has also been carried out in Britain. Since the bat's leg, being small and soft-skinned, is not suitable for ringing in the same way as the scaly leg of a bird, the usual practice today is to use a ring which can be clamped on to the wing bone. (See W. M. and J. H. D. Hooper, 'Cave-dwelling Bats' in *British Caving*.)

Cave bats were largely responsible for the beginning of the exploration of the largest and longest cave in the world, the vast Carlsbad Cavern in the U.S.A. A wandering cowboy spotted a huge black cloud emerging from a nearby mountain; on closer inspection, the black cloud proved to consist of millions of bats flying out of the above-named cave on their nightly search for food.

The most remarkable bats were found in the caves of Mexico. They are the most dangerous of all cave bats and differ completely in their habits from others of their kind, which live on flies, insects and fruit. These bats, *Desmodus maximilian* and *Dyphylla spix*, which belong to the family Phyllostomatoidea, characterized by sensitive outgrowths of skin on the head forming 'nose-leaves', are the only true blood-sucking bats, and probably identical with the vampires of medieval legend. (The actual vampire bat, *Vampirus spectrum*, is a harmless fruit-eater.)

Columbus and Cortés refer in the reports of their voyages of discovery to the mysterious blood-sucker which they met in the New World. But for a long time this creature remained unknown to zoology, despite accounts from missionaries and settlers in America of the puzzling death of cattle from blood-sucking flying animals. Several centuries elapsed before this blood-sucker was identified with the legendary vampire of the Middle Ages. It was then given the zoological classification *Desmodus rotundus*.

Charles Darwin was the first to observe a blood-drinking bat. But the earliest fully-documented account came from the French physician, Dr. Guillon. In 1910, his patients in the Guiana leper colony were bitten by blood-sucking bats while asleep. Then, in 1929, the natives of the village of Siparia on the island of Trinidad in the West Indies fell ill with a strange paralysis of the limbs, which was initially diagnosed as poliomyelitis. But inoculation of apes with the spinal serum of these patients showed that the symptoms were caused by the virus of rabies. The Rockefeller Institute, which investigated this outbreak, was at first baffled, since the island had been clear of rabies since 1924. Then the investigators chanced on a report from Santa Catherina in Brazil, where thousands of cattle and horses had died of rabies since the beginning of the twentieth century. Seven thousand dogs had been destroyed in the belief that they were the carriers of the virus. But when bats were observed attacking grazing cattle it became clear that these creatures were the true carriers. Close study then revealed that the bats tore open the victims' skin with their sharp teeth, and lapped up the flowing blood with a quick lick of the tongue.

A similar case occurred in 1951 in the Mexican village of Plantanito. Villagers and cattle were attacked by bats, and those who had been bitten died of rabies after a few weeks. Little was known about these bats, but they were finally traced to caves in the adjacent mountains. The Mexican government took vigorous steps to exterminate the sinister blood-suckers, killing them in their caverns with flame-throwers and poison gas.

CAVE SWALLOWS AND THEIR EDIBLE NESTS

The European loves his hundred varieties of cheese, which are despised by the Chinese as rotten milk. On the other hand, the Chinese likes rotten eggs, which we disdain, and esteems as an especial delicacy the nests of a particular species of swallow, the salangane, which nests mainly in caves. The salangane is allied to our swift. Most varieties of salangane build their nests of seaweed, moss and feathers, which they bind together with their saliva. Such nests are inedible. But there are three species of salangane distributed throughout South-East Asia which make their nests exclusively of viscid saliva, which they secrete from the thick swellings under their tongues particularly freely during the mating season.

During this period a viscid, glutinous fluid flows incessantly from their beaks. It can be spun into a thread with the aid of a small stick. In the air, the mucus hardens to a substance resembling gum arabic within a few hours. The nests made from this mucilage are about the size of a goose's

egg and weigh around seven grammes. It takes three nests
to make a plate of soup, which is the form in which the nests
are principally eaten.

The bird makes up to a hundred flights to the point at
which it is building the nest, pressing the viscid mucus
against the wall with its tongue until it has constructed a
semi-circular platform on which, in the course of a month, it
builds up a bowl-shaped nest of tiny drops of saliva. In this
nest the bird lays two long, dull-white eggs. The salangane
does not use the same nest twice because it quickly rots,
especially in a humid atmosphere, becomes black and mal-
odorous, and falls down. There are no less than eighteen
species of salangane—which take its name from the island
of Salangan off the Malay Archipelago—spread across
South-East Asia and the islands of the Indian Ocean.

The three species of salangane that produce the light-
coloured nests which are best for eating, live in huge flocks on
Java, where they inhabit caves in the cliffs hollowed out by
the surf. They flutter through the spray of the breakers in
dense swarms, flying into the depth of the caves as the
waves fall back and leave the entrance free. When the tide
is out, the natives enter these caves with ladders made of
rattan cane from the calamus palm, with the aid of which
they can get at the nests that hang in thick clusters on the
ceiling and in clefts high up the walls.

The salanganes also nest in large flocks in the interior of
the islands, for instance in the vast limestone caves of Borneo.
Here it is rather easier for nest hunters to obtain their valuable booty. Even so, it is a dangerous trade. Armed with
rattan ropes, bamboo ladders, a four-pronged fork and a
blazing torch, at the end of a pole several yards long, the
natives gather the nests from places it seems nobody could
reach without breaking his neck. It not infrequently happens
that one of them goes hurtling down to his death.

The nest gatherers belong to a special caste, and the trade
is handed down from father to son. They sell their harvest to

Chinese, most of whom have rented the caves from the government and systematically exploit them. In days gone by, the monthly rent of a cave was often several thousand guilders. In the years before the Second World War, it fell at times to three hundred guilders, because many of the land caves were infested with snakes, which were driving out the salanganes and reducing the crop of nests. A number of the birds then moved into houses near the shore, bringing prosperity, for example, to the little half-derelict town of Grisee two miles west of Surabaya, the capital. Semarang and Buitenzorg on Java also derived considerable profits from breeding salanganes.

The nests are gathered three to four times a year, as soon as the young can fly. The second harvest is the best, and the most expensive nests are those which are freshly built, light in colour and semi-translucent. About two hundred of these go to a kilogramme, which before the war sold for £9 on the spot. But even the yellow and discoloured nests, dirtied with the excrements of the young birds and mingled with seaweed, lichen and other foreign material, find a market.

Although half the young perish when the nests are gathered, the number of salanganes is perpetually increasing, particularly as they have no enemies except owls, snakes and some daylight birds of prey, and have been preserved from decimation, since 1924, by strict game laws.

The majority of the nests go to Shanghai, where they are re-distributed. But some of them are bartered with neighbouring islands. In normal times five million nests at a value of £500,000 were consumed annually in China. After carefully cleaning them, the Chinese cut the nests into strips and boil them in milk and sugar to a soft, stringy soup. Boiled in meat soup, they are esteemed even by the white man for their digestive properties, for they have a high pepsin content. The nests are said to be especially tasty when simmered for twenty-four hours with fat meat, a capon and a duck and quantities of aromatic herbs.

Their great liking for these nests has led Chinese and Japanese to make artificial nests by pressing out algae and seaweed, which are very popular in the Far East on account of their high food value. But these artificial nests, say connoisseurs, lack the powerful aphrodisiac action of the natural product.

To supplement the supply of nests from Java, the Chinese encourage salanganes to nest in their houses. They often clear out the top storey, darken the rooms, divide them up with wooden partitions, beams and planks, and make holes in the walls to facilitate nesting. Although salangane-cotes of this type are a gold-mine to their possessor, bringing him an easily earned income, they also entail certain disadvantages. The dung from the birds, and the many bats nesting alongside them, often piles up to a depth of nearly two feet. But even this ammoniacal manure is valuable and finds buyers. The bugs and fleas that invariably accompany the salanganes are a worse nuisance. But the owner willingly accepts these initial discomforts, for he is soon able to build himself a new house with the money gained from selling the nests.

THE CAVERN OF EL GUACHARO

One of the strangest caves in the whole world is in Venezuela, near Caripe in the modern province of Monagas. The region has been declared a national park and named, in honour of the German naturalist and traveller, Alexander von Humboldt, the Monumento Natural de Alejandro de Humboldt. Von Humboldt sailed into the Cumana roadstead on July 16th, 1799, accompanied by the French naturalist Bonpland, and there began his journey into the interior, the results of which were later published in the vast thirty-volume work in French entitled *Voyage aux régions équinoxiales du nouveau continent, fait en 1799–1804*. Almost as soon as he landed, he heard marvellous stories of the cave of Caripe and developed the desire to investigate it for himself. A few months later, he and Bonpland were staying in the Capuchin monastery of Caripe, whence they set out into the Guacharo Valley, where the cavern is situated, accompanied by a few missionaries.

Von Humboldt gives a detailed description of the cave in his book. He begins by saying: 'The fame of the Caripe Valley rests, apart from its exceptionally cool climate, upon the great Cueva del Guacharo. In a country where people have such a great predilection for the marvellous, a cavern from which a river springs and in which thousands of night-birds live, whose fat is used in the missions for cooking, is naturally an inexhaustible subject of conversation and argument. Hence the foreigner has hardly set foot in Cumana before his ears are surfeited with stories of the eye-stone of Araya, the countryman in Arenas who suckled his child, and the cavern of the Guacharo which is supposed to be several miles long.'

Von Humboldt then describes the landscape through which he and his companions passed on their way to the cave, the rare plants he discovered, and the luxuriance of the tropical vegetation surrounding the entrance to the cavern. He then proceeds to discuss the peculiarities of this cave and its inhabitants, the guacharos, or oil-birds.

At the point where the light begins to fade one hears the raucous cry of the night-birds, which, so the natives believe, are only at home in these subterranean chambers. The guacharo is the size of our hen; it has the voice of the nightjar and the procnia, and the form of the vulturine birds, with tufts of stiff silk round its curved beak. [Von Humboldt describes this bird at length in the second volume of his *Observations de zoologie et d'anatomie comparée*, under the name *Steatornis*, 'fat-bird'.]

In its habits it resembles both the nightjars and the frogmouths. Its plumage is dark grey-blue, with little black streaks and dots. The bird's eyes cannot stand daylight; they are blue, and smaller than in the nightjar. The wings have a span of three feet six inches. The guacharo leaves the cavern at nightfall, particularly when there is a moon. It is about the only granivorous nocturnal

bird known up to the present; the construction of its claws is
enough to show that it does not hunt like owls. It eats very hard
seeds, like the nuthatch. The Indians assert that the guacharo
does not go after either insects of the order Coleoptera (beetles)
or moths, on which the nightjar lives. . . . It is difficult to conceive the frightful din produced by the thousands of birds in the
dark interior of the cavern. It can only be compared to the caw-
ing of our crows. The shrill, piercing cry of the guacharo rever-
berates from the rock-vaults and echoes back from the depths of
the cave. The Indians showed us the birds' nests by attaching
torches to long poles. They were situated sixty to a hundred feet
above our heads in funnel-shaped holes, with which the ceiling
was riddled. The deeper one penetrates into the cave and the
more birds are disturbed by the copal torches, the louder becomes
the noise. If it grew quieter for a few minutes around us, the
plaintive cry of the birds nesting in other branches of the cavern
rang out.

Von Humboldt goes on to describe the fat-harvest in the
caves.

Every year around midsummer's day the Indians go into the
caves with sticks and destroy the majority of nests. Several thousand birds are beaten to death, while the parents fly round the
Indians' heads with a fearful cackle, as though in defence of their
brood. The nestlings which fall to the ground are immediately
disembowelled. Their peritoneum carries a heavy growth of fat,
and a layer of fat runs from the abdomen to the breech and forms
a kind of knob between the bird's legs. The fact that grain-eating
birds, which are not exposed to daylight and make little use of
their muscles, become so fat, recalls age-old experience in fatten-
ing geese and cattle. . . .

At the time of the 'fat-harvest' (*cosecha de la manteca*), as it is
called in Caripe, the Indians build themselves shelters of palm-
leaves at the entrance and in the vestibule of the cavern. Here
they melt down the fat of the young, freshly-killed birds and pour
it into earthenware vessels. This fat is known as guacharo dripping (*manteca*) or oil (*aceite*); it is semi-fluid, clear and odourless.
It is so pure that it can be kept for more than a year without be-

coming rancid. In the monastery at Caripe no other fat was used than that from the cave, and we did not notice that the food acquired any unpleasant smell or taste from it.

The quantity of oil procured is in no way proportionate to the slaughter which the Indians wreak every year in the cave. It seems that they do not obtain more than one hundred and fifty to one hundred and sixty jars of absolutely pure *manteca*; the rest, which is less clear, is stored in large earthen vessels. This native industry is reminiscent of the gathering of dove-fat in Carolina, of which formerly several thousand casks used to be obtained. The use of guaracho fat in Caripe dates from time immemorial; the missionaries have merely regulated the method of obtaining it. According to the missionaries' system, the Indians have to supply guacharo oil for the everlasting church lamp; the rest, we were told, is bought from them. . . .

The guacharo species would long ago have been exterminated if various circumstances had not combined for their preservation. From superstition the Indians rarely venture far into the cavern. It also seems that the same bird nests in nearby caves which are inaccessible to man. . . .

If the crop and stomach of the young birds are cut open in the cave, they are often found to contain sundry hard, dry seeds, which, under the curious name 'guacharo seeds', are a celebrated remedy for the ague. They are carefully collected and sent to the sick in Carico and other low-lying fever zones.

The cavern is the source of the Rio Caripe, which, after its confluence with the little Rio de Santa Maria a few miles farther on, becomes navigable.

Von Humboldt also remarks that the Indians regard this cavern inhabited by night-birds as a fearful and mysterious place, where dwell the spirits of their ancestors. Man, they say, ought to hold in dread places upon which neither the sun (*Zis*) nor the moon (*Nuna*) ever shines. To 'go to the guacharos' means the same as to be 'gathered to one's ancestors', i.e. to die. Hence sorcerers, *piajes*, and poison-mixers, *imorons*, used to hold their nocturnal hocus-pocus at the entrance to the cavern, where they sought to call up the supreme evil spirit Ivorokiamo. 'The cave of Caripe is the Tartarus of the Greeks,' comments von Humboldt, 'and the guacharos fluttering with mournful cries above the water recall the Stygian birds.'

Von Humboldt was the first to introduce the guacharo, which was previously unknown in Europe, into zoology under the name *Steatornis caripensis*. He brought a drawing of it back to Europe with him. He also discovered subterranean vegetation in the cavern. This did not contain any new plants, but was merely an etiolated growth sprung from seeds brought into the cave by the birds. He was unable to identify the plants, which consisted of pale stems up to twenty-four inches in height with a few rudimentary leaves.

Once the cave had become world-renowned, it suffered from a great deal of vandalism. Tourists and souvenir-hunters, and also local people, broke off many of the yards-long straw stalactites and stalagmites which formerly adorned the interior. The guacharos were perpetually frightened away by the visitors, with the result that a large proportion of them moved to other, inaccessible caves. For centuries the birds had been fair game to the Indians, and only the latter's fear of penetrating into the whole of the approximately two-mile long cave had saved the guacharos from extinction. Today the cavern is national property, and may be entered only in the company of official guides. Hunting and killing the birds is forbidden.

Among contemporary Venezuelan naturalists, Dr. Eduardo Rohl has rendered particularly outstanding service in the preservation of the cave and its surroundings. He also possesses the most comprehensive collection of the various works of von Humboldt in French, German, English and Spanish—many of them very rare first editions.

INVESTIGATED AND UNINVESTIGATED CAVE FAUNA

Amongst the smaller forms of life to be found in caves, insects

are the most common. They are noteworthy not only for
their numbers, but also for the multiplicity of species. Chief
amongst them are Coleoptera (beetles), including ground-
beetles and short-winged beetles; many species of Diptera
(flies), and wasps, bees, and even fireflies. In Spain there is
a cave inhabited by bees, whose honey goes to feed the inmates of a nearby monastery. In the Waimoto Cavern, New
Zealand, live numberless glow-worms, which at times illu-
minate a vast hall. They draw threads across the interior of
the cave like spiders, and catch insects in them. At the
slightest sound these glow-worms contract and lose their
luminosity.

Some bats and birds are cavernophilous, that is to say,
they spend only part of their lives in caves. But there are
other creatures which are cavernicolous: they are born, live
and die underground. We will consider some of the principal
cavernicoles found in European caves. (Tropical caves have
not yet been studied from this point of view.)

Coleoptera occur in almost every European cavern. An
excursion in the Holstein Segeberghöhle produced over a
thousand *Choleva holsatica*, a beetle with a thin body, long
antennae and large legs. Another species of cave beetle is
Leptinus testaceus, a blind albino beetle which occurs not only
in caves, but also in burrows of rabbits, hamsters and moles,
mouse-holes, and beehives, where it probably lives on the
excrement of its hosts. Its body is flat and the soft wing is
missing from underneath the hard wing-covers. Like many
other cave animals, it possesses long antennae. Because of its
dual mode of life and its unusual bodily shape, it is numbered amongst the parasites as well as the cavernicoles. Like
the cavernicolous fungus gnats, which will be discussed later,
true cave beetles—found above all in Balkan caves and the
Postofna (Adelsberg) grottoes—show atrophy of the trachea
(respiratory tubes) and the stigmata (respiratory orifices), so
that these beetles are assumed to breathe through their skin.
Franz Lengersdorf describes this peculiar method of breath-

ing in the six-millimetre-long *Lepdotirus hochenwarti*, found in
the Caves of Postojna—the first cave beetle to be discovered.
The exceptionally large, oval, flattened abdomen of this
beetle is covered by two inflated wing-covers, which fulfil
the function of respiratory chambers. This unusually large
abdomen also serves to regulate moisture and preserve the
beetle from drying up in an arid environment. It has six
long segmented legs and two long antennae divided into
eleven segments, in keeping with the large abdomen, while
the thorax is long and narrow. Since the beetle is perfectly
blind, legs and antennae are equipped with fine, sensitive
hairs.

In many caves silvery-grey threads of mucus may be observed, which glisten in the light. These threads—other
cavernicolous insects leave a similar trail—are the work of
the transparent fungus gnat, which secretes mucus from its
salivary gland to facilitate its progress and protect its thin
and delicate skin from injury. These threads often hang in
the air, anchored to the wall by lateral threads. Despite its
delicacy and fragility, the cavernicolous fungus gnat (*Polylepta eptogaster*) has a fantastic structure when seen through
the microscope. Unlike other insects, the larva's system of
tracheae is incomplete and only takes in the large, torpedo-
shaped head. The missing respiratory system is replaced by
the absorption of oxygen through the skin, which is only
possible in the dampness of a cave. If the fungus gnat is
brought out into daylight, it quickly dries up and dies. The
larva, which lives on the algae that cover the cave walls, is
the preliminary stage of the gnat. As with all true cavernicoles, whose whole life is passed in caves, the cavernicolous
fungus gnat—of which no less than five species were found in
the caves of the Siebengebirge alone—may be met with at all
stages of development at the same season. *Polylepta leptogaster*
was first discovered in 1907 by Father H. Schmitz, S.J., in
the caverns of the Louw- or Garnenberg, near Maastrich.

In 1924 Franz Lengersdorf found in the artificial caves of

the Siebengebirge a species of gnat, *Neosciara ofenkaulis*, which had never been seen above ground. Although this gnat possesses fully-developed wings, it does not use them, but only runs along on its legs. Lengersdorf reports that it darted behind a piece of rotten wood, where it also laid its eggs. The wings are useless to the insect in the darkness. On the other hand its sense of touch is highly developed, not only in its long legs, but also in equally long antennae. Whereas the proportion of the length of the antennae to the length of the body is between one and three to one in surface species, in the cave gnat it is between five and six to one. Another remarkable species of gnat, *Epidapus atomarius*, has also been met with in caves. In this species the female has no wings, but possesses, in addition to the antennae, absolutely transparent sensory rods which act as a kind of radar apparatus for moisture. The male possesses much longer antennae, probably as a means of seeking out the far more lethargic female.

Gnats of the same family found in exceptionally damp caverns often show signs of degeneration, in the shape of pronounced bloating of the abdominal segments, which are squeezed tightly together.

The dampness of caves also attracts dung-flies (Borboridae) and the celebrated *Drosophilia*[1] (family Helomyzidae), thick swarms of which frequently cover cave walls in summer. Other cave-dwelling insects are Culicidae (mosquitoes), the yellowish-brown Trichopterae with long wings and antennae, and the Phoridae, which differ from surface species in

[1] This insect, *Drosophilia melanogaster*, is used in biological research into the chromosomes, the bearers of hereditary characteristics. This tiny insect is of great value to geneticists because it not only produces an exceptionally large number of progeny in a year, but also shows an unusual number of mutations. In the course of three million tests carried out up to 1944 seven hundred mutations were observed. The varieties could be distinguished by differences of body shape, hair distribution, colour, wing shape, and eye colour, of which there were thirteen divergent shades.

having a tuft of hair projecting to left and right on the fifth abdominal segment.

Amongst the animals that once dwelt above ground and then crept into caves when the temperature fell, and there evolved a new pattern of life, is the wingless *Schaefferia emucronata*, which resembles the millipede, is unpigmented, and yet has bluish spots. Contrary to other primitive insects—e.g. the cavernophilous species of Neelus, Sminthuridae, Megalothorax and Arrhopalidae—which are more or less humpbacked, Schaefferia has an elongated body. It possesses only four atrophied legs at the front. But in compensation it has a kind of jumping organ or springtail, the furca, divided into three segments. The furca, like the whole of its back, is covered with bristles. Like the *Drosophilia*, the specimens of *Schaefferia* found in the Charlottenhöhle in the Swabian Alps, the Berghäuser cavern, the Rentropshöhle, the Hölloch, the Kellerhöhle in Sauerland, and the Harz caves, show considerable mutation in the number of bristles (dens), the hinder-part (mucro) and the eyes (omma). Similar mutations are visible in the cave crab. All these creatures are troglobites, i.e. permanent dwellers in the Dark Zone, the deepest level of the cave world. Their mutations are determined by this unchanging habitat.

Certain moths spend part of their lives in cavern entrances. Such creatures are known as threshold trogloxenes; amongst them are *Triphosa dubitata* and *Scoliopterix libatrix*, which begin to swarm in late summer and probably change into chrysalids within the caves. A variety of *Triphosa dubitata* is found in the caves of the Swabian Alps.

Spiders are frequent inhabitants of caves. Completely white spiders the size of the human hand have been discovered in the Pyrenees. In German caverns one meets *Plesiocrerius lusicus*, which is blind and passes through the whole of its development in caves, independently of the seasons. It has been found in the Klutert cave, with its wealth of cavernicolous life, and in the caverns of the

Pyrenees. A characteristic of this spider is that atrophy of its organs of sight has been accompanied by hypertrophy of the sensitive hairs on its body. It is the only genuinely caverni-colous spider so far discovered in Germany. Cave spiders are the natural enemies of many threshold trogloxenes, particularly of the spider *Meta menardi*, which likes damp places and spins a cocoon-like nest for its eggs that hangs by a thread from the ceiling of the cave. *Meta merianae*, on the other hand, makes his home in dry caverns.

The notorious 'Death's Head Spider' is a legendary cave-dweller of the Merano region. The story runs that a peasant who entered the Naturno cavern became entangled in this spider's web, the threads of which were as strong as horse-hair. He forced the spider to release him by making the sign of the Cross three times. Nevertheless, the peasant received such a fright that he never returned to the cave.

Among crustacea which spend part of their lives on the surface and part in subterranean waters, there are a number of particularly interesting types.

Foremost amongst these are the little colourless and blind shrimps (Amphipoda). These tiny creatures inhabit cave pools and are characterized by a great wealth of mutations, leading to a multiplicity of species which are found in the majority of German caves.

Rougemont caught the first blind amphipod in the well in the Garden of the old 'Anatomie' at Munich in 1876, and christened it *Crangonyx subterraneus*. It was defined as a developmental stage of *Niphargus*. But when no subsequent example came to light, the creature was removed from the list of German fauna. Franz Lengersdorf, the expert in cave fauna, then came upon further specimens of this amphipod in a small pool between the main road and the Elbe near Schandau in 1931. In the meantime further examples of the Munich amphipod had been discovered in wells at Prague and Lille, in the south of England, and in the Hermanns-höhle, Germany. Like certain cave gnats and the cave louse, the cave shrimp has highly-developed sense organs in the shape of feelers and sensitive bristles.

Besides the amphipods or shrimps, cave pools are inhabited by tiny water fleas (Copepoda) no larger than a pinhead. They have been found in the caverns of the Siebengebirge, in Rumanian caves and in the great cavern of St. Canzian, which used to be in Italy but is now in Yugoslavia. Two peculiar species of water fleas are *Viguirella fodinata* and *Bathynella chappuisi*. The former has been found in a mine adit by the Saar, while the latter was discovered by Franz Lengersdorf in the Hönnetal, the valley of twenty-two caves, and also by A. G. Lowndes in the stone mine at Corsham, Wiltshire, in 1927. These animals possess an organ of propulsion situated on the maxillary gland. *Viguierella* develops in six larval stages. *Bathynella* differs in shape from the normal water flea. It is a worm-like creature, 1.5 to 2 millimetres long, transparent and eyeless. The front half of its body is covered in bristles. It darts about cave pools with an undulating motion, and lives on protozoa, the so-called Rhizopoda. The female lays only one egg, so that reproduction is very slow, as has been observed in many cave creatures. On the other hand, seasons are unknown in caves, because the temperature is uniform; consequently breeding can take place at any time.

The high degree of humidity prevailing in many caves has led to a number of cave fleas becoming amphibious. Several species are encountered both in water and on the damp floor, walls or stalagmites. The creatures are so tiny that the degree of moisture present is sufficient to envelop them and keep them alive.

Many types of aquatic worm occur in the ground-water of caves. *Dorydrilus wiardi* and *Trichodrilus lengersdorfi* have been found in the caves of the Siebengebirge and Sauerland. The former lives on sludge, the latter prefers a more carnivorous diet. The half-a-millimetre-long primitive Annelida (earthworm), *Trolochaetus beranecki*—a kind of larva with rudiment-

1. The Heidenlöcher or Heathens' Holes at Überlingen, Lake Constance

3. Cave dwellings in the loess of Shansi province, Northern China

4a. Entrance to the rock-cut temple of Elephanta, an island in Bombay harbour

4b. Curiously shaped cones of rock with 'helmets' in the Valley of Ghost (known locally as the Hunters' Village) in the Turkish province of Urgub

5. Rock dwellings, known as Chimneys of the Evil Spirits, in Cappadocia

6. The birthplace of Christ at Bethlehem is situated in a cave

7. South African cave painting in the Martinshoek Valley. The large ash-grey antelope is of recent date, the small pink antelopes considerably older, the black figures of Bushmen and Bantus recent

8a. The Liet-Höhle near Warstein: A 60-foot fissure with sinter and tubular formations

8b. The Liet-Höhle near Warstein: The subterranean river that contributed to the formation of the cave

a. The Liet-Höhle near Warstein: A striking group of stalactite curtains in the cave

b. The Liet-Höhle near Warstein: Twisted exudations of calcite on the cave walls

10. The great subterranean lake, one of the largest in the world, in the grottoes of Han, Belgium

11. The subterranean Weebubbie Lake in the Nullarbor network of caverns, Australia

12. The 300-foot-deep Crystal Lake in the Mammoth Cave, Kentucky

13. The Hall of the Sabbath in the grottoes at Rochefort, Belgium

14. The 'Gothic Columns' in the Adelsberg stalactite cave

15. Passing through a Pyrenean cavern in rubber dinghies

16a. The 'Ice Palace' in the Eisriesenwelt

16b. The Eisriesenwelt: The last resting-place of the discoverer, Alexander von Mörk

17a. Ringed horseshoe bat in an Austrian cave

7b. Small horseshoe bats in the Charlottenhöhle near Hürben, Swabian
Alps

18 Blind fish (*Amblyopsis spelaeus*) in the subterranean waters of the Mammoth Cave, Kentucky

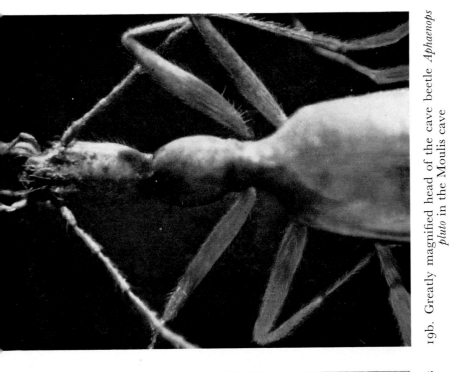

19b. Greatly magnified head of the cave beetle *Aphaenops pluto* in the Moulis cave

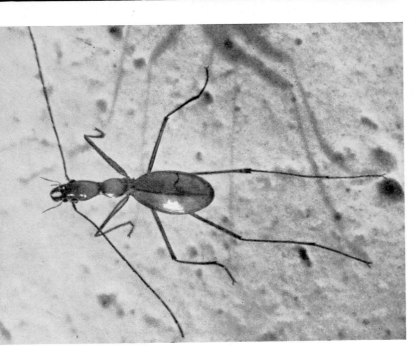

19a. The cave beetle *Aphaenops pluto* in the Moulis cave, showing exceptionally long feelers and legs

20b. Hand imprints in a burial cave of the Worora tribe.

20a. Tantalhöhle: descending an aluminium

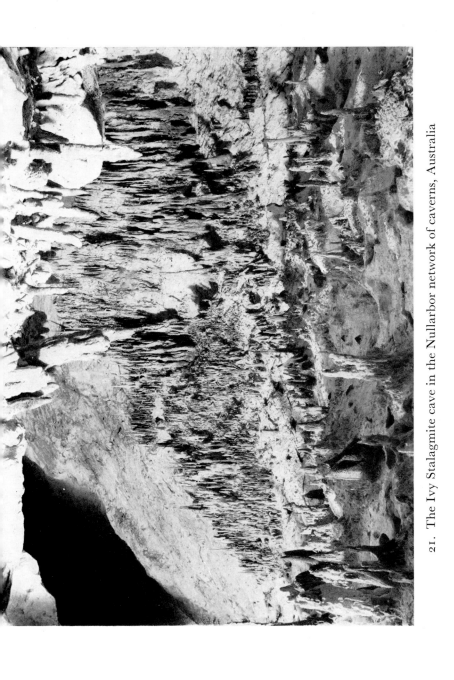

21. The Ivy Stalagmite cave in the Nullarbor network of caverns, Australia

22a. Curtain formations, fringed with stalactites, along the roof of the 'Gothic Passage', Clapham Cave, in the Peak district of Derbyshire

22b. Swithin's hole in the Mendip Caves, Somerset

23a. The Cheddar Gorge

23b. The Wookey Hole Caves, under the Mendip hills

24. Fingal's Cave at Staffa, Scotland

ary legs covered in hair, which can move about both in water and on land—has been met with in the caves of Wilmersdorf and Reyersdorf. Franz Lengersdorf describes it as a pre-glacial relic. Two species of Turbellaria have been observed, blind, colourless creatures about ten to twelve millimetres in length. One of these worms has a suction-cleft in the front of its head as a means of locomotion. In 1932 Dr. Griepenburg found the ten- to fifteen-millimetre-long colourless Turbellaria *Krumbachia* in a pool in the Klutert cave and also a Prostomida, *Prostoma clepsinoides*.

Prostoma is one of the most curious of cave creatures. It is one of the stenothermal aquatic animals: it can live only in water of a particular temperature. Griepenburg experimented with this worm and found that it died if the water was cooled to 41° F. or warmed to 59° F. It has a retractile trunk armed with a sting. The worm winds itself round its prey in a spiral, stabs it with its sting, and then squirts venomous fluid into the wound, which kills or paralyses its victim. The worm draws its prey to it with its trunk and devours it at leisure. If its capture is particularly large, the worm can live on it for half a year.

Amongst other cave worms, certain Filaria, which have been found in such places as mine adits, are worth noting. The genus *Mermis* lives in the larvae of insects. Franz Lengersdorf reports finding a fly, *Helomyza serrata*, near Sundwig in Westphalia, which was smothered in *Mermis* worms. From this the naturalist concluded that the worm had laid eggs shortly before the final stage of the insect's development at the larval stage.

Rotatoria are also among the plentiful worm fauna to be found in caves; but their minute size renders them difficult to catch, so that they have been little studied.

As already mentioned, there are no seasons in caves. Consequently cavernicoles breed at all times of the year. This is clearly evident from observation of water and wood lice (Isopoda) in caves, which have been found in all stages of development at the same time and place. Everyone knows the oval, pale grey, many-legged wood-lice that haunt dung heaps or gather under stones and rotting wood. The several species include a cavernicolous louse, *Asellus cavaticus*, that is allied to the water louse and never seen above ground. *Asellus cavaticus* is distinguished from other Assellidae by absence of eyes and pigment.

The tactile organs are far more highly developed in *A. cavaticus* than in surface species.

Amongst the small creatures that have found their way into caverns by mistake, or been swept in by running water, are snails. Unlike the majority of cave-dwelling animals, snails do not exhibit the usual leucism, or loss of pigment. Indeed, it has been observed that they become darker in colour than the surface forms. A similar phenomenon has been noted in gnats: those in cooler and damper caves proved to have acquired a darker colour than others of the same species in warmer and drier ones. Experiments have been made in influencing the pigmentation of the moisture-loving cave snail, which becomes darker when the temperature is lowered and red when it is raised.

Little enough is known about the life-cycle of surface-water fish, so it is not surprising that cavernicolous fish are still largely a closed book. It is possible that certain fish spawn in underground rivers. Few fish have been found in the accessible waters of European caverns. In 1930, Dr. Biese discovered in a pool about a thousand feet from the entrance to a stalactite cave in the Harz Mountains a trout that had lost all its red spots and pretty well all the rest of its pigmentation. It was not clear whether this trout had entered the cave by mistake, or whether it was a genuinely cavernicolous species. Cave fish, Amblyopsidae, constitute a family allied to that of the carp. *Amblyopsis spelaeus* is five inches long, colourless, eyeless and viviparous. Like *Typhlichthys subterraneus*, it lives in the underground waters of the Kentucky Mammoth Cave, U.S.A.

Next to the bat, one of the most evolved and highest forms of cave life is the proteus, an amphibian which retains throughout life external gills, which are provisional larval structures in most Amphibia. Owing to the variations in the organ formation of this animal, seven different species were distinguished by the Austrian Fitzinger in 1850, when its biology was not yet fully understood. This classification was later abandoned.

This strange creature of the underworld has exercised the minds of naturalists for centuries. The first writer to describe the proteus was Baron J. W. Valvason in his book, *Die Ehre Dess Herzogthums Crain* (Laybach, 1689). It was more fully described by Jos. Nicol. Laurenti in 1768. The first proteus was found in the Magdalene Grotto at Postojna, near Trieste, by Löwengreif in 1797. By 1890, the proteus had been discovered at ninety different places, chiefly in the subterranean waters of Carniola, Carinthia and Dalmatia, and always in absolute darkness.

The proteus, which takes three years to reach maturity, shows perpetual changes throughout its development, but especially during the breeding season. These changes involve varying coloration and alterations in the shape of the tail, head and crest. Organically, too, the proteus exhibits a number of curious features. It lacks a true muscular tongue and possesses three thyroid glands, one double and one single. Its lungs—which it possesses in addition to its three pairs of external gills—are long, tube-like organs with delicate walls. As the Frenchman Rosconi, who made a close study of the proteus, realized in 1846, this amphibian has tiny eyes no bigger than a pinhead and entirely covered by skin. In the young proteus they appear through the skin as a dot of black pigmentation; as the animal grows older they cease to be visible at all. These eyes have neither cornea nor orbit. Above them are several minute organs which must once have been connected with the atrophied organ of sight. The body is normally white in colour, faintly tinged with red by the blood, which also gives the gills a rosy hue. The animal reaches a length of about a foot, has a long tail, four weak limbs placed far apart, and bearing respectively three and two toes. When kept fully exposed to light in confinement, the proteus slowly develops dark pigment, ultimately becoming black.

Up to 1883 very little was known about the life of the proteus. In a paper entitled, 'Die Fortpflanzung des Proteus anguineus' in the *Zoologischer Anzeiger*, 1882, Marie von Chauvin reported that she had succeeded in breeding the creature in captivity. During the breeding season in May, the proteus changes its outward appearance. The male, which is normally scarcely distinguishable from the female, becomes grey and two rows of dark spots appear on its tail. The female, which takes on a reddish colour during the breeding season, lay eggs approximately eleven millimetres in diameter, which she attaches singly to stalagmites. Chauvin's experiment proved, as the great anatomist Hyrtl had guessed in 1850, that the proteus is one of the oviparous amphibians. After ninety days the larvae, which are twenty-two millimetres long and resemble the adults, emerge from the eggs. Amongst the peculiarities of the proteus is the fact that in water whose temperature is over 59° F. it lays eggs, but when the temperature is under 59° F. it gives birth to live young (*The Cave of Postojna and Other Curiosities of the Karst*, by Dr. Alfred Serko and Michler Ivan, Ljubljana, 1953).

In the nineteenth century, naturalists were already preoccupied with the change in the coloration of the proteus which takes place when it is exposed to light. It did not occur to anyone at that time that this darkening of the pigment might have something to do with changes in the oxygen metabolism—a point on which we shall have more to say later. But it had already been observed that the proteus possessed a very fine sense of touch and that, in compensation for the rudimentary eyes, the olfactory sacs and auditory apparatus are very highly developed, so that the animal is able to adapt itself to any change in its environment. In the 'nineties, American naturalists, studying American amphibians, noticed that they were equipped with powerful sensory organs on the skin, and finally it was established that the proteus, too, is sensitive to light which emits no heat, and shrinks from the touch.

The proteus lives on worms, water fleas and other cavernicolous fauna. Its power of movement is somewhat limited, for its legs are small. For locomotion it also makes use of its powerfully developed tail, which becomes much longer during the breeding season.

This brief survey of cave fauna lays no claim to completeness. The breadth of this domain of zoology may be gathered from the fact that in the small caves of the Siebengebirge alone there are no less than nine species of bat and twenty-four other types of animal. Many surprises await the biologist working in this field. What we have said is enough to show the diversity of this fauna, which may, in some respects, be said to parallel that of the great ocean deeps.

Many people may wonder what the animals that inhabit the dark cavities of the earth, where there is virtually no vegetation, can find to eat. The same law prevails in the caverns as on the surface: eat or be eaten. The ooze, the water that seeps down through the fissures, mosses and algae, mouldering wood, vegetable and animal debris, matter unwittingly brought into the caves by men and beasts, and the primitive organisms that constitute, as it were, the plankton of the grottoes provide the food of cave-dwelling creatures. Cave worms feed on slime and the minutest fragments of plant and animal remains; shrimps on the tiniest organisms in the underground waters. Insects feed on excrement and dead animals, and spiders on flies. Mites exist as parasites on bats. Then there are guanobites and guanophiles which live on bat excrement or guano. These include many beetles and snails.

It would not be out of place here to inquire how the bio-speleologist catches his specimens; for it is a difficult business hunting for the animals hidden in the dark tunnels and clefts by the light of a torch. The French naturalists Racowitza, Jeannel and Chapuis, and the Tyrolean Janetschek, among others, have concerned themselves particularly with the distribution of cavernicolous fauna; the Germans Dudich, Lengersdorf, Graeter, Schmitz, Spandl and others have concentrated more on studying individual specimens from anatomical, ecological, physiological and ontogenetic points of view.

Bio-speleologists have evolved numerous methods of capturing the creatures whose presence in the caves they suspect. The Barber trap, for example, consists of a large glass filled with ethylene glycol, in the middle of which stands a small vessel containing bait. The large glass is buried up to the rim in the soil, so that animals attracted by the bait fall into the ethylene glycol. For catching aquatic creatures, the naturalist employs a plankton net with a bait. Armed with collecting-jars, an acetylene lamp, paint brushes, a small rake, a hammer, tweezers, a net and a few other small accessories the naturalist can scour the cave, rejoicing if he returns home with plenty of booty, which he can examine at leisure. If he is lucky, he may discover a new insect which will henceforth bear his name.

No publicity surrounds the laborious and unsensational work of searching out the forms of life native to the world of caverns. But it lends interest to caves that are without obvious attractions or appeal to the eye. To the bio-speleologist such caves appear full of mystery and wonder with all their myriad varieties of living creatures. They are mines of delight to anyone who still feels the urge to track down the secrets of creation and contemplate them with admiration and amazement.

THE PURPOSE OF STUDYING CAVE FAUNA

Not all creatures found living in caverns are cave animals. A distinction is generally made between those living permanently in caves (troglobites), those which live close to the entrance only (trogloxenes), and those which live either in the dark zone or in the cave entrances (troglophiles). No clear division is possible, since the permanent habitat of each creature cannot always be established.

Many naturalists were already interested in cave fauna during the nineteenth century. The blind proteus was the first cave creature to capture their attention. After this, some curious beetles were discovered in Southern European caves in 1835. But several decades passed before a detailed study of the cavernicoles was made.

The first survey of European cave life on any scale was Professor Otto Hamann's *Europäische Höhlenfauna* (Jena, 1896), which included four hundred species. The care with which this book was written testifies to the interest taken in the subject by naturalists at that period. The author consulted no less than three hundred and eighty-four smaller works which had been published earlier. An even broader and more comprehensive study is Robert Leruth's monumental work, *La Biologie du Domaine souterrain et la Faune cavernicole de la Belgique* (Brussels, 1939). Its five hundred large pages contain an almost exhaustive survey of the subject, and as many as four hundred and eight French, English and German works on cave fauna are quoted. But as early as 1934 to 1937, B. Wolf published an *Animalium Cavernarum Catalogus* listing no less than eight hundred cave animals. In 1940, W. Arndt drew up a list of seven hundred and forty-five species that had been found in large caves only. These include two hundred and eighty-five aquatic and four hundred and eighty-one terrestrial creatures. Of these sixty-nine were stated to be indisputable cave animals, forty-four of them being crustaceans. Altogether there were one hundred and sixty species of protozoa (unicellular animals), and six hundred and twenty-nine of metazoa (multicellular animals), of which two hundred and forty-two were insects, made up of one hundred and four Diptera (two-winged flies), one hundred and ten Arachnidae (spiders), ninety-seven crustaceans, thirty-three species of millipede, seventy-three species of worm and thirty-seven molluscs.

Although European caves are no longer the habitation of great beasts, they are the retreat or the natural habitat of innumerable small creatures. Anyone who explores them soon learns that they are the repositories of a strange world of underground life, which is worth studying from many points of view.

Numerous caves throughout the world are noted for their fauna, which deserves more detailed consideration than it can be given here. The Klutert cave in Sauerland is famous for its animal life, which contains species unknown in any other part of Europe. Caverns which are particularly rich in small forms of life include the Karst and Moravian caves, the Carniola caves, those of Montenegro, Hungary and Dalmatia, the Belgian caves, which have been very fully studied as regards their fauna, the caverns of the Pyrenees, the Mexican caves of Cacahuamilpa, and the caves on the Philippines, to name only a few.

A great many problems await solution in the darkness of the caverns. Although their study may appear to the layman a mere scientific pastime, they do in fact offer means of acquiring knowledge of considerable practical value in various domains of life. One of the most burning problems of bio-speleology is that of the reproduction and development of cavernicoles. The father of the Moulis speleological laboratory, Professor Jeannel, has drawn attention to the fact that the larvae of cavernicolous Coleoptera (beetles with four wings, of which the two hard upper wing-covers are useless for flight, which is reserved for the two lower ones —e.g. *Aphaenops, Antrocharis, Leptodierus, Antroherpon*), which are amongst the most highly specialized creatures, are so rare that insect collectors pay as high a price for them as philatelists do for rare stamps. Amongst little-known animals are millipedes and *Typhloblaniulus* (blind-animal), tangled masses of which are to be found in Pyrenean caves. Up to the present, not a single specimen of *Titanethes* (one of the Asellidae) has ever been found carrying eggs, although thousands of this species have been caught. In the Moulis speleological laboratory the attempt is being made to reconstitute the complete life-cycle of the troglobites, and to find out where the animals normally repair to breed.

The most noteworthy phenomena observed in cavernicolous animals are albinism and blindness. It was originally supposed that the blindness was caused by the albinism, for an eye without pigment is always more or less inadequate, for embryonic reasons which we do not yet understand. The albinism and blindness which characterize the majority of cave creatures seem so obviously bound up with the absence of light that, until recently, naturalists did not hesitate to see in this a relationship of cause and effect. This seemed a satisfactory explanation, but the logic of nature often differs from imperfect human logic. Since the knowledge of natural history has to be acquired not through logic, but from experience, it was thought necessary to go deeper into the question of albinism and blindness.

Many caves are the resort not only of troglobites which lack both pigment and eyes and develop entirely within caves, but also of a number of animals which, although they are looked upon as troglobites, possess pigment and eyes in spite of the fact that they have never come into contact with daylight; these include many snails. On the other hand there are several albino animals that do not live in darkness, e.g. the halophiles (salt-animals). From this it was evident that other causes, having nothing to do with light or darkness, were responsible for the lack of pigment. The chief of these are humidity and temperature.

Every cave, even the driest, is relatively damp, for moisture perpetually seeps down through the mountain or rises from the ground water in the cave. During a warm summer the dampness is less than during a rainy autumn or winter. Caverns at high altitude are naturally drier than those in low ground or on the banks of a river. As already stated, every cave—or at least every group of caves—has its own fauna, which is often very circumscribed. There are some cavernicoles which prefer small caves; others prefer large ones; many live in caverns of all sizes, while several live both above and below ground. There are those that like warmth, and those that like cold. Franz Lengersdorf, for example, found several specimens of a species of gnat, *Neosciara cochliata*, in a Silesian cave, which otherwise occurs only in Greenland. Another cold-loving creature is the springtail (*Neelus minutus*), which has been found in the Iberg cavern in the Harz Mountains, but which is chiefly met with in Finland, the Soviet Union and North America. The Northern Siberian mite *Rhagidia recussa* has been discovered in the Unicorn Cave and the Heimkehle, both in the Harz Mountains, the latter being partially an ice grotto.

The French naturalist Professor Fage put forward some very interesting views on the origin of cave-dwelling creatures in a book on cavernicolous spiders (1931). His starting point is Meyer's and Plantefol's investigation of the respiratory phenomena of mosses. These biologists ascertained that phenomena connected with the respiratory process are feebler the higher the water-content of the moss. Professor Fage applied this observation to the cavernicoles and deduced from it that animals living in an atmosphere saturated with moisture accumulate a very low percentage of oxygen. Now, it is well known that the formation of pigment is mainly the result of the oxidation of organic compounds aided by oxidizing diastases (ferments). A reduction of the respiratory process brings with it a reduction of melanogenesis and, at the extreme limit, its disappearance. It has been clearly established that the respiratory metabolism of cavernicolous animals is lower than that of the allied forms above ground. In the section 'Investigated and Uninvestigated Cave Fauna' reference was made to certain creatures showing atrophy of the tracheae, or respiratory system. This is far more evident in the aquatic than in the terrestrial forms.

In 1950, the French worker Mme Derouet published a paper giving the results of her investigation of the respiratory intensity of the cave spider *Meta menardi*, which has already been referred to, as compared with that of *Araneus diadematus*, a large surface spider. Their reactions in a dry and in a humid environment are totally different and almost the reverse. In the latter case, the diminished respiratory metabolism is manifestly not dependent on the humidity of the air, but on the low and constant temperature of the water in caves.

The differing respiratory metabolism was proved by three American biologists, W. D. and M. P. Burbanck and J. P. Edwards, in 1947–8, using two American shrimps—*Cambarus rusticus* from the Missouri and the blind and albino *Cambarus setosus* from the underground river in the Samlin cavern. At each experiment three animals were enclosed in a bottle containing a litre of boiled and chilled water covered with a layer of oil. The survival time of each animal was noted. Results showed that the surface animal survived for a far shorter period than the cavernicolous animals: the average survival time being 272 minutes for the surface animals and 892 for the cavernicoles. The American biologists point out that the cavernicoles are no more resistant to suffocation; for in every case the animals, whether surface or cavernicolous, succumbed if the proportion of oxygen reached a certain limit—about 0.2 cubic centimetre per litre. Thus cavernicoles are just as susceptible as surface animals to oxygen reduction, but their respiratory metabolism is only about one-third of the latter's. The respiratory activity of cavernicolous animals influences the whole of their other behaviour: they are lethargic in their movements, and slow to reproduce; the males are unaggressive, lacking in vigour from the outset and ageing quickly. All their metabolism follows the same pattern.

Mme Derouet, referred to above, carried out some remarkable experiments on aquatic creatures in 1949, in Professor Fontaine's laboratory. Her subjects were two species of amphipod which possess two types of leg, with which they can swim and jump, and which are capable of living either in fresh water or brine. The procedure was similar to that employed by the American biologists. The amphipods were sealed in bottles containing seven cubic centimetres of oxygen per litre of water. Oxygen consumption averaged 1.06 cubic centimetres for *Grammarus pulex*, the surface species, and 0.20 to 0.25 for *Niphargus virei*, the cavernicolous species. Thus the oxygen consumption of the subterranean species is between a quarter and a fifth of that of the surface animal. This observation completely confirmed the Americans' results.

Thus there is every reason to suppose that the cavernicoles' lack of pigment is due to diminished oxygen metabolism rather than to darkness. After this discovery it becomes incumbent upon bio-speleologists to pursue their studies of the biological processes of cavernicolous animals further, employing modern methods to test their reaction to outside influences and so eliminate old traditional misconceptions.

Though interesting and rewarding, this study is not easy, for cavernicolous animals are divided into innumerable species, mutations and families, many of them confined to particular sites. A number of them are so sensitive that they cannot bear either light or the atmosphere of the surface, where they immediately perish. As soon as these minute insects are exposed to daylight, they are attacked by microscopically tiny fungi. Many caves or groups of caves possess forms of life peculiar to themselves. German caverns contain a different fauna from those of Southern Europe, whose fauna differs again from that of the Pyrenean caves.

Much of the knowledge gained by bio-speleology from the study of cave animals is of great importance to the theory of evolution. Hence a good many experiments are made in crossing different sub-species or genera of cavernicolous animals and analysing the results. It is also important to find out what causes the mutations in many cavernicoles— whether they may be the result of radio-activity at work in caves, or whether they are due to the age of this remnant of an earlier marine fauna.

This applies particularly to the Isopoda, aquatic crustaceans which are believed to have once lived in the sea and to be relics of a time when the ocean covered what is now dry land. About a dozen of these cave-dwelling crustaceans are known. Four are confined to Europe, three to North Africa and the Sahara, and four to the coastal regions of the Gulf of Mexico (Texas, Mexico, Cuba). Bio-speleologists hold that these creatures, whose exclusive habitat is the water of caves, have retained a certain tolerance towards the sea-water in which their ancestors lived, and that they serve as an indication of the limits once reached by the ocean.

FLORA WITHOUT LIGHT

Far less numerous, and also more difficult to find, are the cave plants. Plants containing chlorophyll, with whose aid they convert the carbon dioxide in the air into starch and sugar, cannot flourish in lightless caves, tunnels and fissures. Cave flora, like cave fauna, is subject to different laws from those which obtain on the surface.

Fungi and bacteria are the growths most frequently represented in caverns. Fungi, which can thrive without light, generally take root in decomposed fragments of wood, and there reproduce themselves. Bacterial growths are common, especially near the entrance to caves and in places where animals live and drop their excrement. Cave walls are often covered with a slimy mass composed of the bacteria *Micrococcus quellaris*. A thin growth of grass, which is not green but colourless, is also quite often found.

But the least trace of light, even that of an electric bulb, is enough to awaken green life. Every visitor to caves open to the public has noticed how green vegetation develops around the lamps, either on the lamps themselves or on neighbouring stalactites. These are lawns of algae, moss, or embryonic ferns. On damp spots, long white shoots may be seen that have sprouted from seeds carried into the cave by flowing water.

Where there is total darkness, on the other hand, all green life disappears and only moulds, whose spores have been carried in by water, can spread. These are snow-white growths which generally cover organic matter, rotting wood, or plant debris. Bacteria also settle on bones, bat droppings and decomposing cave animals. Little round patches of mould (penicillin) are also found on the cave earth, probably originating from traces of urine.

The writer found some curious plants in the Klutert Cave, strange threadlike growths hanging from the ceiling. Their roots, if they can be called roots, were in a sort of white, flocculent wad of cotton-wool. A blackish, fungoid formation was suspended on the long, frail, bluish-white stalk. It was possible, with great care, to detach the growth from the rock, but as soon as it came into contact with the outside air it shrivelled and dried up. Nearby was a brown, filamentous growth resembling a coconut fibre, which had established itself close to a piece of rotting wood. Beside it was a plant consisting of small grey-brown stalks springing from a single root. A dense red-fibred network, known to German speleologists as 'Barbarossa's flowing beard', often forms on rotting wood.

In the caves of the Urgebirge emerald-green mosses, (*Schistostega osmundacea*), frondiferous mosses, liverworts and small ferns are frequent. The sea-caves of the rocky coast of Italy possess a rich marine flora, in many ways similar to the flora of ocean depths to which a little light still penetrates.

Strange facts have been learned concerning the formation of calcite deposits by cave plants in the Franconian Jura. Mosses and algae, which grow in water containing lime, become enveloped in a thickish coat of tufa. Geologists call this type of tufa-formation cyanophycean tufa. It generally forms on the roofs of caves, and consists of films of limestone, about a centimetre long and generally triangular in shape, covered on the side facing the cave entrance with a thick blanket of blue algae (*Hapalosiphon intricatus*). The most remarkable thing about this phenomenon is the fact that the tiny threads of the algae do not participate directly in the tufa formation. This is the work of other, single-celled, lime-secreting blue algae, which settle in the interstices between the living algae and the film of limestone. These are *Aphano-theces* and *Glococapsa*, which belong to the family *Chroococcaceae* and are also found outside caves. The further one advances into the cavern, the rarer becomes the hanging tufa, and finally it ceases altogether at the point where no light ever penetrates.

E. Dudich and Dr. Paul Magdeburg observed in the Aggtelek stalactite cave in Hungary and the caves of the Franconian Jura respectively, a layer of gleaming black, apparently mineral deposit. At one time this was believed to be soot from the torches of earlier cave-dwellers which had set on the walls. The two workers subjected the black crust, which may also be seen in other caves, to microscopic examination. They discovered that it contained iron and was in fact composed of the comparatively rare iron-bacteria *Lepto-thrix ochracea* and *Leptothrix crassa*. This is a creature which, like the plants, converts inorganic matter into organic life. As energy for assimilation, Dr. Magdeburg concludes, the iron-bacteria employ chemical energy liberated by the oxidation of the salts of bivalent iron, as they are transformed into salts of trivalent iron. The energy of light, which is lacking, is thus replaced by chemical energy, an astonishing process. In all probability, troglobites—animals which pass the whole of their existence within the darkness of a cave—live on these iron-bacteria, so that caves constitute a closed habitat entirely independent of the outside world.

As already mentioned, certain blue algae are lime-secreting organisms. In most caves in limestone mountains one meets cave formations known as 'Devil's sweetmeats' or 'cave pearls'. These are knobs and balls of limestone which are not attached to the ground beneath them. In the centre of each of these concretions is a small foreign body consisting, in the opinion of some geologists, of small particles of clay or stone which are kept perpetually in motion by the falling drops of water containing lime, and are gradually encrusted with limestone.

Magdeburg has also examined cave formations of a different type, which are firmly attached to the walls, roofs and floor of caves. He dissolved these concretions, which are made up of separate layers, in diluted hydrochloric acid and discovered on the surface of the fluid a thin film which, on examination, proved to be composed of iron-bacteria and blue algae. From this he concluded that the blue algae were in some measure responsible for the formation of the concretions. The iron-bacteria could not have produced them on their own.

The algae accompanying the iron-bacteria in these limestone formations have a bluish-green cell content, although they grow in total darkness. This is a curious phenomenon. Chief amongst these blue algae are *Aphanothece naegalii* and *Gloeocapsa biformis*, which are found outside as well as inside caves. That blue algae thrive in complete darkness is well known to botanists. But what do they live on? Since these blue algae exist side by side with iron-bacteria, there is doubtless some biological connexion between them. Probably the iron-bacteria supply the necessary oxygen compounds to keep the blue algae alive, while both together provide food for certain cavernicolous animals.

A great deal more could be said about cave plants; for the flora of caves is not everywhere the same. It differs between north and south, between temperate and tropical latitudes. To review the domain in any detail would demand far greater space than is available here. But this brief survey is enough to show how strange is the plant life of caverns, and how full of fascinating problems for the botanist.

6

THE FORMATION OF CAVES

❖

THE ACTION OF NATURAL FORCES

THERE is hardly a cave, the date and manner of whose origin is known for certain. The geologist who is concerned to establish these facts can only make conjectures, based on the formation of the geological strata. It is, however, clear that caves were produced by powerful natural forces—earthquakes, volcanoes and other natural catastrophes, folding of the earth's crust and the action of water. There are just a few caverns whose genesis can be definitely established, and from these certain general principles can be deduced.

Amongst such caves are those of the Field of a Hundred Fissures near Mihintale in Ceylon, which constitute a striking example of the formation of fissure-caverns in historical times. The caves of this region came into being during a tremendous earthquake that afflicted the island of Ceylon in 1645. For eleven days on end, so the chroniclers relate, subterranean forces shook the northern part of the island, while clouds of smoke and dust rose more than three thousand feet high above the land, and sulphur-yellow flames poured out of the sundered earth, burning and blackening everything for miles around. Today this district is riddled with fissures, many of them seventy feet across and nearly three thousand feet deep. Most of these chasms have only a narrow opening at the top, but widen out lower down into yawning chambers in the rock. The majority are completely unexplored. Only occasionally do practised Singhalese climbers venture into the abysses down shaky rope ladders, in order to finish off the wild animals which have fallen into them during their nocturnal prowls.

Throughout the centuries, scientists have been preoccupied by the problem of the origin of caves. Thus Herodotus reports the underground course of the River Lykos, and Pausanias, Strabo and many others mention caverns in their writings. Ancient geographers meditated on the causes of underground rivers. Although they arrived at a number of illuminating hypotheses concerning the origin of caves and the flow of subterranean streams, which they held to be due to the collapse of the earth's crust, there was nonetheless a strong element of fantasy in their theories.

Thoroughly primitive conceptions about the origin of caves were still current in the eighteenth and even in the nineteenth centuries. Immanuel Kant's *Physical Geography*, written between 1780 and 1790, shows that even this great philosopher was not free from them. Kant had his own ideas about the effects of cold in caverns, the formation of dripstone (stalactites, stalagmites, etc.), the development of rocks and other underground phenomena.

In the book *Beschreibung merkwürdiger Höhlen* (Leipzig, 1805), by Rosemüller and Tillesius, the causes of cave formation are given as earthquakes, underground conflagrations, and revolutions in the interior of the earth, which have brought about the upheaval, fragmentation and displacement of solid masses. Thus water and fire were regarded as invariably the prime factors.

Cardanus and other natural philosophers believed that the great bituminous veins of the earth gradually melted under the effects of subterranean heat and left caverns behind. Other great thinkers, such as Whiston, Woodwards, Leibnitz and Descartes, also propounded theories that were more or less accurate.

The Frenchman Théodore Virlet advanced very detailed and perspicacious views in his book, *Des cavernes, de leur origine et de leur mode de formation* (1836). He saw caves as the result of disturbance and destruction of the earth's surface at various geological epochs, outlets through which gases and water have burst, the products of erosion, upheaval of the earth's crust, etc.

In Schmidl's book, *Die Grotten und Höhlen von Adelsberg, Beug Plania usw.* (Vienna, 1854), Wilhelm Zippe declared that the formation of caves and cave formations were due respectively to the solution of carbonate of lime and to deposits of lime contained in water, an opinion entirely in agreement with that held today. In 1858, Vincent Leopold, writing in the *Jahrbuch der k.k. geologischen Reichsanstalt Wien*, took the view that underground rivers were chiefly responsible for the formation of caves and subsidences. Fuhlrott, the discoverer of the Neanderthal skull, also listed a number of causes of cave-formation in a small pamphlet, *Die Grotten und Höhlen von Rheinland und Westfalen* (Iserlohn, 1869). In the nineteenth century, the geologist E. Tietze wrote a series of works concerned with the formation of caves.

In the eighteen-seventies, many French geologists still believed that caverns were formed by the emergence of acid vapours from the interior of the earth during bygone geological eras. In 1873, Dr. Oscar Fraas expressed the opinion that caves were the product of ancient underground rivers which communicated with the surface through fissures and funnels. He rejected the view of the old Plutonian school, which invoked acid emanations eating through the limestone. The formation of a cavern, he said, always presupposed the prior action of water, a theory that had many advocates in France during the last century.

The British geologist William Boyd Dawkins gave a very full account of the geology of caves in his book, *Cave Hunting* (1874). He regarded water as the principal agent in their formation, stating that caves in limestone cliffs are only

passages hollowed out by water following the line of least
resistance or emerging through cracks formed in the earth's
crust as it cooled and contracted. Dawkins does not consider
the problem of fissures.

In his book, *Geologie* (Vienna, 1875), Dr. Franz Ritter von
Hauer speaks clearly of the action of water containing carbonic acid under pressure and high temperature in producing
caves. Earthquakes, so this author contended, were the result
of caverns collapsing.

Other writers considered the genesis of subterranean
cavities in greater detail. The celebrated French speleologist, E. A. Martel, writing in the last decade of the nineteenth century, envisaged three causes: folding or splitting
of the rock, erosion by water, and disintegration of the rock
brought about by some chemical action. At the time of
writing Martel had examined over a hundred chasms in the
Cévennes, France, which led him to the conclusion that other
factors beside water were responsible for the formation of
caves, e.g., volcanic phenomena. He devoted himself with
particular enthusiasm to the study of the Karst region and
the underground watercourses of the Postojna (Adelsberg)
Cave, and the caverns of Reka and Rakbach.

The number of geologists who concerned themselves with
the causes of cave formation in the nineteenth century runs
into hundreds. Not one of them was able to formulate a
general explanation that was universally accepted. Discussion is still alive amongst geologists and speleologists.
Hermann Bock champions the water theory according to
which all subterranean cavities were hollowed out by gigantic underground rivers. The Tennengebirge, which contains
the great Ice Grotto, is representative of the great limestone
stages which form the eastern part of the northern limestone
Alps. The rock, in which caverns have formed, consists
mainly of limestone resting on dolomite (double carbonate of
calcium and magnesium). The upper layer of barren Karst
rock presents a fantastic array of domes, vertical walls, sharp

ridges, deep gorges, etc. The rocky crevices hold the snow for a long time. The water, laden with carbonic acid drawn from the atmosphere, filters into the calcium carbonate (dolomite) and converts it into soluble calcium bicarbonate. Thus, thinks Bock, the caverns and fissures are being perpetually enlarged, especially as the water carries with it sand, pebbles and mud, adding mechanical erosion to its chemical action.

B. Biese cannot accept this theory. In common with other geologists, he takes the view that caves were formed by fissuring of the rock, which does not, of course, rule out the supplementary action of water. But he denies the primary role of the latter. The water eats away the foot of the rock wall, which then collapses under the effect of gravity. This process continues until a state of equilibrium has been established. (See the section 'Goetz's Cavern at Meiningen'). This explanation is not valid for all caves, however.

The layman who has visited caverns as a tourist, or who knows them from descriptions, makes only a very summary distinction between them. He recognizes only stalactite, rock, crystal, or ice caves. The geologist, on the other hand, distinguishes many different types of natural cavities: crystalline rocks, fissure caves, potholes, caves hollowed out by the sea, caves produced by erosion or the flow of water, niches or rock shelters, caves due to corrosion, caves resulting from subsidence of the soil, ice caves, etc. Natural or primary caverns result from fissuring, crystallization, or fracture. Fracturing is brought about by mechanical forces, folding or upheaval of the geological strata, and then modified by the water that flows through the clefts. What the geologist calls secondary caverns are formed by underground rivers flowing through existing cavities and enlarging them, either by chemical action (corrosion), or by mechanical action (abrasion). Such rivers are amongst the most grandiose phenomena in the whole subterranean world; particularly when they develop into waterfalls, the discovery of which is always a thrilling experience. When a watercourse completely occupies a cavity, it re-appears somewhere else in the shape of a spring.

Many famous caverns must be described as artificial, in the sense that they have been created by the hand of man in the form of mines or quarries. This category includes the sandstone caves of Valkenburg, the Roman Catacombs, salt mines, the Fairy Caves of Saalfeld, and many rock-cut shrines and temples.

This brief survey cannot claim to cover every type of cave. Many subterranean cavities require a category all to themselves. Such are Fingal's Cave in the basalt of the island of Staffa, Inner Hebrides; those hollowed out by the action of the waves on the seashore; the caves of gypsum, sulphur and saltpetre to be found in Brazil, which are particularly rich in skeletal remains; and the unexplored caverns formed by hot springs. Then there are the caverns of which a part is dedicated to some sacred purpose or distinguished by some phenomenon held to be supernatural. These include sepulchral caves, caverns in which oracles are heard (Delphi), underground churches, miraculous grottoes (Lourdes), etc.

Apart from these grottoes open to the public, the most impressive subterranean cavities are the immensely deep fissures, accessible only by special means and at grave risk— chasms like those of the Field of the Hundred Fissures in Ceylon, referred to earlier. Europe possesses equally prodigious abysses, which only the boldest of underground explorers can enter.

On August 24th, 1925, the members of the Società Alpina delle Giulie set up a world record by descending to a depth of 1,485 feet in the Raspo Abyss, north of Pinguente. The previous record of 1,086 feet was established in 1841 in the Grotta di Trebiciano, in the Carso Triestine. But in 1926, the explorers of the Trieste Thirtieth of October Group reached 1,584 feet in the Montenero Abyss, south of Idria. The following year, the intrepid Veronese cavers of the

Sucia Club thought they were descending to 2,102 feet in the cavern Spluga della Preta, in the limestone Alps of Lessino, but subsequent exploration proved the depth to be 1,949 feet.

The majority of deep fissure caves were explored after the Speleological Club of Mariazell reconnoitred the Tonion Shaft (a pothole in the Tonion Alps inhabited by bats) to a depth of 1,838 feet, which is probably not the last word on this chasm. In 1934 cavers from Florence descended to 1,782 feet in the Antro della Carchai in the Etruscan Apennines, where, after travelling along a horizontal stretch more than a mile in length, they came upon a lake 160 feet long. A mile and a half from Isonzo is the Verco Abyss, where the members of the Società Alpina delle Giulie, of Trieste, went down 1,710 feet in 1928, and came to a stop before impassable water and rock falls. Between Schneeberg and Abbazia, on the edge of a basin-shaped valley, lies the Clana abyss, in which the explorers of the Thirtieth of October Group got down to 1,386 feet.

There are potholes of comparable depth in the Pyrenees, for example the Gouffre Martel, discovered by Casteret in 1934 and explored to 1,590 feet, and the Gouffre de la Pierre-Saint-Martin, where a descent was made under dramatic conditions to more than 1,650 feet in 1952. Between Lunz and Mariazell on the southern slope of the Oetscher (6,244 feet) in Southern Austria, are the Oetscher Caves, one of which—the Geldloch—was explored to over 1,300 feet by Franz Mühldorfer in 1923.

In 1954, new depth records were set up in France. The two French cavers Jean Caoux and Georges Garby reached a depth of 2,460 feet in the mountains of Grenoble. In the same year, the speleologists de Riquer and Schoek-Duval discovered in the Grotto Napla six rock basins full of water, one above the other and all communicating. The lowest of these basins is 3,300 feet below the entrance to the cavern.

To conquer these stupendous potholes the explorers utilized the numerous tiers of which they are composed, and

without which the descents would have been almost impossible. Some deep holes are divided into storeys, of which
the first ends at between 300 and 500 feet, the second at 800
to 1,000 feet, and the third at 1,300 to 1,500 feet.

The men who venture into these profound subterranean
cavities must be animated by a quite special spirit. These
sinister and unknown depths offer no reward in the shape of
magnificent dripstone formations, sparkling calcareous
crystals, or the majesty of eternal ice. Everywhere is a hostile
mystery where death lies in wait, where the eye meets nothing
but bare, wet rocks, mud, fissures, sharp spines of rock, pits
hollowed out by water, walls half gnawed away, deep pools
of water, huge masses of fallen rock, cavities of all sizes, impassable water traps and subterranean rivers, which sometimes gush out of the rocks and sometimes tumble from stage
to stage and vanish into impenetrable depths.

Anyone who penetrates this domain, in which the titanic
forces of nature are evident on every side, cannot help feeling
a profound emotion. Did these forces rise up out of the
bowels of the earth to shatter and destroy the rocks? Were
they let loose by the movements of the earth's crust itself? Or
are these chasms the outcome of some past seismic disaster,
during which the mountains heaved up, the valleys were
hollowed out, and the rivers adopted their courses? It is
unlikely that we shall ever know.

SUBTERRANEAN LABYRINTHS

Certain caverns, some of them fully and others still only partially explored, constitute veritable subterranean labyrinths
and are a source of endless amazement to anyone who wan-
ders through them. One such labyrinthine cavern is the
Klutert cave between Hagen and Wuppertal, near the small
town of Milspe. Little attention was paid to this cave, which
had been known for centuries, because—by contrast with

the neighbouring stalactite grottoes of Sauerland—it offered little attraction to the sightseer. Nevertheless, with its three hundred explored main passages and forty-six 'crawls', totalling three and a half miles in length, it is one of the biggest caves in Germany. During the Second World War, it served as a refuge from aerial bombardment. Six thousand or more people sought shelter in its narrow passages, which afforded them perfect security.

Even if the cavern lacks the charm of stalactites and stalagmites, it possesses a quantity of geological, zoological and other curiosities, which give it a character of its own. The whole grotto is rich in strange hydrological phenomena. The rushing and splashing of water reaches the ear from deep clefts in the rock, indicating the presence of unseen subterranean rivers. At many points small pools or rivulets may be encountered, which are washing away the clay soil and slowly but surely undermining the rock.

The various watercourses have been given names of their own. One intermittent rivulet, which sometimes flows and sometimes dries up, is called the Foaming Brook. The Murmuring Brook fills part of the cavern with a twittering sound. Standing waters include the Pacific Lake, the Royal Lake, Western Lake I and II, of which the former stands above the latter in a rocky basin, the Eastern Lake, and the Well. Some of these little lakes are up to twenty-seven feet deep; their water is crystal-clear, and they extend far beneath the rocky massif. They are the habitat of the half-inch-long Klutert shrimp.

The geological structure of the cavern is also full of romantic charm. It is a fissure cave, like Goetz's Cavern or the cave in the Hohes Liet, near Warstein. Masses of rock project menacingly from the walls and even from the roof. Here and there clefts in the rock go back 200 feet or more into the mountain. A multitude of narrow tunnels branch off from the main passages along which it is possible to walk, and lead to other passages or to areas that are still unexplored. Everywhere one has to trudge along a floor of sticky clay, or climb flights of steps to the upper chambers. Every passage, every fork, every grotto, every fissure has a name of its own, as in other caves. A particularly remarkable cleft is called the Diamond Rift, although no diamonds have ever been found in it. Some especially impressive grottoes bear the names Bismarck Hall, Castle of the Grail, Silver Chamber, Rain Castle, Hall of Song, and so on. Where stalactites once hung there is nothing to be seen today but stumps, looking like rows of broken teeth. One part of the cave is called Coral Street, another Streuselkuchen Street. All over the walls one can see fossilized shells and other traces of marine fauna. Here and there, cracks in the rock have laid bare petrified roots that testify to the world-wide cataclysm to which both the mountain and the cave perhaps owe their existence.

In days gone by, the cavern often served as a place of refuge. Prince Maurice of Nassau sheltered in the Ancestral Hall during the Wars of Liberation (against Napoleon I), as recorded by a commemorative tablet. In another cavern, called the Church, divine service was celebrated during the Thirty Years War. This is recorded in the parish registers of Voerde. Rosendahl, a leader in the Wars of Independence, also sheltered here until he was betrayed into the hands of the French and shot.

The cave of Han, in Belgium, has been called a 'subterranean Babylon'. The River Lesse flows through it into an underground lake, one of the biggest of its kind in the world. In these huge caverns the corrosive action of the water on the limestone, and the constructive power of the limestone in solution, have created a miraculous architecture. The result is a fairy-land of towering flowstone and glittering dripstone, visited every year by thousands of wondering sightseers. The grottoes present some unforgettable spectacles of breathtaking beauty. The vaulted roof of the Hall of the Dome rises to a height of 426 feet; the limestone formations of the Cave of Mysteries make one think of an enchanter's castle, and the visitor will long recall the delicate veil of stone in the Hall of Curtains. The nearby caves of Rochefort are full of traces of the primeval forces that created them, and a multitude of clefts penetrate deep into unexplored regions. The visitor stands astounded in the Hall of the Sabbath, an immeasurably vast chamber with vertical walls that take on magic colours when a balloon carrying a magnesium flare is released and drifts upwards towards the roof.

Western Europe is rich in remarkable caves. The Pyrenees, in particular, have captured the attention of speleologists, by their ice caverns, dripstone grottoes, and deep potholes. Traces of prehistoric man are plentiful in the Pyrenean caverns.

Mystery surrounds the abysses, to which the eyes of the whole world were drawn for a moment in 1952 by the tragedy that overtook the speleologist Marcel Loubens in the Gouffre de la Pierre-Saint-Martin. But the valiant explorer's sacrifice has not daunted his comrades, who are continuing his work. Space does not permit the discussion of more than a few of these chasms, apart from those which have already been referred to in another context.

One of the finest of them is the Gouffre de Périllos, which contains a huge chamber. An abyss made up of several stages and fifty feet in diameter gives access to it. The descent can only be made by practised speleologists. The first thirty feet have to be traversed by ladder down a vertical rockface. Once this obstacle has been overcome, the caver enters an immense chamber 130 feet high, 330 feet long and 200 feet wide. There he will see two pillars fifty feet high, twenty feet in diameter and about seventeen feet apart, bearing wonderful mouldings. At the back of this vast hall, the walls fall like heavy curtains, providing shelter for enormous swarms of bats. In many of the pits formed by dripping water, are found the 'cave pearls', already mentioned, which occur so frequently in Pyrenean caves. Very few are to be found in museums, and they are unfamiliar to many geologists. The cave pearl is a pisolith that forms in the eddy of calcareous water falling from a certain height into a shallow basin. A small piece of gravel or a grain of sand kept in constant movement by the falling water becomes encrusted with lime, and finally develops into a small ball, which may be as large as a pigeon's egg.

A smaller chamber, known as the Chapel, opens out of the main hall. Here a forty-six-foot opening was discovered in 1938, leading to a subterranean watercourse, which has not yet been explored.

There is a similar cavern by the bridge over the River Roboul that rises near Périllos. A shaft 170 feet deep, at the bottom of a gorge, leads into a hall 100 feet in diameter, the floor of which is covered with viscous red clay. In shape the cave is like an irregular funnel tilted upwards. A narrow bottleneck gives access to a second hall eighty feet lower down. The masses of mud in this chamber suggest that it is often flooded with water. At a depth of 350 feet, the cavern again splits in two, and probably comes to a dead end. A peculiarity of this cavern is its pestilential odour, produced by rotting vegetable matter and dead sheep, which the local shepherds fling down the shaft. Because of the numerous bottlenecks and narrow branching tunnels, this cavern is particularly difficult to explore fully.

Near the village of Vingrau, children discovered a small cave with a large entrance seventeen feet across, from which a passage 106 feet long leads into a chamber containing two shafts. In this chamber a number of human and animal bones have been found, including a bone amulet. Since there was no complete skeleton amongst them, it is supposed that these bones were carried here by animals. This cavern, which is very dry, has been baptized by the peasants of the district the Grotte des Enfants, after its finders.

Exploration of the Grotte de Maury, which was begun in 1939, was resumed after the war, particularly in 1949 and 1950. It must once have been occupied by human beings. In

1939, a brain pan with highly developed brow ridges was found, and subsequently the bones of a man, a woman and a child together with utensils, bone tools, sherds of pottery dating from the Gallo-Roman era or earlier, and others decorated with brown and red clay came to light. In one of the caves stands a stone table, which points to human use, probably for purposes of magic.

Five hundred and fifty yards west of the village of Périllos is a curious fissure known as the Whistling Grotto. Natural cavities that emit sounds are not rare. Fingal's Cave in the basalt of the island of Staffa, in the Inner Hebrides off the north-west coast of Scotland, is a musical cave. It is only 230 feet long and forty-three feet across at the entrance, narrowing to twenty-three at the back. The walls are made up of regular hexagonal columns of basalt. The sea pouring in, coupled with the noise of the wind and waves, give rise to sounds that range from a deep thunderous rumble to the sweet notes of some unearthly music.

Similarly, the Whistling Grotto of Périllos may be compared to a gigantic organ pipe. The 238-foot shaft grows narrower to a depth of seventy-three feet, and then drops the remaining 165 feet absolutely vertically. The temperature in the shaft is relatively high. When the outside temperature is 45° F., that within is 57° F. A very powerful current of air comes from this chimney. It is probably produced by the wind that blows perpetually across the Périllos plateau, plunging into the numerous clefts in the surface and emerging whistling from the shaft.

The Alps likewise contain plenty of subterranean labyrinths to keep cavers busy. One of the most important discoveries made since the Second World War was the Tantalhöhle (Cave of Tantalus) in the Hagengebirge, near Salzburg. According to the description given by the speleologist Gustav Abel, no other cavern is more difficult to explore. The entrance, which is very inaccessible, was discovered in 1947, 5,742 feet up the southern slope of the Hagengebirge.

First comes a fissure, then a small chamber, after which a wider gallery leads to a 200-feet deep pitch that issues in huge halls 100 feet wide and 200 feet high. But this is not the bottom, which was reached during the large-scale expedition of 1950 at a depth of 1,320 feet below the surface. The deeper one descends into the interior, the more frequent become the vertical walls following the line of the fault—the largest of which is 400 feet long and 200 feet high—and blocks of rock piled up by the forces of nature. At the end of the first third of the cavern lies a vast hall 80 feet high, 330 feet long, and 130 feet wide, leading to a passage 33 feet high littered with fragments of rock. The Grand Canyon, which is 330 feet high and 100 feet wide, is even more astonishing than the Great Hall. Immediately beyond it lies the Hall of the Seven Shafts, which is equally large and contains a number of deep holes, the mouths of which are mostly only eighteen inches across.

There is hardly another alpine cavern that possesses such a wealth of geological curiosities as the Tantalus Cave. These include concretions of sand in the most diverse shapes, curiously eroded rocks, great deposits of gravel, pea ore (oölitic limonite), quartz, clay of various colours, dazzling white stalactites, delicate straw stalactites two to four millimetres in diameter and a yard or more long, flowerlike calcareous formations which are particularly delightful in the Hall of Stone Flowers, where they deck the whole roof, calcite crystals, etc. There is little water in the cave. Only at one point does a brook flow for 170 feet before vanishing into the depths. Since the hall shows numerous unexplored chasms, the water level is assumed to be very low—somewhere around 2,320 feet down. Some parts of the cavern, especially the entrance grotto, possess ice formations. The average temperature is 36° F. Few animals can exist at this temperature. The 1950 expedition found only bats, gnats and springtails. A strikingly large number of fossils were discovered.

According to the measurements taken by Gustav Abel and Franz Koppenwallner in 1950, this stupendous cavern is almost eight miles long with great variations in altitude. Immediately after the entrance it descends to 1,320 feet, then rises 660 feet, after which it goes down 660 feet again. The cavern is between approximately one thousand and three thousand feet below the summit of the mountain.

In September, 1952, a new expedition, made up of ten men and one woman belonging to the Salzburg Caving Club, left Salzburg to explore the Tantalus Cave. They continued for 194 days without a break, in the course of which the speleologists traversed twenty-five miles of underground passages. The party included some French cavers, who declared unanimously that the extent and technical difficulties of the Tantalus Cave eclipsed anything they had encountered in their own country.

The new expedition profited by the experiences of 1949. During the latter venture, the descent was made with a steel hawser paid out from a hand-operated winch. Although the second expedition had at its disposal a special steel cable, six millimetres thick with a hemp core, possessing a resistance to breaking of over twenty stone, it was decided to use ladders of steel cable with aluminium rungs, which gave the climbers much greater security than the thin, rotating wire rope of the type that proved fatal to the French cavers in the Gouffre de la Pierre-Saint-Martin.

Preparations had been long and costly. The equipment, stowed in exceptionally large rucksacks and weighing between seventy and a hundred pounds, was chosen with the greatest care. It would have been impossible for the explorers to carry it on their backs in the narrow and muddy tunnels. They therefore employed sacks of a particular kind, called *waldl*, which could be dragged along the ground behind them containing tins of petrol, rope ladders, sleeping bags, and personal belongings. The descent was prepared by setting pitons and wire ropes in the rock face. The 'Atlantis Villa', a hut built to stand up to falling stones, rain and snow, was laboriously erected at an altitude of 5,380 feet as Camp One, where the last preparations were made. In the same way as for the ascent of a high mountain, bivouacs were established at various points in the cavern, where the explorers could spend the night, collect supplies, and make ready for the next stage of penetration.

This second expedition did not achieve any sensational result outside the limits of the first. Its aim of passing right through the Hagengebirge to the second exit, whose existence is suggested by the powerful current of air blowing through the cavern, could not be realized.

The Lurgrotte or Lurloch[1] is one of the most famous subterranean cavities of the mountainous region round Graz. It is the underground course taken by the River Lur between Semriach and Peggau when it is in spate. The normal underground bed of the Lur can be followed for a few hundred yards, after which it disappears in narrow channels through the rock. When in spate, however, the river pours through the mountain on a three-mile course through galleries, domed chambers, halls and clefts. The majority of the grottoes contain marvellous stalactites, some of them of colossal size, others red in colour and combined with crystals. Fifty-two living species of animals have been found in this cavern, not to mention the bones of cave bear, mammoth and bison. The Lurloch was discovered in 1894 by the Styrian Gesellschaft für Höhlenforschung, but it was only penetrated to about 1,820 feet. In 1908, members of the Steierischer Höhlenklub advanced 10,065 feet. At this point a stream was encountered that has its source in the cavern. In 1908, this

[1] In 1894, this cavern was the scene of an event as dramatic as those which took place in French and Swiss caves in 1952. Seven speleologists from Graz were marooned in the cave by a rise in the water, and only rescued nine days later by an operation unique in the annals of speleology. The occurrence is related in detail by Hans Hofman-Montanus in his book, *Die Welt ohne Licht,* from eye-witness accounts and newspaper reports.

stream was first sailed in a boat. The cavern was measured by Hermann Bock of Graz in 1909. It was inundated by floodwater in 1910, and became impassable for several years. At the western entrance to the cavern is a twenty-three-foot waterfall that once drove the turbine of a sawmill. The cavern was reconnoitred once more from 1924 onwards, and in 1935 it was traversed from end to end, for the first time. Since 1946, it has been administered by a commercial company with the co-operation of the local government authorities. It has now been enlarged and opened to the public along a total length of more than a mile and a half.

This does not exhaust the subterranean labyrinths of the Alps, but to describe, or even list, them all would occupy too much space. Instead we will look elsewhere.

Great Britain possesses a great many caves that have been assiduously explored. In 1909, Joe Hall of Castleton came upon Oxlow Cavern, near Castleton, Derbyshire, while prospecting. The Romans are said to have mined here, employing prisoners whom they kept in the cavern until they died. Apart from old alluvial deposits, nothing was found to support this belief. The cave is reached via two shafts, and together with Maskhill Mine forms a vertical arc whose deepest point is 600 feet down. It offers all sorts of surprises to the visitor: waterfalls, curiously-shaped rocks, walls of glistening crystal, stalactites and stalagmites, and artificial adits and platforms dating from earlier excavations.

On the main road from Settle to Morecambe, near the little town of Clapham, in Yorkshire, stands Gaping Ghyll, which was first explored in 1872 by John Birkbeck. Later, Professor T. McKenny measured its depth and found it to be about four hundred feet. In 1895 E. A. Martel went down with a rope ladder and spent an hour and a quarter in the main hall, which was at that time considered to be the sixth largest in the world. Other explorations were carried out in 1896, 1903, 1904, 1908, and 1909, and disclosed fresh passages and unsuspected halls, totalling three and a quarter miles. It contains all the formations usual in caverns, with the exception of underground lakes.

Today the descent is safe and simple. The visitor sits in a suspended chair, held in by a safety-belt, and is able to admire the precipitous walls and a waterfall that foams forth out of one of them, at his ease. The chair travels along beneath the domed roof of the main hall with the visitor hanging in mid-air like a spider at the end of a thread. If the sun enters through the shaft, a rainbow forms round the moving chair. Down below, in the darkness of the cavern, the occupant of the chair can see the lights carried by other visitors like so many glow-worms. The descent takes no more than a minute.

Amongst the caverns of the Scandinavian countries, one in the Rana district of Norway is particularly worthy of mention. It is situated close to the little town of Mo, at the inland extremity of the Rana Fjord, inside the Arctic Circle and some five and a half miles from the coast, between Mo and the glacier of Svartisan. This is the cavern of Harmane. Its five entrances are all at an altitude of about seven hundred feet, at the foot of a vertical limestone cliff. Natvig measured it in 1923, and gave it a length of 3,000 feet; but Dr. G. Horn, who took fresh measurements subsequently, estimated its length to be about 7,200 feet. It is believed to be even longer than this and to link up with the caverns of Tukihuset and Torrbekkeng farther to the south, though the communicating passages are unfortunately blocked at present.

It is simple in plan, with few ramifications. The entrances, ten to fifteen feet wide, are mostly circular or elliptical in shape. At many points the cavern is traversed by crevasses going down a hundred yards or so, but too narrow for descent. This cave is pretty dry, with only a little rill here and there. The shape of the interior suggests that it has been hollowed out by water. Fallen blocks are found near the entrance, from which the passages run down at a gentle

slope. Finds in this cavern have been limited to the skeleton
of a single cave bear. There is nothing to suggest that it was
ever occupied by human beings.

There are many other caverns in Scandinavia, several of
them celebrated in the sagas, but lack of space prevents us
from discussing them here.

THE VALLEY OF THE TWENTY-TWO CAVERNS

The Hönnetal, the valley of the Hönne, is particularly rich
in caves. This river rises 1,450 feet up the southern flank of
the Kohlberg, west of Neuenrade (*Kreis* Altena), runs past
Frühlingshausen (*Kreis* Arnsberg), Binolen, Ober-Röding-
hausen (*Kreis* Iserlohn), Lendringsen, Menden and Bösperde,
and flows into the Ruhr near Fröndenberg at an altitude of
400 feet. The Hönnetal is especially interesting from a geological point of view. Tectonically, it lies in the Remscheid-
Altena-Arnsberg col and the Lüdenscheid-Affeln depression.
According to Dr. Julius Andree, the numerous caves in the
valley are due to the erosive action of the Hönne. In his
study of the caves, published in 1923, Cl. Lipperheide calculated that fifty-four tons of limestone were dissolved by the
Hönne every day. The majority of the caves are, therefore,
the work of the river.

The Hönne has a curious course. From its source it flows
in a south-easterly direction; it then bends sharply to the
north-west a little over half a mile south-west of Neuenrade,
holds this course for half a mile or so, and then flows due
north near Frühlingshausen. It goes underground in the
region of Binolen and re-appears about three-quarters of a
mile farther on by the Klusenstein. 'Here the action of the
water, which has previously resulted in the creation of a
valley, tends more to the formation of caves. It may therefore be assumed that the hollowing out of the valley itself
has been aided by the falling in of underground channels,'
writes Cl. Lipperheide. Andree is likewise of the opinion

that the Hönne Valley between Binolen and Klusenstein
was formed by subsidence, as indicated by the precipitous
limestone walls known as Die Sieben Jungfrauen or Hörster
Leyen.

In addition to the caves carved out by the river, the Hönnetal contains a few fissure caves, for example Preuss cave,
the two Karhof caves, the Honert cave and the Kötten cave.
Many other caverns are clearly not due solely to the action
of the water, but show signs both of fissuration and water
erosion. These include the Feldhof, Haustadt and Burschen
caves. Stalactites occur only in the Recken and Feldhof caves.

In all, the Hönnetal possesses twenty-two noteworthy
caverns, some of which—notably the Balve cave, which has
been mentioned several times in the course of this book—
have become famous for the signs of human occupation
found in them. Three of the twenty-two caves have recently
been destroyed by quarrying.

Their height above the river varies from the lowest, the
Preuss cave, at eight feet, to the Ziegenhöhle (Goat's Cave),
the highest, at 150 feet. Cl. Lipperheide sees in this difference
in altitude evidence of an earlier terrace structure, similar to
the three Pleistocene terraces found in the Ruhr Valley.
Andree supposes that the humid climate of the inter-glacial
periods, with its frequent rain, snow and hailstorms, greatly
encouraged the development of caves in the limestone, while
the cold water, with its consequent high carbonic acid content, must also have contributed to their formation.

Apart from the finds made in the Balve cave and the
Leichenhöhle, which have already been referred to, signs of
human and animal occupation came to light in the Feldhof,
Burschen and Honert caves higher up the slope of the valley
—particularly during digging carried out after the First
World War. Systematic excavation of the Feldhof cave
during 1925 and 1926 revealed five levels, containing fragments of wood charcoal, broken bones and skeletal remains
of cave bear, reindeer, wild horse, wolf, rhinoceros and cave

hyaena. Artifacts were found only in Levels I and II. It is noteworthy that very much the same faunal remains were found in this cave, the highest up the valley, as in the Balve cave, which is the lowest. Only a few stone implements were found in the Burschen cave (sixty feet), while in the triple Honert cave, 130 feet above the river, pottery sherds, animal bones and fragments of a human skull were unearthed as long ago as 1891. The second of the four levels, composed of brown cave earth, yielded remains of elephant, urus, wild horse, etc., as well as five stone implements and a number of human remains. The topmost stratum contained little oval plates of copper, punched copper leaf, and five three-pfennig pieces of the cities of Hamm and Soest, dated 1736, 1738 and 1740. Andree surmises that these are relics of an old coiner's workshop. The meagre remnants of human skulls and teeth obtained from this cave are hardly sufficient to suggest that it served as a dwelling or tomb. There is little doubt that they were swept into the cave by flood water, since neither ornaments nor other parts of the skeleton were found with them.

The caverns of the Hönnetal are of outstanding interest, both from the point of view of their geological formation and for the prehistoric finds obtained from them. The valley has therefore been made a national nature reserve.

THE MARIEN-HÖHLE AT BAD FRIEDRICHRODA

Of the five great caverns of Thuringia, the Marien-Höhle or the Virgin's Cave is the most striking, by virtue of its formations of crystalline gypsum or selenite. The crystal in this cave, popularly known as 'the Virgin's glass' or 'Our Lady's ice', is so pure and transparent that it deserves its poetic names.

At the beginning of the seventeenth century a gallery was dug in the Höhlenberg in the course of a search for copper-bearing shale or iron ore. At the end of 400 feet, the miners came upon calcium sulphate—no unwelcome discovery, since this is a useful building material. Up to 1904, it was prepared in kilns outside the mine; but the industrial buildings gradually disappeared, to make way for the increasing number of sightseers visiting the cave, who brought in more money than the kilns.

The Virgin's Cave is relatively small: not quite four hundred feet long and about a hundred feet wide. After passing along a gallery, the visitor descends twenty steps into the true Cave of Glass, a chamber thirty feet high and forty feet wide with walls of the clearest crystal. When the cavern is lit up with Bengal fire, the formations glow in magical splendour. Most of the crystals are hexagonal; they project in all directions. Geologically they are gypsum crystallized in simple or double monoclinic prisms, a hydrated calcium sulphate, colourless and transparent for the most part, but sometimes tinged with grey, yellow or red by alumina or iron oxide. Gypsum is found in clays and marls, and in cavities in gypsum and salt mountains. The pearly tablets formed by splitting are called 'Virgin's glass'. Fibrous, granular (alabaster) and squamous gypsum are also found. In commerce, the word generally refers to calcined gypsum from which the water of crystallization has been driven off. It then possesses the property of re-absorbing water and afterwards hardening. Virgin's glass can be split into very thin sheets. At one time it was used for windows.

The nine mighty pillars left in the cavern by the former miners, to carry the vaulted roof, give the Virgin's Cave the appearance of a cathedral. Thirty feet below it is a second cave, from which calcium sulphate was also extracted, but which cannot now be entered.

THE GLASRÖHREN-HÖHLE IN THE HOHES LIET NEAR WARSTEIN

The cavern in the Hohes Liet, near Warstein, is a good example of the fresh puzzles which are always cropping up in-

side Sauerland caves. It was not explored with any thorough-
ness until after the Second World War. It had been known
ever since the discovery of an insignificant cavity during
mining in the Feldmann limestone quarry led Rector
Henneböhle-Rüthen to look for other caves. His surmise that
there was an extensive network here proved to be correct.

The Liet cavern, like Goetz's Cavern at Meiningen, is a
fissure cave with longitudinal and transverse halls and galleries thirty to a hundred and twenty feet high, some of
which go down seventy feet below the level of the quarry.
Their morphological structure is very complex, resembling a
mine with shafts, adits and seams. Like many other Sauerland caves, the Liet cavern is situated in a limestone mountain of Upper Middle Devonian age.

The Hohes Liet offers a typical example of the disappearance of a river in the Karst country. The rivers Wäschegraben and Enkebach, coming from the mountains of slate
and greywacke that lie to the south of the limestone mountain, are swallowed up by large funnel-shaped depressions
in the limestone, to re-emerge about a mile to the north-west
of their point of disappearance. As in tracing other subterranean watercourses, the flow of these two rivers has been
checked by introducing salt, aniline dyes or harmless bacteria into the water where it goes underground. These substances and organisms were observed to emerge two days
later at the point of resurgence.

Professor Lotze of Münster established another interesting
fact. Close investigation proved that what happens here is
not a simple underground flow, but a very complex geological
process. It was observed that more water issued from the
spring than went down where the Wäschegraben and Enkelbach disappeared. At the same time, the spring may dry up
while the two rivers are still furnishing considerable quantities of water. When the weather has been wet for a long
time, the volume of water remains equal at the exit and the
entrance of the underground course. It was therefore clear to

the geologist that the phenomenon is bound up with geological conditions inside the mountain. There must be large cavities in the interior of the mountain that act as dams, giving out water once they have filled up, even if they are not receiving any more from the rivers, and after their contents have dropped below a certain level holding the water they receive from the rivers until they are full again. During wet weather, when the flow of water from the rivers is continuous, these reservoirs give out the same quantity as they receive.

Professor Lotze describes the genesis of the Liet cavern as follows.

To begin with, the bedding planes and joints were very narrow. In those days the Wäschegraben and the Enkelbach flowed on the surface, along the eroded valley which now, having dried up, links the point of submergence of the rivers with that of their resurgence. The fissures were enlarged by rain- and snow-fall and water seeping down from the streams, while the base level of erosion dropped as the rivers cut deeper into the soil. The rivers then began to flow underground and the cave system was enlarged in all three dimensions. At first the subterranean course was not large enough to accommodate the volume of water at periods of heavy rainfall, so that during such periods there was an overground flow as well. After a time this disappeared, making way for present conditions, in which the underground watercourse alone exists.

The Liet cavern possesses another feature that distinguishes it from all other Sauerland caves. This is the presence of calcite formations, which are still forming today and are of great beauty and variety. The stalactites, stalagmites and curtains are particularly pure and snow-white in the Liet cavern, many of them looking like translucent wax. But the thin straw stalactites that hang from the ceiling, attaining in the Twenty-Metre Crevasse a length of up to eight feet with the diameter of a pencil and covering the whole vault, are unusual.

Professor Lotze explains the formations of these straws or tubes in this manner.

'A drop of water emerging from the ceiling was covered, as the result of condensation, with a very thin film of calcite. A second drop following the first burst the film, but a minute ring of calcite remained at the base of the drop. As the process continued, this was continually lengthened and thickened until it became a tube.' Lotze emphasizes that the conditions under which the process took place must have remained absolutely unaltered to permit the development of such regular formations.

This hypothesis leaves a good deal unexplained, however. For one thing, why should a drop of water fall from the same place for hundreds of thousands of years?

In addition to the glass tubes, the walls also present curious calcite formations which are lanceate, bulbous, or in some cases rosette-shaped, as clear as glass, and reminiscent of stems of coral. This calcite formation occurs very rarely in caves. It is also found in the Gruta Maravillosa, the Wonder Cave, near Aracena in Southern Spain, and in the Hall of Diamonds in the Eisriesenwelt (Ice-Giant World), a cavern in the Austrian Tennengebirge.

Besides these formations, the Twenty-Metre Crevasse contains a form of calcite that looks like frost, and some exceedingly fine crooked capillary tubes which Professor Lotze sees as a preliminary stage of the larger stems and spikes.

Thus the Liet cavern occupies a special position among the Sauerland caves, and offers many surprises to the biologist, geologist, mineralogist, hydrologist and speleologist which are hard to find elsewhere.

GOETZ'S CAVERN NEAR MEININGEN

Goetz's Cavern at Meiningen also presents a number of interesting features. It is particularly important for the light it throws on the formation of the Thuringian landscape, and

especially on the way in which the steep limestone cliffs of
the Werra and Saale valleys, and the abundant springs of
this region, came into being. The area is remarkable for
the deep cracks in the limestone and the collapse of long
stretches of cliff, which have in many cases brought down
huge masses of rock. Goetz's Cavern is the result of one
such fall. This natural monument is now open to the public.
Since the grotto contains only modest dripstone formations,
the clefts in the grey rock would only have been of interest
to the geologist and speleologist, but for the magic lent to
the otherwise bleak interior by cleverly contrived artificial
lighting.

This cavern shows clearly the mighty forces that must have
been necessary to rend such vast masses of rock. It was not
created, like other caves in the Harz Mountains or Sauerland, by the dissolution of gypsum or limestone. Where other
caves show wide underground chambers and vaulted halls,
Goetz's Cavern presents only yawning fissures that cleave
the Dietrichsberg near Meiningen with irregular gashes.

The cavern was only discovered by Rudolf Goetz after the
First World War, while he was working an underground
quarry. It must have been open in very early times, however,
for skeletons thought to be of prehistoric date were found in
it. According to the Meiningen chronicler Güth, it served as
a shelter in days gone by, though there is nothing to suggest
that it was ever in permanent occupation.

Goetz died in 1925. In May, 1932, Professor Hess of
Wichdorff, the district geologist, began to clear the cave of
debris with a team of twenty-five men, preparatory to carrying out a methodical examination. The work of clearance
took two years and entailed sinking a seventy-foot shaft in
the mountainside, for bringing the rubble to the surface.
More than seven thousand cubic yards of clay, pebbles and
fragments of rock were excavated, after which the cavern
was shored up against the danger of collapse.

Geologists consider that Goetz's Cavern did not come into

existence by chance, but as the inevitable outcome of the formation of the earth's crust. It shows visible evidence of the processes which took place in the interior of the mountain in the course of millennia, only becoming manifest in their final result. It gives the geologist a picture of the changing shape of the Thuringian countryside through the ages. Primeval seas covered the land and banks of shale piled up before the waters receded. Folds in the earth's surface rose up into mountains and disappeared again, leaving a barren landscape dotted with oases and towering volcanoes. This was inundated by a fresh sea, which dried out and left a desert of huge masses of coloured sand. Again the surface subsided and the sea poured in afresh, bringing with it deposits of chalk derived from sea shells. Once more the earth's crust heaved up and forced back the sea during the Tertiary mountain-building episode. Then the area was covered by the lava masses of the Rhön, which were later eroded by the waters of the Tertiary era and split by forces from within the earth, which threw up precipitous cliffs or gentle slopes. This is how Professor Hess visualizes the geological formation of the area.

Goetz's Cavern was produced by fissuration of the muschelkalk (a rock of the Middle Triassic Age, in Germany, which is absent in England). Its clearance laid bare the openings to six rifts which geologists believe to be due to the sinking of masses of rock towards the Werra Valley, in such a way that the front fissures are wider than those farther back in the mountain. Whereas the first cleft is two yards wide, the fourth is only sixteen inches. This gradation of the fissures is due to the outer rock having more freedom to shift. Geologists have no difficulty in explaining these features, which may frequently be observed in hard rock, even in horizontal sandstone under relatively light pressure. One reason for their development is the presence of a layer of soft red clayey sandstone, mixed with gypsum at the base of the mountain. When water infiltrates into this stratum, the clay swells, becomes soft and slippery, gives under the weight of the mountain resting on it, and creates a slipway down which the rocks slide. This process of slipping can be very clearly seen in the Swabian Alps, for example in the Hell Holes at Urbach and the Hanging Stone near Zollern.

But this sliding down may also be brought about by the solution of gypsum and salt. If these minerals are dissolved by water and swept away the strata above them subside. A particularly good example of this may be seen in the rock gardens of Besigheim, where the muschelkalk rested on a substratum of gypsum and salt that was carried away by water.

Surface water easily infiltrates into the clefts so formed, bearing with it the silt which is found in all caves. When the water meets strata of clay beneath the red bunter sandstone, it can percolate no further and forces an outlet for itself in the shape of a spring. Such springs are frequent in the vicinity of Goetz's Cavern, on the west side of the valley of the Werra.

If Goetz's Cavern lacks the grandiose beauty of famous dripstone caves, it is nevertheless of great interest from a geological point of view. It reveals with striking clarity the effects of gravity at work on the surface rocks of the earth. The vast dimensions of a fissure cavern of this kind make it the equal of any stalactite cave.

As in other caves, the various fissures of Goetz's Cavern have been given names of their own. Forty paces inside the entrance the visitor comes upon the Birthday Rift, thirty feet high, forty feet long and ten feet wide, so-called because it was first entered on the birthday of its discoverer, Goetz. A few steps farther on the rock is split to a height of fifty feet, and just beyond this, in the Little Kettle Hall, the walls show horizontal ripples due to the action of the infiltrating water on the bedding planes of the rock. The Little Kettle is linked by a small transverse cleft to an eighty-feet-high fissure violently rent by powerful natural forces. The Cathedral is a domed hall sixty-three feet high and possessing singular acoustics. In the glow of artificial light, a great variety of strange formations—jagged rocks, grottoes, niches, vistas—create the impression of a subterranean kingdom of gnomes.

Through a sixty-six-feet-long communicating tunnel, the visitor enters the Great Gorge, whose 160-feet-high walls look as though they had been cut into the mountain with a knife. Not far from it rises the equally tall, but narrower, Little Gorge, whose rocky walls can be ascended to a height of forty feet by steps. Round a huge block of stone and up a twenty-foot flight of steps, the visitor enters the Chapel and Pulpit, where he will see what grandiose beauty may be assumed by grim rocks in a subterranean world. Finally the visitor comes to the Chamber of the Dead, where a number of human skeletons were uncovered in the course of excavation.

THE CAVERNS OF
THE BAVARIAN DOLOMITIC LIMESTONE

Franconian Switzerland (the Swabian Jura) is a region of Central Europe in which caves are especially abundant. The cave area stretches south-east from Lichtenfels between Bamberg and Bayreuth to Regensburg, and then continues westward, almost at a right-angle, into the neighbourhood of Dinkelsbühl and Nördlingen. At the end of last century only a hundred and nine caves were known in Bavaria. By the outbreak of the Second World War the Bavarian land-register listed six hundred and thirty caverns in an area of two thousand four hundred square miles, more caves than any other district in Germany. In reality there are probably more than this, for many of the caverns extend far underground and have so far escaped enumeration.

This group of caves, vast in extent and variety, has attracted attention for centuries. Certain caverns were explored by isolated individuals, whose palaeontological discoveries created a sensation in scientific circles and had considerable influence on research in the eighteenth and nineteenth centuries.

The Bavarian caves are situated in the limestone and dolomite of the Franconian Jura, which stretches from the Danube to the Main. Dolomite or dolomitic limestone contains an appreciable quantity of the mineral dolomite (named after the geologist Dolomieu). It is a natural double carbonate of calcium and magnesium. It is used, after calcination, as a refractory mass (fireclay) in the Thomas Steelworks. All over Franconian Jura the caverns proved to have formed chiefly in dolomite. This is the case with the Schwaihaus cave north of Regensburg, the famous Robbers' Cave in the valley of the Naab near Etterzhausen, and the Osterloch in the valley of the Vils north of Kalmünz. There are also important caverns in the Velburg neighbourhood, around Amberg, and in the Königstein plateau, all of them in dolomite. The northern area of the Swabian Alps, the true Franconian Switzerland, is richest in caves, three hundred and seventy having been counted here.

The hydrological conditions that prevail in dolomite caves are particularly striking. Watercourses in this part of the country sink into the ground and re-appear elsewhere as springs of such force that they can be used to drive mills and water-wheels. After flowing a short distance above ground, they often disappear down sink holes or trickle away down cracks and fissures in the rock, only to emerge again as a powerful surface flow. Dolomite is as soluble in water as limestone. The irregular flow of water favours the disintegration of the dolomite, leading at many points to bare rocky deserts devoid of vegetation, while at others it carves the landscape into fantastic and sometimes beautiful shapes.

Some geologists attribute the dolomite caverns of Bavaria to the erosive action of the sea at the time when it still covered this region. In an essay on *The Caves of Eastern Bavaria*, the geologist Brand writes:

Here, as in the limestone islands of the Marianas Archipelago, the limestone cliffs of Italy, France and England, and many coastal regions of the earth, the moderate surge of the shallow sea hollowed out tunnels, deep holes, and caves at the points of least resistance. In many places these cavities collapsed, covering the beach with a confused mass of boulders. Many present-day sea-shore caves show a profile very similar to that of fluviatile caves.

Thus geologists such as Brand believe that the caverns of Franconian Switzerland came into being at a period when the sea, as the result of vast seismic upheavals, poured far in over the land from the south and helped to mould the land-scape. After the retreat of the sea, the rivers began to gnaw away the limestone and dolomite and enlarge existing caves. The details of this process are not clear, and the whole sea theory is somewhat doubtful. The cave area exhibits too much variety to be reduced to a common denominator, especially as the formation of caverns by flood waters, sub-terranean sapping and erosion is still going on.

The cave region of Franconia, with its 2,400 square miles the largest area of karst in Germany, has been divided by the Bavarian land-registry office into twelve plateaux, bear-ing the names of the following localities: Hollfeld, Potten-stein, Betzenstein, Königstein, Alfeld, Velburg, Burglenglfeld, Hemau, Altmannstein, Titting, Monheim, and Nördlingen. Hollfeld has a hundred and ten caves, Pottenstein sixty-one, Betzenstein two hundred and two, and Königstein a hun-dred and thirty-nine. The surveying and mapping of these caverns has been in progress for several years.

Many Bavarian caves have been the site of abundant palaeontological finds, as shown in the section entitled, 'Classics of Speleology'. They had begun to attract attention by the remains of Pleistocene mammals found in them at the end of the Middle Ages, and some of them became world-famous, particularly the Gailenreuth Zoolite Cave. It is a striking fact that the Bavarian caves have not produced the same wealth of remains of great Pleistocene beasts—mammoth, rhinoceros, primitive horse, bison—as those of northern Germany. On the other hand the Franconian caves have yielded immense quantities of bones of small animals. These are thought to be remnants of indigestible matter swallowed by birds of prey with their food and afterwards vomited and preserved in the clay. Bones of rodents are particularly numerous, but there are also bones of various types of chicken, accompanied by curiously polished stones from the stomachs of the latter. The remains of steppe-hamster, red ground-squirrel and striped mouse are ascribed by palaeontologists to a period when the countryside was covered by steppe, while those of snow-hare, snow mouse and white grouse are assigned to the Ice Age. But these are only conjectures.

As in other horizontal caverns, relics of man in the shape of stone implements were to be expected along with the faunal remains. In 1866, Pastor Engelhardt of Königsfeld reported to the Bamberg Natural History Society the traces of human occupation he had found in the valleys of the upper reaches of the Wisent and Aufsess; in 1876, the famous historian Ranke visited the Franconian grottoes, where excavation had been undertaken by the Institute of Palaeontology, Munich; in 1880, an Exhibition of Prehistoric and Anthropological Finds was held in Berlin under the patronage of the German Crown Prince. All this stimulated many museums to expand and complete their prehistoric collections. The result was a wild hunt for prehistoric objects in any cave or barrow that could be found, and when nothing more turned up, many people had recourse to forgery, fabricating the most fantastic objects from bone and sandstone and presenting them intermingled with genuine pottery sherds. The faking of prehistoric material was particularly rife between 1885 and 1895, and it is not impossible that a few museum pieces which are still much admired date from this period!

The rifling of caves that took place during the nineteenth century resulted in the destruction of a great deal of material which would have been immensely valuable to present day scholars. Round the turn of the century, methodical investigation was initiated by the Natural History Society of Nuremberg, in which a particularly meritorious part was played by the curator, Dr. Hörmann. These and other researches led to the claim that many of the Franconian caves had been occupied by man—during the Palaeolithic Period. This hypothesis is based on the similarity of the finds with those made at Le Moustier in France, and the advent of man in Franconian Jura is ascribed to the Mousterian Age. The caves that yielded the most abundant traces of human occupation were the Hohlefels at Happurg and the Hasenloch near Pottenstein. From the latter, Ranke obtained a hundred and twenty-five flint implements of Mousterian character. Some caves yielded flint points in the shape of a laurel leaf and bone tools, which were thought to belong to the Upper Palaeolithic Period. There were also a good many finds dating from the Mesolithic, suggesting that at this period men settled under overhanging rocks or in rock shelters close by a river. This is inferred from utensils of jasper, fishhooks, awls and needles of bone, and ornaments of staghorn; but no graves have been found to furnish conclusive proof of the presence of human beings in the area during the Middle Stone Age. Nor have any discoveries been made that point to human life in the region during the Neolithic, when man had begun to practise agriculture and stockbreeding.

Interesting as these finds are, they leave too many questions unanswered to be taken as proving permanent human settlements in the area during these great periods of culture. 'Our present knowledge of these bygone ages no longer permits us to regard evidence of the presence of men of the prehistoric Age of Metal in caves as proof of habitation, that is to say of the use of the caves as normal and permanent dwellings,' writes Richard Erl in an essay entitled *The Caves of East Bavaria in Late Prehistoric and Historic Times*. It looks as though prehistoric man may not have lived in such primi-

tive abodes as some theorists would have us believe. Many
bones, stones and antlers found in caves bear engravings
showing hut-like constructions, but none show representations of caves. This suggests that in northern latitudes, too,
primitive man dwelt in huts built from the products of the
forest, and not always in caves.

THE SANDSTONE CAVES OF VALKENBURG

The sandstone caves of Valkenburg are amongst the most
remarkable caves in Europe. They were not formed by
nature, like the dripstone caves or the crevasses, but dug by
the hand of man, bit by bit over thousands of years. One
gigantic cavern created by human agency over a period of
thousands of years must be a curiosity not easily paralleled.
Valkenburg, where this cavern is situated, lies on the River
Geuel in the province of Limburg, the south-eastern tip of
Holland. It is sometimes called 'the little town with the hundred hotels'. In olden times, Limburg was covered by the sea,
and it is to the sea that the hills of Limburg owe their
existence. The sandy limestone out of which these hills are
carved is the product of calcareous shells of crustaceans that
lived and died in the seas of the Mesozoic era. Under the
pressure of the ever-increasing accumulations of such
material, these deposits were compressed into a fifty-foot
thick layer of yellowish, friable, soft standstone. The stone is
so soft that it can be cut with a knife and is easy to work. The
author, who went to school in Valkenburg for several years,
can recall how he and his schoolmates used to carve heads
and other things from the stone with pocket-knives. Since
time immemorial, the stone has been used for building. It
would have been too soft for this purpose but for certain
special properties. In its original form the stone absorbs
moisture to an extent equal to its own weight. But when it is
exposed to the air it frees itself from this water, sets firm, and
provides a stone that stands up very well to weathering. This

only takes place with quarry-fresh stone mined underground like coal. Hence the immense workings around Valkenburg, which inspire amazement in every visitor.

The Romans, who passed down the Rhine as conquerors, hewed the yellow sandstone and used it in the building of their houses and fortresses. The enormous cavern cut by the Romans, 170 feet high and extraordinarily impressive in its unusual shape, was not discovered until after the First World War. The methods by which the Romans hewed the stone were naturally different from those employed nowadays. Today the stone is cut horizontally with blunt saws, whereas the Romans cut it vertically, i.e. from above downwards, which enabled them to create these gigantic vaults.

The whole network of caves extends over an area of about forty acres, and the galleries are over three miles in length. The visitor who makes his way through this labyrinth with a guide is amazed by the fantastic world here created by nature in collaboration with man.

The hydrological conditions in the sandstone workings are very curious. At one point, for instance, there is a four-acre lake of pure spring water crossed in places by currents. The water slowly rises and then falls again, until the lake is completely dried out, over regular seven-year periods—a phenomenon for which geologists can offer no explanation. In the old Roman grottoes there are two striking spots at which the water falls from the roof in drops, with meticulous regularity, and immediately sinks into the ground. At one point three drops fall each time, in the other one single drop. Neither frost, rain nor drought have any influence, one way or the other, on this dripping water. Here again the geologist is baffled.

Many relics of extinct animals have been discovered in the course of mining operations, including those of *Plioplatecarpus*, *Megalosaurus* and the forty-foot *Mosasaurus*. The most interesting skeletons have been reconstructed and may now be seen in various European museums. Sculptors have carved full-sized models of these creatures in the soft sandstone of the caves themselves. Amongst the most striking of these sculptures are a giant lizard, a thirty-foot tortoise that seems to be creeping out of the darkness of the cavern, and a very impressive carving of St. George and the Dragon. Numerous other sculptures, including a Madonna, a head of Christ wearing a crown of thorns, and busts of famous Dutchmen, make the stone-mines veritable museums of art. There are also a number of paintings and drawings executed on the smooth sandstone walls in charcoal, casein or resistant paint. They portray the history of the province of Limburg, the life of its seigneurs, scenes from the Cretaceous, Carboniferous and Diluvial Periods, pictures of everyday life, and portraits of the Dutch royal family. The sculptor who carved the statue of Atlas supporting the roof of a vast cavern lost his reason after being startled while at work by a quarryman's dog. The fine statue of the Magdalene has the profile of the old Queen of the Netherlands, which is shown on ancient guilder coins. Time and again these caverns were used during periods of war or revolution as places of refuge. This happened during the Seven Years War, and during the French Revolution a number of priests with their faithful took shelter there for twenty months. In the eighteenth century, the caves served as hideouts for the brigands who long terrorized Southern Holland and the neighbouring districts.

The Valkenburg caves became world-famous in 1910, when the faithful replicas of the Roman Catacombs, which had been constructed in them, were opened to the public. The money for this work was raised by Monsignor Diepen, Bishop of Hertogenbosch, and members of his family. The reproduction of the tombs, sarcophagi and murals was carried out with rigorous exactitude under the supervision of archaeologists, Dr. Cuypers, a Dutch architect, and the Archaeological Commission of Rome. Painters and decorators were even sent to Rome so that these simple craftsmen could study the paintings in the Catacombs and reproduce them at Valkenburg. The background made it impossible to copy the dark brown background colour of the Roman Catacombs, which was replaced by the yellow of the sandstone. The Valkenburg catacombs reproduce, with considerable fidelity and in close proximity, things which, in the Roman Catacombs, are spread over a wide area.

The first section, with the Catacombs of Calixtus, Thrason, Pontianus, Petrus and Marcellinus, Priscilla, Cyriaca and Hermes, was opened in July, 1910, by the celebrated expert on the Catacombs, Maucchi. The second section, the Catacombs of Domitilla, Agnes, Comodilla, Praetextatus, St. Sebastian and Valentius, was opened on July 2nd, 1912, by Baron Kanzler of Rome, Secretary of the Commission for Christian Archaeology and Director of the Vatican Museum of Christian Art.

THE MAMMOTH CAVE, KENTUCKY

Besides the Carlsbad cave, America possesses another giant cavern, the discovery of which dates from the time when the wilderness round the Green River, Kentucky, had not yet been pushed back by civilization. Tradition has it that a hunter named Houchins was led by a black bear to a gaping hole, in an out-of-the-way spot on the river bank, which opened into a cavern of vast dimensions and more than three hundred yards in length. Many of the early pioneers, with love of adventure and thirst for knowledge in their blood, advanced year by year deeper and deeper into the subterranean labyrinth, wresting from it, with exertion and risk, one secret after another. Even today it has not been fully explored.

But it was not curiosity alone that led to the penetration of this cavern. There was a practical purpose. Since the beginning of the nineteenth century, it was known that the cave had been occupied by vast numbers of bats, whose accumulated excrement was the probable source of a rich mine of saltpetre. At that time saltpetre was indispensable to the manufacture of gunpowder, so that these deposits furnished an invaluable source of supply during the war of 1812. The precious substance was lifted by slaves and transported on ox-carts. To satisfy the demand, new deposits had continually to be sought by entering deeper and deeper into the interior of the labyrinth. Exploration of the deposits ended with the war, and the Mammoth Cave has been opened to the public since 1816.

In 1837, Stephen Bishop, a Negro slave, crossed the apparently bottomless underground lake in this cavern on a cedar raft, which enabled the extensive galleries on the other bank to be explored and led to the discovery of three underground watercourses: the Hall River, the Echo River and the Roaring River. Five passages radiate from the main hall, known as Great Central Station. One of these passages was blocked by a roof fall. It was not cleared until 1923, when the effort was rewarded by the discovery of what is perhaps the finest section of the cavern—the frozen Niagara, a gigantic calcite concretion in the shape of a waterfall, and some beautiful cave-onyx formations. At this point, too, is Crystal Lake, thirty-eight feet deep and containing the purest spring water. An embankment, which rises 300 feet from ground to water-level and then 200 feet above this, prevents the water of the Crystal Lake from flowing into the Green River.

The most important discoveries in the Mammoth Cave were made by the guides, an occupation that is handed down from father to son, the majority of the present guides representing the fifth generation. The guides had long wondered where the mysterious Roaring River would lead, if anyone were bold enough to advance far beyond the narrow defile. After his audacious crossing of the lake, Bishop had reported hearing the noises of a waterfall. In reality the river has no waterfall. The sound is produced by the beating of its ripples against the walls of the grotto, which throw back a positively deafening echo. When the guides went fishing in the river they felt an urge to advance as far as possible along its course. Roaring River contains the famous blind cave-fish, *Amblyopsis spelaeus*. Once, and sometimes twice, a year the guides make their way up the river in order to gather in a supply of these fish, which constitute an interesting curiosity for visitors.

Even today, nobody has succeeded in following the river to the end. It is an unreliable and spiteful stretch of water. A downpour above ground may cause the river to rise at the rate of six feet in an hour, filling the whole defile and barring the return of anyone unwary enough to be caught inside.

In 1938 two guides, Karl Hanson and Leo Hunt, forced their way through a number of long and very narrow tunnels and came upon a subterranean paradise. Snow-white gypsum crystals deck several hundred yards of ceilings and walls. Innumerable grottoes of all dimensions and embellished with crystals open to the gaze. The eye is everywhere delighted by gypsum flowers, some like small daisies, others resembling exotic lilies with outspread petals. Rods of crystal, straight and sharp as a needle or twisted as a corkscrew, project from the walls. These needles also grow in thick clumps on the floor and ceiling; they are four to eight inches long and sway in the least breath of air.

The fauna consists of bats, cave-crickets with excessively long antennae, and beetles. Remains of vertebrates prove that the section of the cavern discovered in 1938 once communicated directly with the surface, for it is unlikely that the animals traversed the two and a half miles that separate it from the existing entrance. A direct entry to this cavern has recently been cut in the hillside, to save visitors the necessity of crawling on hands and knees along the tunnels followed by its first discoverers.

7

SUBTERRANEAN WONDERLANDS

✳

DECHEN'S CAVE, SAUERLAND

The Dechenhöhle, or Dechen's Cave, one of the earliest known stalactite caves in Sauerland, was discovered on June 10th, 1868, by two workers employed in the construction of the Letmathe-Iserlohn railway.

The discovery was reported by the railway company as follows:

In June, 1868, railway workers clearing debris fallen from the rocky slopes of the Sunderhorstberg came on a deep opening in the precipitous limestone cliff. It proved to be the entry to a cavern richer in stalactites and stalagmites than any other in the Devonian limestone range of Rhineland-Westphalia. This cavern was named after the Inspector of mines, von Dechen, in recognition of his services to geology.

The cave was subsequently explored by many geologists, including von Nöggerath, Fuhlrott (finder of the Neanderthal skull), and Karl Vogt. It was found to contain abundant remains of the extinct cave bear, cave hyaena, species of deer, and wild horse. Karl Vogt has left the following description of this wonderland of stone.

The great clefts and cavities have been enlarged by subterranean streams which later dried up or changed their courses. The caverns are never completely dry, because water perpetually seeps through the numerous cracks and crevices in the walls and ceilings. At one point the water trickles along a projecting spine, at another it accumulates in big drops on the roof, which hang there until pulled down by their own weight. In other places it rains down, pattering on the ground and splashing up a fine spray. And wherever a drop of water emerges, a tiny calcite crystal is left behind, and where one such particle remains, others are added to it and a concretion slowly forms. This process goes silently forward day and night, year after year, millennium after millennium. The trickles of water on the walls build up into ridges and projections. Where an irregularity in the walls slows the flow of the water and therefore increases the rate of deposit, the concretion is thicker; where the water flows more rapidly, it is thinner; until finally the trickle develops into an elegantly draped curtain, with pleats and folds that take on a magical appearance as soon as a flame is lit at the back of the translucent formation. But where a drop hung at the very beginning, a cone formed and grew continually thicker and longer, while another cone grew up to meet it from the point where the drop struck the floor, until the two tips met and joined into a column, which now seems to be carrying the roof. Plants have also played a part in this process. Rootlets penetrate the rock and become immensely elongated as they stretch out in search of soil. Algae, moulds, and even ferns creep along the dripping rock. All these plants gradually become enveloped in a sheet of limestone; by absorbing the carbonic acid released by the water they encourage the formation of concretions, which quickly suffocate them. The filaments decompose and vanish, but their shape is preserved: small tubes, long, thin and transparent, hang from the ceiling; a fine lacy fabric spreads over the walls. While this process is going on, the floor of many caves becomes covered with flowstone, an extremely hard crystalline concretion, several feet thick, beneath which lie all sorts of treasures. Thus the simple process of sedimentation from infiltrating water gives birth to an overwhelming variety of shapes; all that can be predicted in advance is that the clearer the water and the more undisturbed it can carry out its creative process, the greater will be the wealth of dripstone forms, the purer the structure and colour of the calcite.

Much thought has been devoted to the genesis of drip-stone and the length of time it takes to form. The simple statement that stalactites and stalagmites are the result of a drop of water falling for hundreds and thousands of years at the same spot leaves a great deal unexplained. This process alone could never have given birth to the columns and arcades, the mouldings on walls and ceilings, the draperies, waterfalls, and all the other dripstone formations of a substance that resembles alabaster. Other forces must have been at work here besides the thin trickle and drip of water, which may have played a part in producing these concretions but cannot have been solely responsible. Dripstones exhibit a great variety in their structure. Some stalactites are hollow, others solid; some are porous, others compact; some are as twisted as corkscrews or shaped like carrots or fruit; others are angular, showing no trace of the vertical course of the falling drop. Other dripstones are incrusted with tufa or crystals; stalagmites rising from the ground often carry concretions of tufa or crystal on their tips. These phenomena do not contradict the role of water in forming dripstones, but they make it very doubtful whether this role was exclusive. Vast groups of dripstone formations are also to be found in low-roofed tunnels. Such formations do not look in the least as though they had been produced by drops of water falling for thousands of years. If a flat base is placed under perpetually dripping water in a dripstone cave, it will be seen that after a number of years there is no sign of a stalagmite, but merely a formation of porous tufa spread over an area corresponding to the distance covered by the splashing of the drop as it fell.

Last century, geologists were already making a close study of the genesis of dripstones and attempting to assess how long they took to form. Their conclusion that dripstones were produced by dripping water is still largely unchallenged. The calculations of time, based on repeated experiments, differ so enormously from one another that it is still quite impossible to give even an approximate figure for the rate at which dripstones develop. Thus the bulk of the evidence is against, rather than for, the theory that massive stalactites and stalagmites owe their existence exclusively to tiny drops of water.

Pressure conditions inside the mountain, coupled with thermal and magmatic influences, must have played a major role. There are many similar phenomena that can be ascribed to volcanic (i.e. magmatic) influences, for example the stone cones in the Valley of the Ghosts, Cappadocia, and the caverns in volcanic regions. The varied shapes of dripstones suggest an origin in fusion, rather than dripping water though this is not to deny the part played by water in many of these concretions.

Dechen's Cave was frequently visited and admired during the nineteenth century. In their famous book, *Das malerische und romantische Westphalen*, Schücking and Freiligrath wrote:

In this cavern mighty trunks rise aloft, their branches curving above them and dividing into twigs as they approach the roof. Their growth is as luxuriant as that of the Indian sycamore, of which every branch that grows down into the soil is changed into a fresh trunk. Here fluted columns lie on the ground; there a whole forest of icicles point threateningly down at us. There chandeliers and delicate lamps hang from the cracked cupolas, wreathed about by strange twisted creepers. The stone walls and ceilings look as though they had been covered by genies with embroideries, tapestry, or the finest lace. And behind the transparent curtains glows a rosy light, as though they hid some new and yet more enchanting magic chamber. We seem to see the Moorish architecture with its richly decorative arabesques that still delights the visitor to the wonderful Alhambra. But here, beneath the ground, this architecture possesses even greater power to move the spirit to poetic dreams, transporting it into a veritable fairyland.

At one time the interior of Dechen's Cave was illuminated by candles, but their smoke had a deleterious effect on the pure coloration of the dripstone. In the 'eighties, therefore, a gas pipe was run into the cavern feeding a hundred and fifty gas-jets—a curiosity which probably few recall today. Later, electric lamps were installed all over the cave, which heightened the effect, particularly of the chambers farthest back in the mountain.

The individual chambers received high-sounding names, earned by their shape. The thirty-foot-high entrance hall is called the Chapel, on account of its resemblance to a nave. The Glacier Hall owes its name to a glacier-like formation projecting abruptly from the wall. Close to it is the Bower, seventy feet long, seventeen feet wide and thirteen feet high. There is every sign that a stream once flowed through here, but later infiltrating water created delicate dripstone formations resembling hanging plants and gathered curtains. One of the most striking and splendid dripstone formations is in the Organ Chamber, where, with a little imagination, one can see a giant hand lying diagonally across the 'organ pipes'. The Curtain Chamber is of quite different construction; here dripstone is not so much in evidence, but the walls and ceiling are brilliant yellow striped with reddish lines, and shaped like gathered cloth. The Royal Hall, the biggest chamber in Dechen's Cave with an area of 1,610 square feet, contains a particularly magnificent dripstone formation. In the centre of the hall rise one small and two large dripstone pyramids. Here also were found a large number of bones of cave bear, cave hyaena, prehistoric horse, and various species of deer, which are now in a museum at Bonn. The Pulpit Chamber is a singular shape: it is more or less circular and on the left side a smooth, oval block, resembling a pulpit in appearance, hangs from the roof, flanked by a snow-white stalactite that looks like a chandelier.

From the Pulpit Chamber a flight of forty steps leads upward to the romantically wild section of the cavern, and at the same time to its highest point, the Nixies' Chamber. Between slender columns of dripstone stands a green pool, called the Nixies' Pond, or the Bath of Venus, and looking like a fairy bath of marble. The water is five feet deep, the temperature an unvarying 43° F., and the pool always kept uniformly filled by the drops of water falling from the roof. The water flows out under a stone shaped like a shell at the back of the pool to one side. Ornamental fish that were introduced into the pool soon died. From the Nixies' Grotto a bridge leads past Hell Gorge into a wild and precipitous cleft that runs far back into the dark, mysterious depths of the mountain. A second flight of steps descends into the Crypt, which contains a number of stalagmites that recall the headstones in a graveyard. In the background is a formation resembling a yellow curtain striped with red.

One of the most perfect of all the dripstone formations is to be found in the Palm Court, in the shape of a stalagmite ten feet tall and a foot thick, for which the British Museum once offered £30,000 in vain.

Another hall is called Alhambra, because its numerous dripstone columns and richly decorated walls give it a likeness to the Alhambra in Granada. This hall, with its arabesques, cupolas, denticulations, mounds and dripstone formations, is particularly stimulating to the imagination. On the left a concretion shot through with rose red, foam white and grey-green hues resembles a waterfall turned to stone by the hand of a magician. At another point, a stone plinth carries two shapes that look like a dog and a hen. In a niche in the wall stands a small brown figure, recalling the image of a saint carved in wood.

The Crystal Chamber, which owes its name to several pools in which crystals of calcite are found, a rarity here, has a charm all its own. Here, too, the imagination is stimulated by the diverse forms of the dripstone, resembling a snow-white polar bear or iceberg, or an enormous tortoise.

Like the Organ Chamber, the Imperial Hall is rich in dripstone formations. The walls are rent by strange fissures, the stalactites hang down like ragged curtains, and in the centre rises a pyramidal column with an almost needle-sharp apex. The right-hand wall, shaped like a curtain full of folds and shot through with red stripes, has the property of ringing like a bell when struck.

A long, wide passage leads to the last section of the cavern, the Wild Wolf Ravine, full of fantastically shaped rocks, with queerly contorted walls and a few dripstone formations. The walls and ceilings are covered with short, blunt concretions reminiscent of various kinds of fruit.

In 1912, Dechen's Cave was enlarged to the west. The masses of clay in the 260 feet of new galleries suggests that the Grünerbach, which now flows along the valley, once passed through Dechen's Cave. The gallery has no cavities of any size, but contains several remarkable dripstone formations.

THE ATTENDORN CAVE

On the outskirts of the old Hansa town of Attendorn, Sauerland possesses a dripstone cave which is fully equal to Dechen's Cave in the originality of its concretions and the diversity of its forty-five chambers. It was laid bare in 1907—fifty years after the discovery of Dechen's Cave—by a blasting shot that brought down a mass of limestone. The large chambers, for the most part between fifteen and 130 feet high, contain innumerable stalactites and stalagmites from one and a half to forty inches in diameter and up to fifteen feet high. The water has carved the stone into every imaginable shape. Curtains and draperies up to sixteen feet in height and twenty inches wide hang like fine white and coloured fabrics on the walls and ceilings; sparkling crystals decorate wide areas of the interior. It is easy to imagine that primitive man, in his ignorance of the natural forces at work here, derived from the bizarre forms he saw in this and similar caverns his conception of the gnomes, spirits, elves and all the other phantoms that haunted his legends of the subterranean world. Modern man has broken the seal of the mystery; the universe that nature offers him below the ground is no less marvellous, no less fantastic, but for all his wonderment he enters it with the instruments of the scientist and inquires into its origin.

The Attendorn Cave, which is perhaps even more fissured than Dechen's Cave, was formed under the same conditions as all dripstone caverns. It took four and a half years to render this masterpiece, in which nature presents grotesque shapes beyond the power of human imagination to conceive, accessible to sightseers.

Amongst the cavern's forty-five chambers, the finest items are the Alhambra Grotto, the Glacier, the seventeen-foot Curtain, the Waterfall, the Imperial Grotto, and the Hall of Fame.

THE WIEHL CAVE

The Rhineland, too, has its dripstone cave. This is at Wiehl (*Kreis* Cologne) and, like Dechen's Cave, it was discovered in the 'sixties of last century. Round about 1860, blasting in the limestone quarry on the Pfaffenberg near Wiehl broke into the first galleries of a dripstone cave. Tourism was not such an industry then as it is today, so little attention was paid to the discovery, and the cavities that had been opened up were allowed to become choked with rubble again. This, and the uncontrolled right of entry to the cavern, resulted in a great deal of damage being done, especially to valuable dripstones. Not until 1922 did the municipality of Wiehl take the cave under its protection. This plan was approved by the owners of the property, the Evangelical Community, who made the land round the cave available on a long lease.

When Wiehl was struck by unemployment in 1926, the opening up of the cave offered a welcome opportunity of creating work. The task was not easy, since huge quantities of mud and debris had to be shifted from the passages before access could be gained to the still virgin galleries. Finally the work was finished, and on August 4th, 1927, the cave was opened to the public. This added one further goal for tourists in the Rhineland. The Wiehl cave is the biggest of all Rhineland caves and the only one containing dripstones.

The geological structure of the countryside in which the Wiehl grotto lies is different from that of Dechen's Cave or the Attendorn cave. Nor are the dripstone formations so original and abundant as the two Sauerland caverns.

According to Professor Max Richter's account, the Wiehl cave lies in limestone belonging to the Devonian, i.e. the geological period between the Silurian and the Carboniferous. On the Pfaffenberg, this limestone forms an isolated enclave in the midst of huge masses of shale and sandstone, which were deposited on the bed of the shallow Devonian sea. During the period when the rivers carried little sand and silt into the Devonian sea, coral reefs formed, which were later smothered when the amount of sand and silt swept into the sea increased. The Pfaffenberg limestone is made up of petrified coral, as may be clearly seen from the coral growths and marine plants that are still visible. The limestone is therefore of organic origin, i.e. it comes from marine creatures which absorbed calcium carbonate from the sea water and used it to make their shells, which, after their death, were compressed into solid masses. The Devonian sea must have been relatively shallow, since coral can only live in shallow water. It must also have been tropical, like the seas near the Equator, for coral can only thrive in water of about 70° F.

The subsequent evolution may be imagined thus. After a certain period the coral reef was covered with sandstone, shale and limestone. In the Carboniferous era, which followed the Devonian, the sea gradually retreated northwards leaving dry land behind. Through tectonic action, to which the earth's crust was subjected, the various strata were lifted, fractured, folded, and raised to form hills and mountains. The resulting chain (the Hercynian mountains of Central Europe) extended from the French Massif Central, through the Northern Alps, the Vosges, the Black Forest, the Oden-

14

wald, and the Rhenish Schiefergebirge (Slate Mountains) to
the Harz Mountains, Saxony, and Silesia. Only parts of the
original huge formation still exist, the rest having been worn
away by erosion.

The dripstone formations of the Wiehl cave have a different character from those in the Sauerland caves, being
more massive. The cave, which is entered down a flight of
eighteen steps, has a constant temperature of 46° F., due to
the perpetual evaporation of moisture. The ceiling of the
entrance hall, the floor of which lies thirteen feet below
street level, is covered with rows of small transparent stalactites. From here the path leads into the various chambers and
to the twenty-four points of special interest, to which poetic
names have been given, such as Waterfall, Organ Chamber,
Big and Little Glacier Chamber, Pearl Chamber, Dragon's
Den, Hall of Siegfried, Ravine, Cascade, Devil's Gorge,
Group of Stalagmites, Great Hall, Owl Gorge, Crystal
Chamber, Pulpit, Bell, Glowing Iron, Small Hall, Elephant's
Head, Blue Grotto, Icicle Rift, and Smoking-Chamber. On
all sides are chambers and galleries of every dimension, rifts
up to thirty feet deep, calcareous sinter in a rich variety of
shapes, and crystals that give off a fairy-like refulgence when
they are lit up.

THE RÜBELAND CAVES

Rübeland is the old name for the district between the high
limestone rocks and the banks of the River Bode, round
which so many legends are spun, in the Harz Mountains.
The foundry that sprang up here in the mid-fifteenth century
was called in the Harz dialect, 'De isern Hitt tau'n rühen
Lanne', 'The foundry of the rugged land'. In the course of
the centuries this 'rühen Lanne' became Rübeland.

The 'foundry of the rugged land' was one of the most important of the numerous iron-works in the Bode Valley from
Schierke to Altebrak and Treseburg. It provided the people

of the neighbourhood with work and bread, until it closed down in 1920 to make way for a pleasant summer resort.

The rocky banks of the Bode, in some places wooded, in others bare, deserve the geologist's attention. They contain a black marble that was once sent to all parts of the world, and from which were cut altars, fonts and columns for cathedrals and castles. Halberstadt Cathedral, the Garrison Church at Potsdam, the church belonging to Dresden Castle, and the Ducal Castle at Blankenburg are all built largely of Rübeland marble. Later, Harz marble was pushed more and more into the background by Italian marble, with its finer appearance.

A new blessing descended on the district in the shape of the discovery of several dripstone caverns, equal in beauty to any other similar caves. The first cavern was found in 1536 by the miner Friedrich Baumann, while he was prospecting for fresh veins of iron. He discovered only the smallest and most modest section of the cave that bears his name, but because of its beauty it was also called the 'Queen of the Harz'.

Two hundred years after the finding of Baumann's Cave, in 1762, the foresters Müller and Hartung came upon the Bielstein Cave in the mountain of that name as they were clearing the forest after a fire. As no value was attached to such discoveries in those days, the cave was abandoned to destruction. By the mid-nineteenth century, the interior had been completely pillaged. Then, in 1866, a roadmender named Fritz Sorge found a third dripstone cave, Hermann's Cave. This cavern and the even larger Baumann's Cave, brought world renown to the little, previously unknown locality of Rübeland; for by the outbreak of the Second World War some quarter of a million people had visited the Rübeland caves.

Hermann's Cave, which was scientifically explored for the first time in 1874, consists of a number of interconnected rifts and cavities made in the Upper Devonian limestone by water, and contains a quantity of dripstone formations. The older Baumann's Cave has still larger dimensions. Baumann himself is said to have roamed the cavern for three days and three nights, after his miner's lamp had gone out during his search for iron. On returning to daylight he died from exhaustion.

The biggest cavity of Baumann's Cave is the Goethe Hall, which is 230 feet long, 130 wide and twenty to thirty-five feet high. During his journey through the Harz Mountains in 1777, Goethe also visited this cavern and was so enchanted by it that he spent three-quarters of the first day there and came back the next day for several hours more.

Goethe writes of his visit to Baumann's Cave as follows in his *Kampagne in Frankreich.*

After a good night's rest, I hurried to Baumann's Cave again in the morning, once more accompanied by a guide. I crawled through it and examined closely the natural processes at work there. Masses of black marble that had dissolved and been reconstituted as columns and surfaces of white crystal drew my attention to the unceasing life of nature. To be sure, all the marvellous pictures which a sombre imagination so readily creates for itself out of amorphous shapes vanished on calm contemplation, but to compensate for this, everything that truly existed was all the more clearly evident and I felt myself greatly enriched thereby. As soon as I returned to daylight, I noted down what I had seen, and while my recollection was still fresh I wrote the first stanzas of the poem which, under the title *Harzreise im Winter* (*Winter Journey in the Harz Mountains*), has held the attention of many of my friends to the very last line.

In Wernigerode, Goethe—unrecognized—entered into conversation with the son of Superintendent Plessing, and told the latter what an impression Baumann's Cave had made upon him. Goethe describes young Plessing's reaction to his enthusiasm about the cavern.

At this point he interrupted me animatedly and assured me that he thoroughly regretted the short distance he had gone to see it. The cavern had by no means come up to his expectations. After what had gone before, such morbid symptoms had no power to vex me; for how often had I had to learn that man decries the value of a clear reality in comparison with the murky phantoms of his own sombre imagination. Nor was I any more surprised when, on my asking him how he had pictured the cavern, he replied with a description which the most audacious stage designer would scarcely have dared to employ as a representation of the forecourt to Pluto's kingdom.

The whole vault of Baumann's Cave consists of black marble—a combination of calcium carbonate. In prehistoric times the Rübeland caves must have sheltered great mammals, especially cave bears, skeletons of which have been found in both caves.

Some years ago the blind proteus, hitherto found only in the caverns of the south-east, was acclimatized in Hermann's Cave.

As in all dripstone caves, the most spectacular spots in the Rübeland caves have been given names derived from the shapes of the concretions, which are here extremely rich and varied. The Pulpit, the Monk, the Hall of Columns, the White Robe, the Palmtree, and Proteus Lake are some of the titles they have received.

THE CAVERN OF BARBAROSSA

The Kyffhäuser is a little wooded mountain that rises from a fertile plain in the heart of Germany and is at one and the same time the southern outpost of the Harz Mountains and the northern limit of the hill country of Thuringia. This mountain has an important place in German history and legend. The much loved and heroic Emperor Barbarossa is said to sleep an enchanted slumber within the Kyffhäuser, from which he will one day wake and return. A monument to the victorious Emperor William I and the soldiers who gave their lives for the honour and liberty of Germany has been erected on the northern slope of the mountain. This massive monument of stone rises from a plateau on which the proud imperial castle of Kuffese (Kyffhausen) once stood, the ruins of which may still be seen. All that remains is a single tower, popularly known as the 'Emperor Frederick', and the Chapel of the Holy Cross. The oldest tradition regarding this castle dates from the twelfth century. In 1118, Emperor Frederick Barbarossa had the castle rebuilt, after its destruction, to protect the royal court of Tilleda. By the beginning of the sixteenth century the edifice had collapsed, and was never built up again. Later, the site was excavated and the castle's extensive foundations laid bare.

Nature herself has created an unforgettable memorial inside the mountain in the shape of the Cavern of Barbarossa, which is of particular interest to us within the framework of this book. The cavern was discovered entirely by chance in the Christmas week of 1865, when prospectors searching for copper had dug 590 feet into the mountain. Here they came upon a stupendous cavity, which was soon made accessible to sightseers.

The Cavern of Barbarossa has been formed in Permian gypsum. In the depth of the cave one still finds anhydrite, a form of calcium carbonate giving rhomboid crystals, which also occurs in salt-bearing strata and is produced by gypsum absorbing water. At several points balls of white alabaster—also a type of gypsum—may be seen imbedded in the anhydrite. Anhydrite, like limestone and dolomite, is a rock which readily dissolves in water. Water infiltrating through the cracks and crevices of the mountain transformed the anhydrite into gypsum. At the same time it created cavities by solution. This process was initiated by ground water that first hollowed out cavities with horizontal roofs. As the span of these ceilings grew too large for the rock's resistance, they caved in, leaving vaulted domes. The water that perpetually seeped into the cavities, the action of which may still be observed, contributed to their further enlargement.

Physically, the formation of the walls proceeds as follows. When the water oozing in from outside comes in contact with the anhydrite, the latter greedily absorbs it, increasing its own volume by twelve per cent. Because there is no space for this expansion, the originally flat strata fold, taking on the appearance of a crumpled cloth. Thus the anhydrite on the cave walls is folded artistically this way and that like a starched ruff. Where there was no obstacle, however, expansion of the rock has produced protuberances on the inside or outside of the cavern.

Another process also takes place, which lends a particular charm to the Cavern of Barbarossa. The anhydrite continues to absorb water and dilate, with the result that sheets of varying thicknesses are constantly detaching themselves, curling away from the rock like leaves or bark. These peeling sheets hang from the ceilings of the grottoes like skins or sides of bacon, and have gained for one of the chambers the name of the Tannery. These exfoliations, combined with the manifold shapes on the walls, make the Cavern of Barbarossa unique of its kind in the whole of Europe. In some places, especially on the roof of the Sea of Rocks, curious new formations of gypsum crystals developed where a block detached itself from the roof. At the point of fracture a saturated solution of calcium sulphate appeared in the guise of a saturated gypsum solution, which left behind gypsum crystals shaped like bundles of needles.

The Cavern of Barbarossa, with its seventeen hundred yards of accessible chambers, whose height varies from 60 to 170 feet, is one of the largest German caves. The variety of shapes exhibited by its component cave is almost unsurpassed, and the whole of its 27,000 square yards of area may be traversed in absolute safety, because it is flat and free from rifts.

The singular formations on its walls, its majestic halls, its splendid vaults and domes, its fields of boulders, and its numerous lakes of crystal-clear water up to thirteen feet deep make the Cavern of Barbarossa a unique experience for the visitor.

According to ancient Thuringian legends, current long before the cave's discovery, the Kyffhäuser opens on the eve of Ascension Day, revealing all the marvels hidden in its depths. Human enterprise has turned this legend into reality and unveiled the enchanted kingdom of Barbarossa. For it really is an enchanted kingdom, this group of caverns beneath the snow-white rocks in the neighbourhood of the delightful Bad Frankenhausen, which is known to history through the tragic battle of 1525 that ended in the defeat of the insurgent peasants and the capture of their leader Thomas Münzer, who was beheaded shortly after.

A 530-foot adit leads into the interior of the mountain. At the end of this gallery the first mysterious hall confronts the gaze. The walls and ceilings have a strange, fantastic look, as though covered by the folds of innumerable thick curtains interspersed with curling leaves. In the shadows of the vaulted cave there is a gleam and shimmer that seems to come from some enchanted treasure. According to the legend, this cavern was used by Barbarossa as a reception hall.

Farther on, another chamber on the right, Neptune's Hall rivets the gaze with its own peculiar charm. A narrow path leads past a deep, crystal-clear lake, the bottom of which shines emerald green. Not a fish, not a plant is to be seen in its limpid depths. The water stands there in mysterious silence, reflecting the grotto. Next door to Neptune's Hall lies the Tannery, whose curious ceiling hung with what look like skins has already been mentioned. From the Tannery there is a view through a wide oval passage into the Ballroom, to which nature has given the form of a perfect cruciform vault. In this vast hall, where legend says Barbarossa held his court balls, 'the stone describes graceful arabesques: here ruches are suspended from the ceiling, there a prettily frilled ruff gleams white and the diagonal ribs are decked

with lace, galloons, and ribbons in charming confusion,'
wrote Carla Heidendorff, describing her impressions in the
cavern. 'I close my eyes, overwhelmed—I catch a whiff of
fragrant scent, I hear the silky swish of the brocade dresses
of the ladies, the low clink of the swords of their cavaliers.
Celestial music seems to sweep through the lofty vaulting
of the hall, and feet shuffle rhythmically across the floor.
What was that strange tinkling sound? Isn't that the humpbacked court jester leaping this way and that amongst the
ladies, engaged in his buffoonery? No—these were all phantoms—and everything sinks back into the eternal silence of
these subterranean halls, whose walls pitilessly stifle every
sound.'

The lake of Neptune's Hall is not the only one in this
underground kingdom. In another part of the cave, called
the Swiss Landscape, the rugged rocks of a miniature mountain landscape are reflected in the waters of a second lake.
From the Ballroom a remarkable alabaster structure is
visible having the form of a huge chair and table. Here Barbarossa used to sit, in the manner immortalized in Geibel's
poem *Frederick Barbarossa*:

> *Tief im Schosse des Kyffhäusers*
> *bei der Ampel rotem Schein*
> *sitzt der alte Kaiser Friedrich*
> *an dem Tisch aus Marmelstein.*[1]

One of the most impressive places in the Cavern of Barbarossa is Olympus, reached after climbing a steep path.
This chamber is like an enormous cathedral with a rocky
mountain rising in the centre. Like the Valkenburg sandstone caves, this hall is filled with the everlasting sound of
rain, the perpetual drip of water pattering down from the
ceiling. When lit up by a Bengal light the walls sparkle as

---

[1] 'Deep in the heart of the Kyffhäuser, by the red glow of the lamp,
sits old Emperor Frederick at the table of marble.'

though with numberless stars, and in between hang the pale moons of the alabaster outcrops.

Close to the adit cut into the mountain by the miners in the nineteenth century, which led to the discovery of the cavern, lies the Cave of Grottoes with a third lake. Opening out of it is a cave that has received the prosaic name the Bacon Cupboard, because of the curious superimposed layers of alabaster and their fat-like surfaces.

This does not exhaust all the secrets of the cavern. Beyond the Bacon Cupboard a fourth lake of crystal water lies in magic solitude. At the end of this cave a long, narrow and winding tunnel leads to a zigzag cavity that was first opened up in 1926. Here the mind is again seized with amazement before a sixty-foot-high chamber, resembling Olympus, but filled with a heap of rubble thirty feet high. This is the end of the journey through the Cavern of Barbarossa, where nature has created through the millennia wonders that delight many thousands of visitors every year and show them that the powers of creation do their work not only on the surface, but also in the interior of the earth.

THE CAVES OF THE SWABIAN ALPS

The Swabian Alps contain a large number of very striking caves. One of them, the Karlshöhle, has already been referred to in the section on 'The Home of the Cave Bear'. The years 1892–3 were particularly eventful as regards the discovery of caverns in the Swabian Alps. In the Heidenheim district, the Irpfel cave near Giengen and the Höllhöhle, or Hell Cave, at the same spot were found by Sihle the head-forester and Spiess the apothecary; shortly after this the fine dripstone grotto at Heuchstetten was discovered by Grotz the chimney-sweep and Frei the cartwright; and then the Herwarth cave near Königsbronn by Klemmer the clock-maker. Finally three carpenters, Beutler, Strass and Schlumpberger, came upon the Charlotte Cave at Hürben, the most magnificent and largest dripstone cave in South Germany. From their first entry into this cavern with the aid of a rope ladder the three discoverers brought back unfossilized pelvic bones of cattle and horses' skulls.

The 1,756-foot-long Charlotte Cave is not only the biggest dripstone grotto in South Germany, but also one of the most spectacularly beautiful, rivalling those of Sauerland in the diversity of its concretions. In 1893, the year of its discovery, it was visited only by the inhabitants of the surrounding district; but its fame soon spread throughout the country, and even beyond it, after the cavern had been visited by Queen Charlotte of Württemberg.

As in every dripstone cave, the limestone of the mountain and the formations have assumed strange and bizarre shapes. The first to confront the visitor as he enters is an isolated figure known as the Mountain Spirit. After this he comes upon Vulcan's Forge, St. Paul's Cathedral, and the Hall of Ivory. Every notable spot has its name. There are the Little Castle, the Monks' Refectory, the Rood-screen, the Bears' Defile, whose walls are believed to have been rubbed smooth by the coarse fur of bears as they slipped through. The Royal Hall deserves its name with its roof like fine filigree work. The Grotto of the Gnomes, the Staircase, and the Vault of the Cyclops likewise merit particular attention. The Radish Chamber is a curious phenomenon, its roof covered with strange spherical formations of the same stone as the stalactites. Next to the Tall Chimney, which runs up to a point at the top, is the Hall of the Gods with Olympus, a sensationally beautiful grotto that terminates the cave system.

In the immediate neighbourhood of Lichtenstein in the Swabian Alps lies the Nebelhöhle, or Cavern of Mist, made famous by Hauff's novel *Lichtenstein* and by Duke Ulrich of Württemberg, who went into hiding here. The Cavern of Mist was one of the first caves in Europe to be discovered. A hunter stumbled on it in 1517, when a roebuck he had shot on the mountainside vanished into the ground before his eyes. On looking closer, he found a cleft that led into a cavern. This cleft in the earth was assiduously avoided by the local people. For every now and then it belched forth vapours that clung to the ground in the form of a grey mist. This phenomenon is attributed to the steady temperature of 50° F. prevailing in the cave. If the temperature outside falls below this figure, the warmer air in the cavern emerges in a grey cloud.

In 1920, two students from Stuttgart discovered a second mist cave. They observed a bat flying out of a narrow crack in the rock. They enlarged this crack and passed through it from the old cave into a new one that led to vast dripstone halls. To begin with, the two caverns could only be viewed separately, because the first one lies in the district of Unter-hausen, while the second is in that of Genkingen. In 1934, the two municipalities reached agreement and made a pas-sage between the two caves. This gave the combined cavern a total length of 1,320 feet, while parts of it lie 140 feet below the surface.

The Cavern of Mist contains interesting dripstone forma-tions and large caves up to 230 feet wide and seventy feet high. No important finds were made in its galleries. Roughly in the centre of the cavern a gallery crosses at a height of about sixty-six feet over the main hall, known as Ulrich's Cave. This latter is named after Ulrich, Duke of Württem-berg, who hid there in 1519—shortly after the discovery of the cavern—when pursued by the Swabian Confederacy while returning by night to the nearby castle of Lichtenstein.

On every Whit-Monday the Cavern of Mist is a centre of attraction for the local populace. A feast is held beneath the towering oaks and beeches on the open place in front of the entrance to the cave in celebration of the visit of the first King of Württemberg, King Frederick, at the beginning of the nineteenth century.

The Swabian Alps contain a good many other caves of

special interest. The Schwertelshöhle and the Sontheim
Erdloch or Earth-hole, were hollowed out by rivers that
have since dried up, but the Wimsen cave can still only be
traversed in a boat. Other important caves round Hürben
are Goatstone Cave, Bear's Cave and Decoy Cave, in the
valley of the Lone, all of which are believed to have been
occupied in prehistoric times. Carvings of ivory were found
in the Decoy Cave (Vogelherdhöhle). Apart from these,
there are the Laichingen Pothole that drops vertically to
340 feet and then runs horizontally; Gussmann's Cave and
Gutenberg Cave close to the town of that name; and finally
Olga's Cave, hollowed out of the tufa. The Laichingen Pothole is a very singular cavern. It is entered by a reinforced
concrete stairway down the vertical shaft. At the bottom the
visitor is confronted by impressive halls, vaults and chambers, grotesque dripstone formations, cavities washed out of
the dolomite, and shafts eroded by percolating water.

There are also a number of incompletely explored caves,
chief amongst them the Falkenstein cavern, 1,043 feet long
and hollowed out by the water that still flows through it.

Many of these caverns are of great interest from a speleological, bio-speleological, palaeontological and geological
point of view, but space forbids detailed discussion of their
special features.

THE FAIRY CAVES OF POSTOJNA

Wonders of nature, created by sun and sea, succeed one another in infinite profusion from the Alps to the sunny shores
of Sicily, surpassing in beauty and majesty the works of man.

Whoever crosses the blue Adriatic encounters these
natural wonders in a multitude of different shapes. The in-
comparable beauty of the landscape is continued into the
colourful world beneath the sea, and in the dark clefts in the
cliffs washed out by the water in the course of thousands of
years.

But the wonder of wonders lies between Laibach and Trieste, and nothing else of its kind can compare with it. Nature has strange caprices. The landscape of the Trieste Karst is totally devoid of the charm that characterizes the rest of the Adriatic coast. The region is bare, barren and harsh, presenting to the eye vast stretches of limestone scoured by erosion, hollowed out by depressions and sub-sidence. No one would suspect the existence of a subterranean world, yet this area contains no less than 2,000 cavities of various kinds.

The finest and most famous of these are the caves of Pos-tojna (Adelsberg), fourteen miles in length. Up to 1818, only a small part, the Great Cathedral or Big Dome, was known. In subsequent years new and more magnificent caverns per-petually came to light, which are now the goal and delight of innumerable tourists on account of their singularity, beauty and extent.

The shady park before the entrance to the caves gives little hint of the marvels within. But once inside the cave the visi-tor is immediately astonished by the brilliantly-lit Great Cathedral, through which the underground River Piuka flows. This first hall has little in the way of dripstone forma-tions, but this lack is amply compensated by the halls that follow. The various formations have naturally received appropriate names. First one comes upon the Pulpit, the Butcher's Bench, the Waterfall, the Lion's Head, the Font, St. Peter's Chair, the Sarcophagus, etc.

From these small grottoes the visitor enters the Great Ballroom, one of the main sights of the cavern. For a hundred years balls have been held here at least twice a year, at Whitsun and on the first Sunday in September, often attended by as many as 15,000 people. After this, the beauty and singularity of the grottoes continually increases. The con-cretions include the Statue of the Virgin, the Leaning Tower of Pisa, the Abyss, the Tortoise, the Banner, the Palmtree, the Eagle's Wing, the Charcoal Kiln, and the Hayrick.

At the Tomb, a low dripstone formation resembling a canopy, the path divides. From here the visitor enters a veritable fairyland, shimmering with a multitude of hues ranging from dazzling white to the deepest purple. Here, too, the various items have received expressive names: the Iris Hall, Gothic Column, Shower of Rain, Crocodile, Icicle, Weeping Willow, etc. At the end of this section the elevated Belvedere gives a magnificent view of the dripstone formations. This is the home of the blind white proteus, which is to be found elsewhere only in the caves of Istria, Dalmatia and Herzegovina.

From the Belvedere the path leads through the Gate of Columns into the immense and sinister Concert Hall, the largest cavity in the Postojna caves. The ceiling is 154 feet from the floor and bears a number of splendid stalactites. A small cave opening out of the Concert Hall, the Owl Cave, holds an orchestra of about a hundred musicians. Another cavern houses the Cave Post Office, which was installed to deal with the tremendous postcard traffic. More than seventy thousand postcards are frequently despatched to the outside world from this post office in one day.

The visitor who thinks he has seen the best part of the cave is pleasantly surprised as he proceeds. From the Concert Hall a winding path leads into the great Forecourt of Hell with its wealth of columns, from which the visitor passes through the Chamber of Gems, distinguished by several splendid concretions, and comes first to the foot of Mount Calvary and then to the most precious treasure chamber of all the caverns of Postojna, Paradise. Geologists believe that the River Piuka, which washed out the interior of the mountain, once had its main course here. Every step in Paradise discloses a fresh marvel in stone. White crystals gleam in the pitchy darkness, slender stalagmite columns rise from the floor, the walls are decorated with undulating folds that shimmer white, yellow and red. At the bottom of pools yards deep, white and yellow crystal rhombohedra glisten, their beauty enhanced when rain on the surface of the earth fills the pools to the brim. There is an isolated column that rings when struck, and the sound echoes on through all the niches and little grottoes.

After passing this mass of concretions, the visitor enters a 300-foot connecting passage which leads to the artificial Bertarelli Gallery, 1,634 feet long, and the vast Black Chamber, which is 9,240 feet in length. In the 'twenties a new chamber opening out of this, the Piuka Chamber, was rendered accessible at very great expense.

From this point the path descends again to the foot of Mount Calvary. A multitude of stalagmite columns, each more splendid and brilliant than the next, rise from the 150-foot slope. In the cavern called Milan Cathedral stands a fifty-foot stalagmite column, the tallest in all the caves of Postojna.

At the foot of Mount Calvary, the wanderer is at the end of his journey and also at the terminus of the underground railway, which picks him up, weary from his long roam through fairyland, and carries him through the English Church, the Avenue of Columns, under the Fallen Column and past the Curtain—an especially delicate formation—to the exit.

The visitor emerges into the daylight drunk with looking at a fairyland that stretches several hours' walk beneath the mountain. Carmen Sylva, the poet, who once occupied the royal throne of Rumania, wrote after visiting the Grottoes of Postojna: 'The fairy-tale still has its kingdom under the earth.'

THE CARLSBAD CAVERN,
THE LARGEST CAVE IN THE WORLD

America, the land of unlimited opportunity, also possesses the biggest cave in the world, outstripping by far all its rivals. This cavern is situated in the State of New Mexico, some twenty-seven miles south-west of the little watering-place of Carlsbad (6,000 inhabitants), in the middle of the Carlsbad Caverns National Monument, an area of seventy-eight square miles declared a national park by President Coolidge in 1923. Within this area are numerous caves of all sizes, which are of great interest to archaeologists by virtue of the many sepulchres of America's aboriginal inhabitants they contain. The region has a desert landscape, and is celebrated for its exceptionally abundant cactus vegetation.

The stupendous cavern was discovered in 1901 by Texas-born Jim White, when he chanced to see a vast cloud of Mexican bats (*Tadarida mexicana*) swarming out of a cleft in the rocks. In the summer of the same year, he penetrated into the interior of the cave accompanied by a young Mexican cowboy, and so became the discoverer of the biggest cave in the world.

This prodigy of nature was not opened to the public until 1926, however. In this year, indirect lighting was installed in the cavern with 900 bulbs—and so skilfully has it been done that neither flex, nor switches, nor bulbs are visible. Nowhere are the natural colours affected by tinted lighting, as is the case in the stalactite caves of Sauerland. The concealed lighting sends its fifty to 50,000-watt rays into every nook and cranny. The power is supplied by a special generating station on the ridge above the cave, including that required to operate the two elevators, which cost $160,000 to install and are capable of taking 500 people an hour into the depths of the cavern in a few minutes. Next to the elevator shafts in the Empire Building, New York, those of the Carlsbad Cavern are the longest in the world.

The system of underground cavities at Carlsbad is enormously extensive, and up to the present only part of it has been explored. A particularly remarkable fact is the variation in level between the chambers. The cavity at the highest altitude lies about eight hundred and twenty feet below the surface. A second is roughly a thousand feet down, and a third approximately one thousand five hundred. The two

15

deepest cavities have not yet been explored, and of the whole system only thirty-four miles of galleries and chambers have been examined and measured. Of these thirty-four miles only seven miles are accessible to the public.

No important geological discoveries have been made in the cavities investigated. It has, however, been established that the humidity in the cavern is eighty-five to ninety-two per cent, and that it is impossible to make wireless transmissions.

The passages and larger chambers are distinguished by a great abundance of dripstones, some in the form of stalactites and stalagmites, others in the shape of spiral helictites. The multiplicity of minerals with which the rocks are impregnated have given the dripstone formations all the colours of the rainbow, from the lightest to the darkest yellowish-brown and including pink, green and purple, so that the Carlsbad Cavern is not only the largest but also the most colourful subterranean wonderland in the world. The air amongst these miraculous formations is so astonishingly pure and fresh that it seems as though nature has equipped this underground zone with its own heating and air-conditioning plant.

Each great cavity offers a surprise. In the Green Pond Room the attention is drawn by a jade-green pond full of crystal-clear water that gains an even more unearthly beauty when the artificial light is reflected in it. The King's Palace is a majestic circular hall 820 feet high and 170 feet in diameter, sparkling with dripstone formations. Not much farther on lies the Queen's Room, particularly remarkable for its curtain-like concretions. These formations, which hang from the roof in large numbers, are so delicate that it is hard to believe they are of stone. This hall contains another singular concretion—the Elephant's Ear, that gleams with the hues of pink and yellow roses when lit from behind. An impenetrable thicket of curious calcite formations, resembling a thorn hedge, also catches the eye.

As in every other cavern, each chamber has received a name appropriate to its shape and size, e.g. the Cathedral, or the Hall of Giants. Fireland, where the drying up of underground springs is thought to have caused the tips of the stalactites to become encrusted with crystals, is an absolute fairyland. These crystals hang down over little pools decked with concretions resembling lotus flowers or fungi.

From Fireland an undulating and winding path leads to a prodigious cavity, through which may be seen the second cavern, some thousand feet below the surface. After the crater, the path runs beside pools edged with transparent crystals, and Mirror Lake, a gigantic shimmering crystal formation, and finally reaches the Bottomless Pit, a chasm so deep that it defies measuring instruments.

The most impressive cavity open to visitors is the Big Room almost four thousand three hundred feet long and seven hundred feet wide, with a vaulted ceiling six hundred and sixty feet high. This gigantic chamber, lit by 50,000 watts, is twenty-five times as large as any other known cavern. Here, too, nature has created dripstone formations of all sizes, from the finest needle point to enormous stalactites and stalagmites. One of these stalagmites is nearly seventy feet tall with a circumference of sixteen feet; in shape it resembles the Leaning Tower of Pisa. This cavity is so vast that the whole Capitol at Washington could be placed inside it without touching the walls or ceiling. As though to emphasize her artistic caprice, nature has created alongside it a series of very small grottoes of unexampled splendour and beauty. Most striking of these are the Chinese Temple and the Sun Temple, whose concretions, perhaps the loveliest and most brilliant of all, look like the purest gold encrusted with precious stones.

Notwithstanding his practical turn of mind, the American is also able to appreciate and foster romantic sentimentalism. As a climax, at the end of the tour of the cavern, the lights go out and a male-voice choir is heard, first from a distance and then closer and closer, until it fills the halls like the notes of a gigantic organ. Generally, this is only a gramophone record, but the effect on the listener in the darkness of the cavern is none the less for that.

But the cavern administration has also not neglected the bodily well-being of the many thousands of visitors from all over the world. Weary from his long wandering, the sightseer can obtain refreshments at a gigantic restaurant 825 feet under the ground. No fewer than fifteen hundred people can be accommodated and fed in this unique subterranean inn. The hungry guests are served with great rapidity by means of lunch trays bearing bread and butter, cakes, oranges, nuts, cutlery and a paper table-napkin, and are inexorably guided to a bar-counter where beer, coffee, milk and lemonade are served. The old explorer of the cave, Jim White, was still living here in 1950 and running a stand at which he sold copies of his book on the cavern. He was set up in this business by the State, *honoris causa*, but the company exploiting the cave has a more profitable line.

THE CAVES OF THE GRANDS CAUSSES AND THE AVEN ARMAND

Let us now return to France, which is so rich in subterranean cavities. They occur everywhere, but are particularly numerous in the Pyrenees, where many have been explored by Norbert Casteret and already referred to in this book. There are still others, however, situated in regions where they were not suitable for prehistoric human habitation. Some of these caverns that spread their network several hundred yards below the surface are among the finest in the world. This is the case with the caves of the Causses, and especially with the Aven Armand.

The Causses (from Latin *calx*—lime) are lofty calcareous plateaux in the departments of Aveyron, Lozère, Gard and Hérault, on the western slopes of the Cévennes, with an area of some two thousand square miles. At the present time they form a desolate terrain whose formation must be explained if the genesis of their cavities is to be understood. For this, we must go back a very long way into the past to the end of the era known as the Palaeozoic.

A vast mountain system, represented in France by the Armoricain Massif, the Vosges, and the Massif Central, stretched across Europe. Like everything else, these mountains were subject to the action of time, and today only vestiges remain.

The rain and frost, the wind and waters little by little gnawed them away. The earth changed its shape and fractures developed.

At the beginning of the Jurassic Period, some 150 million years ago, a depression of the land surface took place in the area of the future Causses; the sea poured in and entirely new conditions prevailed.

The activity of certain living creatures that people this sea built up enormous masses of limestone over the ages. Other strata were formed by the accumulation of an immense quantity of debris from living creatures—shells and the skeletons of fish and molluscs mingled with clay on the sea-bed.

Then the seabed slowly rose, and in the areas that are now the Causses this former seabed, made up of layers of limestone mingled with clay and 3,000 feet thick in places, emerged: a new terrain was born.

The cycle began all over again. No sooner was this terrain born than it was exposed to the action of the elements as the old had been. Then, in the Tertiary epoch, a geological event shook the world: a series of gigantic folds developed in the earth's crust. First the Pyrenees, then the Alps. Wedged between these two upheavals, the region of the Causses was dislocated and fractured. The rivers rushed into them with all the vigour of youth. They formed the narrow gorges or canyons—some of them thirteen to sixteen hundred feet deep—that are a characteristic feature of the landscape of the Causses.

One of the potholes, or *avens*, hollowed out by underground rivers in this calcareous terrain, the Aven Armand, discovered by Louis Armand in 1897, may be numbered among the subterranean wonders of the world. It was opened to the public in 1927, after a tunnel 686 feet long had been cut in the steep and slippery hillside to facilitate access.

Passages have been dug to make it easier to admire the more remarkable mineral formations, while electric lighting shows them up and adds to the fairyland quality of this subterranean world.

This cavern was explored at length by E. A. Martel, one of the greatest speleologists the world has ever known. His energy and courage were extraordinary. He travelled through almost the whole of Europe, visiting the most famous caves in Britain, Germany, Austria, Spain and Italy, discovering new cavities or fresh chambers. In France, besides the regions of Vercors and Devoluy, which he studied at length, he explored the area of the Causses, revealing the subterranean riches of a hitherto little-known region. It may also be noted that Martel was one of the first to descend the Grand Canyon of Verdon and draw the attention of the authorities to the touristic interest of this zone.

'The Aven Armand abyss,' writes Martel, 'begins with a perpendicular shaft two hundred and fifty feet deep. It opens out into an immense oval chamber a hundred and sixty-five feet wide by four hundred feet long. Its floor is sloping and bristles with a forest of four hundred stalagmites, three to a hundred feet in height. The fairy-like appearance and fantastic shapes of these trees of calcium carbonate, baptized collectively the Virgin Forest because of their miraculous preservation, is impossible to describe or imagine. It really constitutes the apotheosis of caverns. No cave in the world possesses anything like it, for the tallest stalagmites known anywhere else do not exceed seventy-five feet.

Twenty to thirty of these monoliths reach a height of seventy feet; they are so close together that in places it is impossible to pass between their extravagant trunks; several of them measure up to ten feet thick. Others, by contrast, are veritable fragile tapers only two or three inches in diameter and several yards in height.'

A second shaft in the north-east of the pothole goes 320 feet deeper.

THE HENNE MORTE (1943)

Norbert Casteret had already made a number of attempts to explore this gigantic chasm, situated at the eastern extremity of the Paloumère limestone chain, in the Massif d'Arbas, in 1940, when he reached a depth of 1,140 feet. He returned to the attack in 1943, with a fresh team. All went well until the expedition reached 825 feet. At this point one of its members, Claude Maurel, fell into a waterfall that tumbled down one of the pitches. Although his fall was broken by a pool of water, Maurel had nevertheless crushed his helmet and fractured an arm. After this accident there was nothing for it but to halt the expedition and get the injured man, who was in great pain and practically helpless, back to the surface.

His companions had succeeded in hoisting him on to a projecting rock, when one of those treacherous stones that cause so many accidents detached itself from the top of the shaft and caught another member of the team, Marcel Loubens. The latter, wounded in the head and with a shoulder-blade and four ribs broken, fainted. The situation was desperate. The two injured men had to be brought to the surface from a depth of 825 feet. It is easy enough to imagine the agony of these two men and their rescuers, roped together, tied up, dangling at the end of a rope and deluged by the icy shower of the waterfalls that flowed down the pothole.

The team spent thirty-five hours without food and virtually without light during the last few hours, because of the unexpected duration of the expedition below ground. But thanks to the courage of every one of them, all the members of the expedition came out alive.

The exploration of the Henne Morte was resumed in 1946 and 1947, when the bottom of the chasm was reached at a depth of 1,463 feet. In the course of this expedition, and for the first time, an underground camp was set up 825 feet down, enabling its sixteen members to make preparations for the second half of the descent. This time the team remained underground for 130 hours.

Casteret and Loubens took part, and once more the latter suffered a nasty mishap. While he was clinging to a ladder, he lost his balance and found himself hanging upside down at the end of the safety rope. As an added disaster, his acetylene lamp set fire to his overalls.

The position would have been tragic, but for the presence of mind with which he set his rope swinging and so reached the waterfall, where he put out the incipient blaze.

8

THE UNDERGROUND
WORLD OF SALT

THE HALLEIN SALT MINES OF SALZBURG

IN salt mines that have been worked since time immemorial it is impossible to tell whether nature first created caves in the salt. It is at least probable that water hollowed out cavities and that these led men to deposits of this valuable mineral.

Salt has been for thousands of years one of the most important mineral products of the province of Salzburg in Austria. The town and province of Salzburg, as well as the River Salzach and the Salzkammergut mountains in the same region, all derive their names from the word *Salz*, meaning salt. The ancient implements found in the shafts and adits are dumb but eloquent witnesses to the antiquity of salt mining in this area. The Illyrians already mined in Salzburg with great technical skill, and when the Celts drove out the original inhabitants in the La Tène period they intensified the mining industry and began to trade in salt. Then the Romans came, destroyed the Celtic kingdom of Noricum, and founded Juvavum, now the town of Salzburg. The Romans called the Celts Alaui, which means 'salt-men'.

With the collapse of the Roman Empire, salt-mining in Salzburg also came to an end. It was recommenced in the eighth century by Bishop Rupert, and the gratitude of the population was such that they made him patron saint of salt mining. He is always represented holding a barrel of salt. At that time the Salzburg salt trade covered a wide area, extending to Switzerland, the Rhine, via Bamberg to Fulda, to Silesia, Bohemia, Moravia and Hungary. This not inconsiderable commerce in a single product finally led, in 1123, to the founding of the town of Hallein, where the salt-works of the reigning prince were established.

The mountain that contains the salt mines and to which our attention is here directed is the Dürnberg, which looks out over the salt town of Hallein, the church of pilgrimage of Maria Plain, and the smiling valley in which Hallein lies. The entry to the salt grottoes is below the chapel of pilgrimage erected by Wolf Dietrich and Marcus Sitticus in the seventeenth century. The so-called Mouth-Hole gives access to a timber-clad adit several hundred yards long which dates from 1450. After passing through two trap-doors, which are there for ventilation purposes, the visitor finds himself immersed in the air of the mine which here, as in most caverns, has a constant temperature—in this case about 43° F. He soon comes upon the first traces of salt mingled with sandstone, marl, anhydrite and clay. The deeper he penetrates into the interior the more frequent become the veins of salt; they are not pure, however, but streaked with red, brown and grey. This visit calls for some exertion, for the total volume of the Dürnberg salt mine is equivalent to a cavity more than a mile and a quarter in length, just under a mile in width and a thousand feet in depth.

The system of driving galleries into the mountain is the same as in any other type of mine. These adits—also known as horizons—have been cut at various levels approximately a hundred to a hundred and thirty feet one above the other. Numerous secondary tunnels branching off from them lead to the salt. The salt is obtained by dissolving the mineral in water and then collecting and boiling the resultant brine.

The brine obtained by dissolving the salt underground—which creates cavities—is pumped through pipes to the refineries at Hallein.

Unlike other mines, the Salzburg salt mines are open to the public. The visitor who wishes to go down into these pits has to muster up his courage, for the initial descent is made along two slides of tree trunks, the first 106 feet long and inclined at an angle of 45°, the second 200 feet long at an angle of 50°. This is a very ancient method of descent which was in general use before the introduction of the pit-cage. The miners wear a leather apron—at the back instead of the front—on which they sit to slide down into the mine.

The first thing to meet the visitor's eye after he has gone down these two slides is one of the strangest museums in the world, containing all the objects and implements—shovels, pickaxes, hafts, axes, stone hammers, torches, pieces of leather, and ornaments—dropped in the shafts and galleries two or three thousand years ago and recovered during the process of dissolving the salt.

In 1576, the corpse of a Celt was found perfectly preserved by the salt. This body gave Ludwig Ganghofer the idea for his novel, *Der Mann im Salz*.

A third slide descends deeper into the mountain, to the black salt lake 330 feet long, 230 feet wide and six to ten feet deep, which lies in a huge cavern whose walls are incrusted with salt and gleam with fairy-like splendour as they reflect the light.

But this is not yet the deepest point in the salt mine. A fourth slide takes the visitor to the Commemoration Chamber, which houses a bust of Bishop Rupert and other memorials connected with the history of the mine, as well as a plan showing the extent of this subterranean world of salt. Down the fifth and last slide the visitor comes to the lowest point in the mine, 1,500 feet below the surface, from which he enters the 7,000-foot-long Wolf Dietrich gallery, which Archbishops Wolf Dietrich and Paris-Lodron opened in

1638 after forty-two years had been spent digging it. A truck takes the visitor back to daylight again.

THE WILICZKA SALT MINES

There are also important salt mines in Poland, near the town of Wiliczka, where this mineral has been extracted for centuries in the usual manner. It has been claimed that the length of these chambers and galleries is equal to the distance from Cracow to Vienna, i.e. over 200 miles. The mine, which is altogether 1,000 feet deep, is divided into seven levels. The whole salt-bed stretches so far that it joins that of Bochnia, the second largest salt mine in Galicia.

The beginnings of these salt mines lie far in the past. They are first mentioned in a document which is said to date from 1044. According to another tradition, the presence of salt in this region was first discovered around 1233 by a shepherd named Wilicz, after whom the town was named. Casimir the Great ordered the methodical extraction of the salt in the fourteenth century, and August II imported Saxon miners to increase the output. The beds of salt are here sandwiched between layers of clayey marl, anhydrite and sandstone. During the mining, strong pillars of salt are left standing to carry the roof. Some of the salt is obtained in pure form and can enter commerce after merely being ground, while the rest is impure and has to be refined for consumption by boiling.

What gives the subterranean world its individual note is the existence of a large number of caverns and chambers, many of them of imposing dimensions, containing religious statues carved from the salt. The oldest of these chambers, on the first level, dates from 1700. The so-called Chapel, which dates from the nineteenth century, and is 330 feet below the surface, is eighty feet high, seventy feet wide and seventy feet long. Everything in this singular chapel, apart from the seats, is made of salt—the ceilings, the walls, and even the chandelier, which is composed of salt crystals with the transparency of glass. The statues, of all sizes, glow with a magical refulgence when a light is lit behind them. All these statues, for example the figures of Saint Kunigunde, patron saint of the town and the miners, Saint Barbara, and all the many reliefs on the walls, were carved by miners. Another chapel has been established 440 feet down, in which the miners say a prayer before going on their shift.

Like those of Hallein, the Wiliczka salt mines are open to the public. The visitor passes through a multitude of caverns, one of which attains the imposing height of 110 feet. The roofs of the large chambers are supported by pillars of salt five feet thick. The water from the otherwise extremely dry mine gathers at its lowest level in a sinister-looking black lake twenty-six feet deep and with a thirty-two per cent salt content. The water from this lake is pumped up to the surface for utilization. One exceptionally large cavern is set aside for the entertainment of visitors on Sundays. A miners' orchestra plays for dancing and as the salty air makes people hungry and thirsty the refreshments on sale are in great demand.

Poland has a good many other caves, apart from the salt mines, though none of them are very large. The majority occur in the Tatra Mountains and the Cracovian Jura. This district contains more than seven hundred, of which only a few are of any size. The biggest Polish cavern, the Kasprova Niznia, is about three-quarters of a mile long; the Mietusia cave in the Tatras is 150 yards long. Scientific exploration of the Polish caverns began in 1870, when Jan Zawisza made a wealth of archaeological discoveries in the caves of Ojcow, including remains of mammoth.

The continued emergence of vestiges of the past in caves led to a steady growth of interest in speleology. Other Polish workers, such as Ossowski, Krukowski, Czarnowski, Wrzodek and Cietak, devoted themselves to various aspects of the subject. Although Polish caverns contain only a limited recent fauna, they are a fruitful field for ecological research, in which Demel and Stach have been particularly active.

After the Second World War, the Polish Museum of Archaeology began, in collaboration with the speleologist, K. Kowalski, to draw up an inventory of Polish caves, the first volume of which has already appeared (Kasimierz Kowalski: *Jaskinie Polski*, Polish Museum of Archaeology, Warsaw, 1951). This book discusses the origin and development, the fossil and recent fauna, the climate, the flora, and the significance to man of 508 caves. It also gives an extensive bibliography of speleological literature, most of it dealing with the technique of caving, and a list of biological works, the majority of them by French, German and Austrian writers.

When the second volume has appeared, Poland will probably be the first and only country to possess a complete and detailed survey of its caves.

9

THE UNDERWORLD OF ETERNAL ICE

THE FORMATION OF ICE CAVERNS

THE formation of ice is one of the most curious phenomena that takes place in caves. Whether the temperature outside is that of the coldest winter, or whether the sun is scorching the naked rock with its rays, the same cold reigns within the cavern and the ice here has an eternal character. It is erroneous to suppose that this ice dates from the Ice Age, but it is very possible that it began to form at a time when temperature conditions in our latitudes were different from what they are today. But, like giant refrigerators, these caves form, maintain, renew, and even increase the ice, regardless of the outside temperature.

A number of scientific treatises dealing with ice caverns were written during the nineteenth century. In the 'nineties, Professor Eberhard Fugger of Salzburg assembled a complete bibliography of these works. Before this, Professor Bruno Schwalbe of Berlin had written a good deal on the subject as well as compiling bibliographies. A number of divergent theories on the formation of the ice in caves were current at that time. It was variously attributed to the storing up of winter cold, the cooling of water as it filtered through fine fissures, loss of heat due to evaporation, diminution of temperature resulting from the solution of salts, a survival from the Ice Age, etc. Fugger himself, after close study, drew up a list of no fewer than twenty-one conditions that must be satisfied before an ice cavern could form, that is to say a cavern in which the ice is permanent.

The most famous of these, the Eisriesenwelt (Ice-Giant World) in Austria, is a wind tunnel or dynamic ice cavern, in which the air is in perpetual circulation. It can be pictured as a branch from which vertical shafts rise like twigs. In summer the relatively cold air of the cavern escapes into the open, and the warmer outside air is sucked in down the shafts, where it is rapidly cooled against the cold rock. This process is clearly perceptible to the visitor through the strong wind that continually blows past him. In winter the process is reversed: the warm air of the cavern escapes, and the cold outside air is sucked in. When the interior and exterior temperature have reached equality, the wind drops and there is a momentary lull, which is soon broken as the previous conditions reassert themselves.

The deepest section of the cavern is the coldest, and the warm air from outside is so cooled by the time it reaches this section that it has no effect on the ice. At the end of the winter, when the temperature in the cave has reached its lowest level, the snow on the crest and slopes of the mountain melts and filters down into the interior, where it is turned into ice. The Eisriesenwelt is an example of perennial ice formation in an ascending gallery. Ice also forms in descending galleries, where the mouth is higher than the rest of the cavern, which stores the cold. Examples of this are the Kolowrath Cave in the Untersberg, and the Seeofen in the Tennengebirge.

The ice in these ice caverns is everlasting; it never melts away completely, although the shapes are perpetually changing. As in dripstone caves, water is the magician that conjures up every imaginable shape—columns, towers, bells, ramparts, gates, waterfalls, icebergs, curtains, cones, banners, crystals, frost, etc. When the water contains minerals, the ice is shot through with colours that vary from emerald green to azure blue.

Amongst the changing shapes assumed by the ice special mention must be made of the so-called *Eismandln* (ice men), curious natural statues which often occur in large groups, when they present a strangely moving sight. The temperature is not uniform at all levels of ice caverns. The lower levels are colder than the upper. A drop of falling water is cooled on its way down and frozen to ice on reaching the bottom. A succession of such drops forms a column, which continues to grow until it has reached the zone of warm air. Growth then comes to a stop, but the drops continue to fall and the tip broadens out into a head, creating the likeness of a human figure.

Another curiosity of these caverns is the *Eisauspressungen* (extruded ice), to which attention has been drawn by the Austrian speleologist Erik Arnberger. According to his description (*Die Höhle*, No. 2, 1950), these are bundles of icicles several inches thick and four to eight inches long in places, resembling glass-wool in appearance and structure. Arnberger found them on very porous stones permeated with water. He explains their formation as follows:

When the outside temperature is persistently cold, that of the sections of the cavern close to the entrance gradually falls, and may remain for several days below freezing point. The surface of the porous stones becomes covered in a very fine frost. The water that fills the capillary interstices inside the deposit is also turned into filaments of ice; the consequent increase in volume causes these filaments to protrude from the deposit, where they freeze together in bundles. At the same time, these protruding filaments may lift portions of the frost on the outside of the stone. This process continues until either all the water inside the stone is frozen solid, so that the bundles of filaments are thrust farther and farther out, or until the temperature rises above freezing point again. The curve in these bundles is doubtless to be explained by the variation in the water content of the sediments in different parts of the stone, which results in the rods of ice squeezed out of a small section of the frozen surface of the sediment attaining very dif-

16

ferent lengths in the same period of time. Since the rods are frozen together into bundles, the variation in growth causes the whole bundle to incline towards the side on which the increase in length is least.

Ice caverns are not so numerous as dripstone grottoes, because very special climatic conditions are necessary to enable them to develop. Some, particularly in Austria, attain colossal dimensions. Besides the Eisriesenwelt in the Tennengebirge, Austria possesses the following ice caverns: the Sulzenofen, the Almberg ice grotto near Obertraun (6,220 feet), the Eiskogelhöhle, the Kolowrathhöhle, the Dachstein-Rieseneishöhle where a funicular railway was installed in 1951, and the Schwarzmooskegelhöhle in the Todesgebirge. In the ice caverns of Demenova, in the Lower Tatra (Slovakia), vast underground chambers were opened up by blasting after the First World War; they end in a subterranean lake.

The best-known ice cavern in Germany is that of Schellenberg, which will be described in the next section. Caves which contain temporary formations of ice occur in the Harz Mountains, the Eifel plateau, the Siebengebirge, and Franconian Switzerland. The ice cavern at the highest altitude in Europe (8,910 feet) is the Grotte Casteret, which took its name from the great French speleologist. This will be the third to be described, following the Austrian Eisriesenwelt.

THE SCHELLENBERG ICE CAVERN

The huge mountain mass of the Untersberg, the northernmost watchtower of the Berchtesgaden district, is surrounded by legends. It consists mainly of dolomite and triassic limestone, and contains a number of caves. On the northern flank of the mountain is the Kolowrath cave, on the plateau near the Mittagscharte the Kleiner Eiskeller (Little Ice-Cellar), on the way from Veitbruch to the Klinger Alp the

Windlöcher (Wind Holes), and at the bottom of the eastern face, between the Mittagscharte and the southern wall of the Salzburg Hochthron, the most remarkable of all: the Schellenberg Ice Cavern, which is visited by some ten thousand tourists annually. Many of the natural cavities of the Untersberg are rock shelters, or have not yet been explored.

The ice cavern is about three hours' journey from the charming little town of Schellenberg in the south-east corner of Bavaria, to the north-east of which rises the gigantic wall of the Untersberg. A considerable climb is required to reach this cavern, since it lies at quite an altitude.

It has been known for a very long time by shepherds, hunters and mountaineers. The Bavarian General-Staff map of 1826 shows it as the Eisloch, or Ice Hole, the name by which it is still popularly known today. The first tourist to visit the cave, in 1874, was A. von Posselt-Czorich from Salzburg, who was also the first to enter the Eisriesenwelt. Posselt wrote of the cave in the *Zeitschrift des Deutschen und Österreichischen Alpenvereins* (1880), but made only a quick sketch during his first visit. In 1876 Professor Eberhard Fugger, who also discovered a new entrance, made a more accurate plan. In 1879 the Salzburg Alpine Club improved the path to the cavern, and the same year Posselt re-entered it. Posselt has left a description of this second visit. Armed with crampons, lanterns, magnesium lamps and ropes he ventured down into the deep chambers, after cutting steps and tunnels with an ice-axe. He made a third expedition in 1879. After this, nothing more was heard of the Schellenberg Ice Cavern until 1912, when Alexander von Mörk, noted for his exploration of the Eisriesenwelt, penetrated its lower chambers in his turn.

The entrance to the cavern is a great cleft in the rock sixty-six feet wide and thirteen feet high, from which a moderately steep snow slope that broadens on both sides as it goes down leads to the floor ice of the Josef Ritter von Angermaier Hall. This cavity was named after a celebrated speleologist on the occasion of the opening ceremony in 1925. Angermaier continued to visit the cavern when in his seventies.

This hall, which is 230 feet square and twenty-six feet high, is largely covered with ice. In front of the entry to the Fugger Hall stands a gigantic blunt cone of ice, while the roof above it is pierced by a huge cavity like a funnel into which several smaller ones run. The rock must have been worn away by a powerful flow of water from the mountain, mingled with rock debris. Today only a meagre trickle comes through the opening. In cold years this trickle causes the cone to grow to a height of thirty feet, while ice stalagmites form round it from the water that splashes off. A large stalactite of ice often forms on the ceiling, only to break off with the advent of summer. A number of icicles on the wall in the western section of the chamber, likewise formed by dripping water, recall organ pipes.

The fifty-foot cascades of ice, the frost formations, and the ice walls that gleam like diamonds in the light of magnesium lamps, are particularly striking. The Fugger Hall, though only forty by fifty-three feet in area, is fifty feet high. Its floor is ice, as smooth as glass, and in the centre stands a thirteen-foot cone of ice that sometimes develops rudimentary branches at its apex.

The Fugger Hall is followed by a number of singular chambers. Behind the cone a wall of ice rises to Mörk's Cathedral. A narrow cleft leads into the Ice-Crystal Chamber decorated with sparkling ice crystals. In a south-westerly direction the path leads into the sections of the cavern that have not yet been opened up. These include the Max Gadringer Hall under the Fugger Hall, into which the visitor cannot go but to which the guide descends to light a magnesium torch. This shines up through the thirty-foot thick floor of ice with spectacular effect.

Mörk's Cathedral, named after Alexander von Mörk, is distinguished less by its area than by its height. A semicircular wall of ice twenty-five by thirty feet in area extends from one end to the other, enclosing an altar of ice fifty feet high which presents a marvellous wealth of shapes. A dim twilight penetrates from above through two small holes in the ceiling of ice, and there is a sound like that of low organ music, produced by trickling water.

Amongst the parts of the cavern not open to the public because they are dangerous to cross are the Spiral Staircase, a thirty-foot corkscrew tunnel made by erosion, the Chimney Labyrinth, the Frost Passage, the ninety-foot Deml Passage, the Thomas Shaft leading to the Max Gadringer Hall, and the Muddy Passage. The work accomplished by the forces of nature in these inaccessible parts of the cavern is even more grandiose than in the sections open to the visitor.

THE EISRIESENWELT IN THE TENNENGEBIRGE

The Tennengebirge, between the Salzburg Alps and the Dachsteingebirge, contains one of the most spectacular natural phenomena in the world: the Eisriesenwelt, the largest of all ice caverns and a place of extraordinary beauty.

The speleologist Anton von Posselt-Czorich entered it for the first time in 1879, accompanied by a hunter, and penetrated to about six hundred and sixty feet. It was probably the first time man had ever set foot in this mysterious subterranean cavity, to which a hidden cleft in the rock gives access. As he stepped inside, the speleologist was met by a violent, snarling, icy wind, the origin of which has remained to this day unexplained. Leaving his companion behind, von Posselt-Czorich clambered boldly over boulders and scree into the interior of the cavern by the light of a torch. What he saw in this flickering light caused him to shudder. He entered first a hundred-foot-high chamber shimmering with a glassy green that opened fanwise like a widening waterfall. His reactions were those of every speleologist whose senses have been rendered abnormally acute by the silence and the solitude, giving stimulus to his imagination. He saw greenish-white giants emerging into the light cast by his torch and then retiring into the darkness again. The sound of his footsteps rang hollow and weird against the walls, as though in a tomb, echoing a hundredfold in the dark nooks and crannies where the dim light of his torch could not penetrate. Then the light was reflected by myriads of ice crystals on a wall of ice enveloping a gigantic rock that barred his path. He was forced to turn about. Posselt recounted all that he had seen and experienced in the *Jahrbuch des Alpenvereins*.

For thirty-two years no one else felt inclined to disturb the silence of this treacherous and eerie world of ice. Then, in 1912, the twenty-one year old art student, Alexander von Mörk—who later became the founder of modern speleology in Salzburg—happened to come across Posselt-Czorich's essay as he was browsing through the papers of the Alpine Society. This aroused a desire to see the subterranean wonderland for himself. He entered the cavern with a number of like-minded friends, was met by the same howling wind as he stepped inside, and saw the same scene as that described by his predecessor. But he too got no farther than the wall of ice holding the rock in its grip. After this first trip he was uncertain whether this represented the end of the ice-world, or whether yet more secrets were waiting behind the rampart of ice.

The following spring, Mörk organized a second expedition in collaboration with his friends Angermeyer and Riehl. This time they armed themselves with ice-axes and climbing-irons, in order to scale the barricade of ice. In the usual manner of mountaineers, they cut step after step in the glassy wall and slowly climbed towards the top. When they reached it, Mörk saw to his amazement that it was indeed not the end of the cavern. Behind it a fairy kingdom of unimaginable loveliness that had never before been seen by human eye was revealed by the light of the lanterns. The floor was pure crystalline ice, shimmering with all the colours of the spectrum; the ice of the walls, streaked with yellow ochre, flashed like tongues of flame.

The intrepid explorers advanced over the glistening surface of ice crystals. Once more they were confronted by ice giants, towering figures whose heads were lost in the shadows. The three friends pressed on into the unknown between these seventy-foot towers of ice. Then, amidst the eerie silence of this frozen world, there echoed a roaring sound. Was it another subterranean gale that had been blowing its monotonous organ note for thousands of years? The farther they advanced, the louder grew the sound. Then they found themselves on the edge of a small lake, whose waves came splashing angrily towards them. The cause of the roaring soon became apparent. It was indeed a subterranean gale, which stirred up the waves on the lake and threatened to blow out their lanterns. At one point, the ceiling came down to within a short distance of the surface of the water, and through the narrow space between rock and water the wind was whistling into the cavern, disturbing the surface of the lake, which for the moment barred their progress.

They returned three weeks later with a diving-suit, with which von Mörk crossed the ice water. On the other bank he beheld a spectacle of fairy-like splendour, before which everything the cavers had seen till then paled into insignificance.

But still their equipment did not permit them to wrest from the cave its ultimate secret. The two excursions had whetted their appetites, however, and they made plans to explore the whole of the cavern. A new assault on the eternal ice was to be made in August, 1914. But the First World War broke out and the young speleologist was sent to the Front, from which he was destined never to return. He fell during the first year of war. In 1925, his earthly remains were interred in an urn within the cavern, of which he must be regarded as the true discoverer.

After the War, other bold and enthusiastic speleologists

returned to the exploration of the Eisriesenwelt, amongst them Walter von Czoernig-Czernhausen, Dr. Friedrich Oedl, Dr. Robert Oedl, Hermann Gruber, and Gustav Abel. They forced their way to the very end of the vast labyrinth of ice, of which twenty-five miles have now been explored.

The road to the cavern was not freed until the lake which Mörk crossed in the diving-suit had been drained. Here a new wonder meets the eye, the Utgardsburg, a chamber with a magnificent vaulted roof, from which a crystal gate gives access to a huge cleft whose walls sparkle emerald-green in the light of the lamp. Beyond this cleft lies a chamber 130 feet high and of indescribable beauty, to which its discoverers gave the name Alexander von Mörk in honour of the first speleologist to penetrate into the depths of the cavern.

Today the Eisriesenwelt is one of Austria's most famous sights. The construction of paths and the building of the Friedrich Oedl Hotel close to the entrance, at an altitude of 5,191 feet, have opened the cavern to tourists. From the hotel there is a breathtaking view of the Alpine landscape with all its valleys, mountains and rocks.

The Eisriesenwelt has a sister at the same altitude, the former Sulzenofen, now called the Czoernig Ice Cavern after the great speleologist Baron von Czoernig-Czernhausen, who explored and surveyed some thousand grottoes. This cavern is appreciably smaller than the Eisriesenwelt and does not link up with it.

The entrance of the Eisriesenwelt is immediately behind the Oedl Hotel, a yawning chasm seventy feet high and fifty feet wide that gapes in the tall, smooth wall of the Hochkogel. After mounting a steep stairway the visitor reaches the oval mouth of the cavern, where, on warm summer days, he is met by an icy blast from the interior. This huge oval window looks out on the Achselkopf with the pincer-shaped rocks between which the visitor has just passsed, and beyond this to the snow-covered peaks of the Gasteiner Tauern.

There is no electric lighting in the Eisriesenwelt. Instead visitors are supplied with carbide lamps which enable them to find their way through the icy labyrinth. The floor of the entrance is covered all over with smooth and shining ice. The path leads up into the interior at an angle of 25°. The colossal wall of ice that Alexander von Mörk once scaled with crampons can now be crossed more easily by steps and a wire rope. Since the floor of ice has continuously risen since the cavern was first entered, the path to Hymir's Hall, behind the wall of ice, can only be traversed bending down. Alexander von Mörk himself gave outstanding spots in the cavern names taken from the legend of Thor's journey to the ice giants. Hymir's Hall is dominated by the mighty Hymir's Castle. The hall lies across the axis of the cavern and is linked with a system of overhead passages, from which huge rivers of ice descend with gigantic cones of ice standing between them. If a magnesium lamp is lit behind these rivers they emit a magical greenish-white effulgence. Hymir's Castle consists of an ice formation rising from the ground topped by an enormous mass of ice shaped like a bunch of grapes, which is perpetually fed by water trickling through a crack in the rock above. This long fissure is the source of the whole compact mass of ice from here to the Posselt Hall, including the great rampart of ice.

The path leads on to Friga's Veil in the Nifl Heim, an ever-changing ice formation, then to Odin's Hall, and finally to a primeval landscape made up of gigantic blocks fallen from the roof. Against the wall may be seen a regular formation of ice known as the Bell. In the Asen Heim stands a throne-like formation called the Castle of the Gods. The cold blue-green of the walls is marked by rust-red streaks caused by ferruginous water that oozes in through cracks in the rock. These streaks glow like red flames in the shadows.

The wind still wails in Thyrm's Hall (called after Thyrm, the storm giant of the Eddas) as it did when the ground was covered by a two-foot-deep lake, through which von Mörk waded and which was later drained. A narrow tunnel leads to Ice Gate, the highest point in the cavern, 400 feet above the entrance, where the most magnificent and varied ice formations may be seen, frequently covered with a thick layer of frost that looks like a white fur embellished with diamonds.

From here a steep stairway runs down into the finest chamber of the Eisriesenwelt, which bears the name of the cavern's discoverer: Alexander Mörk's Cathedral. The Ice Gate continues as a huge wall built up in vertical layers, in which the wind, laden with fine particles of sand, has worn niches. Air bubbles enclosed in the layers of ice by the rapidity with which they froze, and looking like bunches of grapes, add to the singular charm of the path that leads to Mörk's Cathedral.

The Cathedral itself, where the marble urn containing the speleologist's ashes rests on a stone altar, is the largest chamber of the Eisriesenwelt. Even a magnesium flare cannot illumine it fully. The size of the hall is the result of several rifts converging on a field of debris from the roof that slopes up towards the north and is bounded on the west by a huge wall of limestone furrowed by channels cut and dissolved by trickles of water.

Opening out of Mörk's Cathedral is the last great hall, the Ice Palace, whose floor is covered in spring with a mirror-like surface of ice, which takes on marvellous reflections when flooded with water during the summer thaw. The Ice Palace is situated 2,300 feet from the entrance. Only a small section of the vast subterranean labyrinth is accessible to the sightseer. An excursion through the additional sections of the cavern would take eight to ten hours. These include the labyrinthine Midgard Passage, the Dome of Terror, the Vertical Canyon, the Kingdom of Diamonds, the Stalactite Dome, the labyrinth of the Slippery Tunnel, the Avalanche Dome, the Mount of Fools, Hades, the Poldi Dome, the

Watchtower, the Erwin Tunnel, Robert's Drop, etc. Even after the Second World War many new chambers were discovered, but they can be entered only by tourists of great persistence and stamina.

THE GROTTE CASTERET

Ice caverns exist all over the world, especially in regions subject to great variations of temperature, e.g. the Alps, the Jura, the Caucasus, and probably in other parts of the world, quite apart from the many caves in zones of ice and snow, which are of little interest to the speleologist. Ice caves in the sense in which he uses the word are subterranean cavities that contain permanent ice formations, independently of the external temperature. One of the most remarkable of the large ice caverns in Europe is that discovered by Norbert Casteret, after the First World War, in the Massif de Gavarnie, part of the Pyrenees. This cave, which lies in the heart of the Monte Perdido massif, is particularly noteworthy because no one had hitherto suspected that there were any ice caverns in the Pyrenees and also because, at an altitude of 8,910 feet, it is one of the highest frozen caves on earth—except for those which may later be found in the eternally ice-covered Himalayas.

The Massif de Gavarnie had been explored and examined by any number of alpinists, geographers, geologists, hunters and naturalists since it was first investigated by Ramon de Carbonnières in 1787. It was reserved for Casteret to discover this frozen cavern which, in many respects, is the equal of the two that have just been described.

'This time,' writes Casteret of his discovery, 'when we reached the vestibule, it did not turn out, as they so often do, to be a mere overhang—it admitted us to the loveliest and most fantastic cavern I had ever explored. A snow ledge and great rubble-heap still hid the inside of the cavern, but when we had surmounted this obstacle we could not hold back a shout. At our feet was a frozen underground lake, and a river of ice came from the bowels of the mountain beyond it.

'The huge chamber was bathed in a strange, slanting, bluish-green light. There were many green-grey reflections on walls and ice. Mysterious noises came from within, heralding the icy wind that blew in our faces. Where the wind met the warm outside air there was a faint mist, through which the frontier ridge, with the Brèche de Roland notch, appeared dramatically framed in the cavern mouth.' (*Ten Years under the Earth*.)

This was a wind of the same nature as that which met the explorers of the Eisriesenwelt, and like them Casteret was confronted by one surprise after another as he penetrated deeper into the cavern. With the audacity that has characterized all his speleological explorations, Casteret crossed the frozen lake and discovered, beyond the point at which the frozen river curved down into it, a subterranean glacier covering 8,400 square yards (nearly an acre and three-quarters), the walls and roof of which were decorated with ice fringes and stalactites.

On his second visit Casteret explored the huge hall which he and his companions had glimpsed on the first occasion. Its roof was a single unbroken vault spanning an ice-floor which he estimated at 3,350 square yards. Huge blocks fallen from the ceiling were set in the ice, which was so clear that tiny pebbles could be seen distinctly at a depth of six or seven feet. This gigantic chamber is furnished with a perpetual influx of ice by water that flows in through cracks in the ceiling and is immediately frozen. One such stream has been frozen to a towering cascade of translucent ice sixty or eighty feet high, the top of which is lost to sight in the darkness.

The cutting, icy wind that met Casteret every time he entered the cavern led him to believe that it must have a second opening, which produced the current of air and led to the freezing of the water flowing from above. On examina-

tion it proved that the water in a lateral cave, not penetrated
by the icy blast, did not freeze. Casteret emerged through
this second opening which lies, opposite the entrance, on the
eastern slope in the midst of 'a wild confusion which the
geologists call *lapiaz*—a name which speaks volumes to anyone who has ever tried to cross such a formation. A slice of
bread has fewer holes than lapiaz, with its chasms, oubliettes,
trap-holes, fissures, tunnels, funnels, knife-like ridges.'
Lapiaz is a particularly difficult terrain to cross. In this case
it covers an area of 100 acres. All the holes in this lapiaz
communicate through a series of chambers, domes, corridors,
and branches fifteen to thirty feet below the ground. From
October to the end of June it is shrouded in snow, which
slowly melts during the remaining three months and pours
down into the lowest cavities of the cave, where it is frozen
to ice by the low temperature induced by the icy wind. In
holes and hollows a few yards below the lapiaz, into which
the sun never penetrates, the snow remains all the year
round. In some of the chambers the snow forms great cones
corresponding in size to the holes overhead. Melted snow
and the water trickling in from above form treacherous pools
of clear water which are invisible in the white snow.

Of his second exploration, made in the company of his
wife, Casteret writes: 'We spent a total of three weeks on it,
living on bread and cheese and glacier water, shivering
under the stars and baking under the Spanish noonday sun.
I have no hesitation in saying that this extraordinary region
of the Monte Perdido in the Aragonese Pyrenees still has
many surprises in store for anyone who will get off the beaten
track, and methodically explore this stony desert.'

I O

MAN RETURNS TO THE CAVERNS

FLIGHT INTO THE UNDERWORLD

At all periods caves have served as places of refuge for those in flight, for those who feared the daylight, who were in conflict with the authority of the State, plotting rebellion, or persecuted because of their religious or political views. Many such cases have been quoted in preceding chapters. In our own day, caverns have been more widely used as refuges than ever before. The collective flight into the depths of the earth began when the fury of war was unleashed over Europe and terrified individuals sought to protect their lives and belongings from the explosive and incendiary bombs raining down from the sky. They welcomed these natural air raid shelters wherever they could be found. The greater part of Europe's books and paintings, and the other art treasures in her museums, would have been destroyed during the War or the turbulent months of its aftermath if they had not been placed for safekeeping in deep shafts or caverns. Caves saved the life of innumerable human beings and preserved countless treasures of Western culture. Thus the war brought about a new age of caves: modern aircraft reduced man very nearly to the level of his most primitive ancestors.

Has this new cave age come to an end with the termination of the War? Have caverns ceased to concern those whose minds are filled with the fear of another war? During the last war it was not only private individuals who sought shelter in caves: whole industries were evacuated to subterranean chambers, where they could continue in safety to produce the horrible tools of warfare. From time to time rumours reach the West of new underground cities and factories beyond the Urals and in distant Siberia, erected by the Soviet to house men and industries in flight from the atom bomb. Whether these subterranean cities are a reality, part of the colossal modern armaments programme, or whether they are merely figments of propagandists' imaginations, we cannot tell.

But there is no doubt that natural cavities constitute a welcome protection in this age of the atom and the hydrogen bomb, and the search for them is a sign of our times. Many people both in America and in Russia have long regarded caverns as the safest shelter from unexpected atomic attack. In New Mexico, not far from the Carlsbad Caverns, the site of the oldest cave settlement in the country, stand the atom towns of Los Alamos and Alamogordo. Specialists in aeronautical medicine are carrying out experiments relating to gravity-free space within the caverns themselves, and rocket experts are sending their projectiles into the stratosphere in the same region.

The preparation of caves as air raid shelters is of great importance, for there seems to be no more reliable defence against radio-active rays than a cavern in the heart of a mountain. Thus, a study group of the New York Research Club have been examining the possibility of utilizing the caverns in the Blue Ridge and Massalutten Mountains, Virginia. These ranges contain an extensive labyrinth of caverns which remain to this day largely unexplored. Several expeditions into this kingdom of the shades have been organized by the club. They have shown that the cave system would be proof against destruction by any atomic or hydrogen bomb and therefore well adapted to serve as an air raid shelter. The view was advanced that large sections of the population of New York, Philadelphia, or even Washington, which is only a few hundred miles away, could be housed in the caverns—provided, of course, that evacuation could be carried out in time. Since there is plenty of fresh water, there is no reason why very great numbers of people should not be accommodated in these caves, if stores of provisions were built up beforehand.

Quite apart from fear of air attack, however, industrial plant is often built underground for purely practical reasons. For years, methane gas has been tapped from the earth. These natural underground accumulations of gas gave gas technicians the idea of utilizing subterranean cavities as natural gasholders, which would be less dangerous than those built on the surface. In 1953, the Ruhrgas A.G., Essen—following the example of the U.S.A.—began planning one such reservoir five miles from Hanover, after Professor Seitz of the Lower Saxony Geological Office had discovered a cavity 330 feet under the ground, near the village of Engelbostel, which tests involving the use of compressed air demonstrated to be absolutely proof against the escape of gas stored in it. This new-style gasholder will hold more than a hundred million cubic yards of gas.

In the same district, at Hänigsen near Hanover, a cavern seventy feet high, thirty feet wide and 100 feet long, 2,000 feet below ground, has been transformed into a potash factory. The sylvite mined there is now transformed into potassium chloride on the spot.

Caves possess an economic importance of another kind, however. With what hope and trust man, exhausted by the frantic pace of modern life, turns to the healing powers of nature, of which he too is a part. Caves are amongst these natural sources of healing. Not only do they provide shelter, but some of them actually cure disease. In ancient times man looked upon the subterranean abysses as places of terror and the realm of evil spirits. But his constant search for knowledge has led him to the realization that they are also the seat of good spirits, which bestow blessings upon man.

Caves are a world of their own, with their own climate, atmosphere and waters, where the elements work in a fashion peculiar to this subterranean world. Some caverns show this singularity to an especially marked degree. The so-called Hot Mountain of the Northern Caucasus, in the Mount Elbruz region, contains the Lermontov Grotto and the Proval, a large cavern on the slopes of the Machuk, which were apparently hollowed out by powerful subterranean streams of sulphur. Ground water later accumulated in the cave and formed a lake fifty feet deep. Because of its high sulphur content this water is azure blue in colour and possessed of therapeutic properties. The whole region abounds in medicinal springs, whose mineral-laden waters are up to 120° F. in temperature.

Medicinal caverns also occur in Western Europe. At Monsumano, Italy, there is a natural cave with a temperature of 96° F., in which a sweating-cure can be undertaken. At Luchon, France, there is another where the vapours emanating from a sulphurous spring may be inhaled. An artificial cave at Montegrotta is permeated by the vapours from a medicinal spring, and at Bad Kreuznach the air from a mine, which is charged with emanations, is drawn off and conveyed to a Radio-Emanatorium. Amongst the largest and most important medicinal caves are the Klutert cave near Milspe in Sauerland and the Radhausstolln near Bad Gastein, both of which merit a detailed description.

Under the heading of healing caverns one might also place the miraculous caves—those of Lourdes and Sassenage in France, that of San Servolo near Trieste, etc. In the Grotte de Sassenage a miracle has taken place every year for centuries on January 6th, when two hollow stones fill up with water. This event always attracts a crowd of believers. The Grotto di San Servolo contains a little pool that never becomes empty, a fact noted in Valvasor's *Chronicle* (1689).

ASTHMATICS AND THE KLUTERT CAVE

Despite its size, the Klutert cave near Milspe would have no greater reputation than others if it were not for one feature that distinguishes it from any other cavern. Amongst the thousands who sought shelter in its galleries during the war were a number of asthmatics, people whose distended and rigid bronchi prevent them from breathing freely and in whom dust, smells, and certain foods cause painful coughing. Strangely, all these asthmatics experienced great relief every time they visited the Klutert cave. To begin with, this was attributed to the shock induced by the air raids. But people who were not subjected to any shock, for example an electrician who spent some time working in the cave, underwent the same improvement.

The phenomenon came to be talked about, and lively discussion amongst physicians and laymen stimulated belief in the cave's curative properties on the part of the sufferers. Many doctors dismissed this belief as just one more example of the search for sensation and miracles to which the postwar world was so prone. But the faith of the mass of the population was not to be shaken, and the doctors of the Ennepetal and Schwelm felt obliged to issue a warning against exaggerated hopes. When patients came to the Klutert cave from abroad in search of a cure—for example, the composer of religious music Petrus Sinzig, from Rio de Janeiro, who was eighty-four at the time and has since died—even the scientific world sat up and took notice, and physicians began to inquire into the causes of the cave's therapeutic action.

The medical officer of Schwelm, Dr. Schultz, was the first to investigate atmospheric conditions in the cavern. He also sent a questionnaire to patients who had visited it. Asthmatics who had already tried various spas for their complaint were able to report complete cure or great improvement after daily visits to the grotto extending over one month. The patient revived, his appetite increased, he slept better, and his general well-being was much improved. No amelioration was reported in any case of silicosis, cardiac asthma or pulmonary emphysema. Patients with tuberculosis, cardiac insufficiency, circulatory disorders and infectious diseases reported prejudicial effects.

After these facts had come to light, the Ennepetal doctors entered into an association, so that they might jointly supervise and guide the patients. Dr. Schultz reported the astonishing results in the periodical, *Medizinische Klinik*, Munich, No. 40, 1950, confirming medically what the patients had already established by self-observation.

This medical testimony to the efficacy of the cavern in certain asthmatic afflictions swelled the flood of asthmatics from Germany and abroad. The little building at the entrance developed into a larger one with modern equipment. During the summer there are often more than a hundred patients at a time in the galleries of the cave. They make their way through the passages armed with blankets and sit down on the benches dotted about among the chambers, or stretch out on the iron bedsteads. They pass two hours here in a silence that is often broken by the rattling breathing of the patients. They all wait passively for the miracle of health, which is slowly—frequently only after weeks of twice daily visits—restored, or at least much improved.

What is the secret of the Klutert cave? It has been scientifically established that the carbon dioxide content of the air in the cave is ten times higher than that on the surface. This increased carbon dioxide is due to the flow of underground streams in the cavern, which bring about a relatively high degree of atmospheric humidity—forty-five per cent—which in turn renders the air of the cave free from dust and allergic bodies. The carbon dioxide induces an increase in the respiratory volume of one to one and a half litres a minute.

It seems that the mineral composition of the rock also contributes to the cure. At many points, the rocks contain rock salt which dissolves in the humid atmosphere and loosens the mucus when inhaled. In several parts of the grotto, Professor Lohse of Münster registered on a Geiger counter at least ten per cent more radio-activity than can be observed on the surface. Radio-activity in the air may also exercise a beneficial influence on the malady.

Dr. Spannagel of Voerde was the first to note the cave's curative action. He affirmed that asthmatics who spent two to four hours a day in it had no further need of medicines or injections. To begin with he was laughed at by his colleagues, but he was right. Official organizations, physicians, physicists, chemists, geologists and scientific institutes have studied, each from their own particular viewpoint, the phenomena that occur in this cave. Today the doctors can say, with full justification: 'In the Klutert cave, Sauerland, we possess the oldest and strangest sanatorium in the world, which brings healing to asthmatics more cheaply than any other.' Up to the present, success has been achieved with eighty per cent of the patients visiting the cave, above all with the young.

THE RADIO-ACTIVE CAVE THAT CURES RHEUMATISM

Austria, which is so rich in caves, possesses one with an even greater power than that of the Klutert cave. This cave, which is not natural, but made up of deep galleries dug through the ages by the hand of man, cures rheumatic and allied ailments.

The Radhausberg near Böckstein in the Gasteiner Tal, in the neighbourhood of the famous watering-place of Bad Gastein, has a very unusual geological structure. The Tauriscans and the Romans dug for gold here. The gold mines of this district reached their heyday in the fifteenth and sixteenth centuries, were then depleted and fell into decline. During the Second World War, the fact that this mountain had once contained gold was recollected. In 1940, a new adit a mile and a quarter long was cut into the mountainside. Very little gold was found, and digging was abandoned for reasons connected with the war.

Miners who had worked in the tunnel, however, discovered something more valuable than gold. They observed to their amazement that those afflicted with rheumatism were cured, and that they developed none of the disorders due to cold to which miners are so prone. It was noted that as the tunnel advanced the temperature steadily increased, till it reached 112° F. one thousand six hundred yards in; after this it fell once more, only to rise again in the southern stretch. It was further observed that iron rusted in twenty-four hours, that copper rapidly oxidized, and that well-packed photographic plates, which were hung on a rock, bore clearly marked black spots after a time. A test carried out by F. Hernegger of the Radium Institute of the Vienna Academy of Sciences showed intense radio-active radiations in the galleries. Furthermore, fine traces of secondary uranium were found. It was conjectured that these traces came from underground waters which had once been linked up with the radio-active springs of Bad Gastein, some three miles to the north. This also explained the fact noted by aircraft pilots that their radar apparatus was thrown out of gear while flying over the area.

All this attracted the attention of the local population. The Research Institute founded at Bad Gastein in 1936 also began to take an interest in the singular phenomena in the gallery, and to wonder whether it might be possible to integrate its curative properties with those of the spa.

Immediately after the war the professors and research workers of Vienna and Innsbruck Universities, the Vienna Technical High School, the Radium Institute of the Academy of Sciences, and the Vienna Natural History Society combined to study the mineralogical, geological, chemical, physical and hygienic conditions of the mine. Their positive findings led, in 1949, to the treatment of various diseases being undertaken there. The Bad Gastein *Badeblatt* (Nos. 38,

39, 40, 41, 43 and 44, 1951) gave an account of the tests made: 'The programme was very comprehensive. The source of the heat was sought for, the rocks carefully studied, the mountain submitted to radio-electric tests, and every trickle of water analysed. The radiations and emanations in all branches of the network of galleries were measured with counters; climatological investigations were undertaken, and patients volunteering to take the cure were kept under medical observation.'

Study of the abnormally high temperature in the grotto brought some curious facts to light. Thermal water, being an extremely good conductor, interferes with the propagation of electric waves. The total cessation of radio reception at certain points in the gallery led to the supposition that the interior of the mountain contains thermal waters. Geologists surmise that these thermal waters must be linked with the seventeen separate radio-active springs which emerge from the mountain at Bad Gastein, three miles to the north, at an altitude of 3,300 feet. This link had already been deduced from the identical deposits left by the water of the two places. In both cases it was found to contain a grey-brown sediment of iron oxide and manganese oxide, which often occurs in dripstone caves, and on its surface tiny particles of radium and uranium compounds dissolved by the thermal water, these latter being frequently in higher proportions than those in the pitchblende of the Joachimstal, from which Madame Curie produced the first radium. In the grotto, uranium appears in the form of pale yellow dots, tiny crystals, or little drops or protuberances that emit a yellowish-green effulgence, like that of the luminous figures on a watch dial, when a quartz lamp with a nickel-oxide filter is shone on them. Only traces of uranium were found, however, and not large deposits as reported at the time in the world press.

Apart from various types of gneiss, the mine was found to contain aplite and lapis albus, a white stone rich in silica mingled with soda felspar and mica. Von Grauvogel, who gave lapis albus its name and also found it in the Bad Gastein springs, used it to treat goitre, scrofulosis and tuberculosis of the bones and glands. Lapis albus is still employed to a considerable extent in homoeopathy. This white stone probably has a similar action to that which is found in the Milk Grotto at Bethlehem (see the section entitled 'The Birth of Christianity in Caves') and also in Bavarian caves.

The most important factor in this cavern remains, however, its high temperature and the strong radio-activity of its atmosphere. Since the conditions of oxygen, carbon dioxide and humidity were equally favourable, it was well suited for therapeutic purposes. The temperature of 105° F. combined with the saturation of the air with water vapour produces a high body-temperature, as in a steam bath. The emanations arising from the disintegration of radium and uranium are of the same order of magnitude as those used in therapeutics since the discovery of radium. But in the Radhausstolln they are spread through a volume of 20,000 cubic yards, which makes the treatment much less unpleasant for the patient than in the confined space in which it is normally given. It has been calculated that at least three grammes of radium would be required to create artificially the conditions which prevail naturally in this cavern.

The Bad Gastein Research Institute carried out very exhaustive tests on healthy volunteers to ascertain the effects of the temperature on blood pressure, circulation and respiration, and especially the amount of emanation absorbed into the body. The results were remarkable. In spite of the high loss of water due to perspiration, which in some cases reached 4,000 grammes, the patients did not show any abnormal thirst. The blood was enriched by an amount of emanation virtually equal to the concentration in the atmosphere of the grotto, which is 3.5 to 6.2 times as much as after bathing for half an hour in the radium-laden thermal water of Bad Gastein. The emanation was eliminated within four hours through the sweat and urine. Searching study disclosed that the inspired emanations circulate in the whole body, entering the tissues and cells and so having the effect of a carefully calculated irradiation of all the organs.

All experience confirms that treatment in the old mine is beneficial in all cases where heat therapy and radio-active irradiation of the tissues is indicated. The Bad Gastein *Badeblatt* writes:

Being a gas devoid of fatty bodies, the emanation concentrates particularly well in organs that are rich in lipoids. Chief amongst these are the endocrine glands, such as the gonads, the thyroid, the adenohypophysis, and the renal cortex. The action of emanations on the last-named organ, which has long been known, gains particular interest, because recent American experiments have shown that spectacular, though short-lived, results can be achieved by the administration of suprarenal substances in severe cases of arthritis. Similar results have also been obtained with the substances of the adenohypophysis, which increase the activity of the suprarenals.

Experience up to the present shows that a stay in the Gastein cave, under medical supervision, contributes towards the cure or alleviation of a whole series of complaints, e.g. rheumatic ailments, circulatory disorders, kidney troubles, neuritis, the after-effects of infantile paralysis, certain endocrine and metabolic disturbances, and allergic affections.

I I

THE EXPLORATION AND SCIENCE
OF CAVES

CAVE EXPLORATION THROUGH THE CENTURIES

THE exploration of caves has gone on for centuries, even if it was not animated by the same spirit of scientific inquiry in which it is pursued today. Encyclopaedias issued during the first period of printing contain little reference to caverns, apart from the information that they are the lairs of dragons and other fabulous beasts. Nevertheless, investigation has shown that even in the distant past men entered and explored caves. Inscriptions have been found in the Tigris Cavern near Lidje, Southern Armenia, showing that this cave was explored by the ancient Assyrians. Mühlhofer came across signs of rock-cutting in the depths of the Grotto of Apollo in Cyrenaica, which contains a spring. The numerous painted caves are undoubtedly among those explored in olden times. But there is no documentary evidence of cave exploration before the Middle Ages.

The aims of caving at that time were almost exclusively practical. In 1490, for example, Hans Breu of Bayreuth explored the Ahornloch, now known as St. Sophia's Cave, for saltpetre, which was then used in the manufacture of gunpowder. Great efforts were made in those days to extract the saltpetre from the phosphate deposits, known as *terre nitreuse*, which occurred in many caves. Entry into horizontal caverns was often inspired by the hope of acquiring gold, silver and other ores without undue effort.

A little four-page pamphlet by Berthol Bruchner, printed in Amberg in 1535 and dealing with a cave, is still extant. The title-page reads: *Marvellous New Intelligence / now on the day of St. Peter and St. Paul / In the thirty-fifth year. / By twenty-five citizens / of the town of Amberg / who entered a huge mountain / by a village / called Predenwind / in which mountain they entered and crawled through / nine hundred fathom-cords* (a measure of distance) . . . The cavern referred to is the Breitwinner Cave near Velburg. The pamphlet also reports that the cavers were equipped with 'lanterns, tinder-boxes, picks, ropes, wine and bread'.

In 1596–7, the Elector Frederick IV had large quantities of mud and dripstone excavated from the Windloch near Krottensee, now known as Maximilian's Cave, with the aim of extracting gold from the mud and saltpetre from the dripstone. Reports state that he failed in both. But other treasures, which could be put to practical use, were found in caves. The sheets of soft white calcareous algae on the walls, called *nihilum album*, were peeled off and sold by quacks as a medicament. The teeth of cave bears were also held to possess curative properties when pulverized, and earth from the Geisloch (Geyser Hole) at Velden, Bavaria, was also employed for therapeutic purposes.

In 1646, the celebrated Jesuit Athanasius Kircher wrote a two-volume work in Latin, *Mundus Subterraneus* (*The Underground World*), in which he referred to a French scholar, Jacques Gaffarel (1601–81), a man of great erudition who made long journeys to Spain, Italy, Greece and Asia Minor, and whose works deal chiefly with magic and occultism. A fragment of one of Gaffarel's books called *Le monde sousterrein*, comprising four pages, the title-page, and the index, is now in the Bibliothèque Nationale, Paris. The intriguing sub-title of this unique literary production runs: *THE UNDERGROUND WORLD or historical and philoso-*

phical DESCRIPTION, of all the most beautiful CAVES, and all the rarest GROTTOES on earth: Vaults, Holes, Cellars, hidden Lairs, and secret Dens of various animals, and unknown peoples: Abysses, Hollows, and marvellous Openings in the Mountains; memorable Pits, and famous Mines of all kinds: Underground Towns: Crypts: Catacombs: Temples cut in the Rock: Wells, and wonderful Fountains: Rock Overhangs: Cisterns, and hollow Baths: And generally of all the most celebrated CAVERNS, POTHOLES, and CAVITIES in the world; and of everything most curious about them.

The author deals with everything that can be included under the heading of 'caves'. Amongst divine caverns Gaffarel numbers Heaven, Purgatory and Hell, nor does he forget the oracular grottoes of antiquity—Delphi, the temple of Jupiter Ammon, etc. He discusses all activities engaged in by people connected with caves, or dwelling in them: referring to the caverns of lawgivers and prophets, Jews, cabbalists, philosophers, poets, seers, those possessed, vagabonds and thieves. He also mentions saints and hermits, e.g. St. Rosalia and St. Mary Magdalene of France, who lived in caves. Gaffarel does not omit cave-dwelling beasts, especially lions, tigers, elephants, crocodiles, serpents, dragons, wolves and bears. But he makes no mention of the small fauna to which modern biologists pay so much attention. He does, however, refer to the miraculous phenomena and mysterious forces at work in caverns. He describes caves that make people cheerful or tearful, lively or drowsy, taciturn or talkative, caves that bring death, that heal or rejuvenate. Thus Gaffarel and Kirchner knew something about medicinal caves, modern examples of which have been enumerated above. These old works on caves lay no claim to being scientific in our sense of the word. They were in keeping with the thought of their time and based on a belief in astrology and alchemy.

Caving without practical objective, but more scientific in spirit, is first encountered in the seventeenth century. In

1618, the Pastor of Neukirch discovered a quantity of human skeletons in the Steinbach cave, which were employed by Ranke for anatomical research 270 years later. There were other explorers in Bavaria, with its numerous small caves, during the seventeenth and eighteenth centuries, e.g. Pastor Meyer from Muggendorf, J. J. Bayer, a naturalist, A. Döderlein, an historian, and Müller, a town-clerk, who wrote *Deliciae topographiae Nibergenses*.

These investigations took place in isolation, however, without method and without reference to existing scientific knowledge. Truly scientific speleology, which is dealt with in the following section, did not begin until the end of the eighteenth century.

CLASSICS OF SPELEOLOGY

The osseous remains discovered in the Steinbach cave by the Pastor of Neukirch, in 1618, would have aroused tremendous excitement among palaeontologists if they had been found today. It never occurred to anyone at the time that they might go back to prehistoric ages. Again it was a priest, Pastor Esper of Uttenreuth, who occupied himself with speleo-palaeontology in the eighteenth century, nearly two hundred years later. In his book, *Detailed account of the recently discovered zooliths of unknown quadrupeds, the caves in which they were found, and various other noteworthy caverns of Oberburg, in the Margraviate of Bayreuth*, which was published in 1771 with copperplate engravings in colour, the author interpreted his finds in the Gailenreuth cave as evidence of 'the coexistence of man with the fauna of the diluvian epoch', which he called 'the era of the disappearance of the first world'.

The appearance of this great work drew the attention of the whole scientific world to the caves on the Wisent. Among those who visited them was the famous French naturalist Cuvier, originator of the 'catastrophe theory',[1] who iden-

---

[1] In our day Cuvier and Esper have found an enthusiastic partisan of their catastrophe theory in the person of the Russian doctor of medicine

tified amongst the remains the skeletons of cave bear and cave hyaena. Up to this point the views of Cuvier and Esper were in agreement. But they came into vigorous conflict when Esper unearthed a fragment of human skull, on September 22nd, 1771, which he regarded as coeval with the bones of diluvian animals. Cuvier took it upon himself to point out the country pastor's error, and the latter suffered the same fate as Fuhlrott ninety years later, when his Neanderthal skull was rejected by the scientific world. The Margrave of Ansbach and Bayreuth sent some of the bones to London, where they were seen and described by John Hunter. Hunter's report stimulated the English geologist Dr. William Buckland to carry out excavations of his own in Franconia in 1816, the results of which confirmed his belief that Esper was right. Buckland's *Reliquiae Diluvianae* (London, 1823) was the signal for widespread excavation of caves and study of their contents.

A number of other speleological writings were published at the same period as those of Pastor Esper. In 1789, Schleiss von Löwenfeld wrote a book on the caves of Sulzbach; in 1795, Köppel described some of the Muggendorf grottoes; and in 1796, Professor J. Chr. Rosenmüller of Leipzig wrote a book on the same subject. In 1810, the palaeontologist Goldfuss, and in 1827 Heller, published descriptions of all the caverns of Franconian Switzerland known at that time.

This was undoubtedly a great scientific achievement, which shows the high level of speleology at the time. The

Immanuel Velikovsky, who wrote a book in America entitled *Worlds in Collision*. The author breaks categorically with the theory of evolution of our solar system, basing his view on the numerous traditions current amongst all civilizations and peoples that our planet suffered, in the not very distant past, a series of great catastrophes caused by collision with a comet. The worst catastrophe is supposed to have occurred around 1500 BC, in the time of Moses. The book caused a tremendous sensation in the U.S.A., provoking protests from scientists attached to the evolution theory, as a result of which the author was forced to change his publisher.

greatest scientific minds of the day felt it worth while to devote their attention to the most extensive cave area in Central Europe, which, at the outbreak of the Second World War, was known to contain more than six hundred and thirty caves. The caverns of this district offered a richer and more varied field of research than those of almost any other. They presented a multitude of palaeontological, climatic, zoological, botanical, thermal and prehistoric problems, which scientists felt the urge to solve.

By 1850, the skeletal remains found in Franconian Switzerland had greatly contributed to palaeontological knowledge. After this date prehistoric research made increasing use of these finds, a development in which the Munich geologist Max Schlosser played an outstanding part, even though the knowledge he gleaned in a series of caverns from 1894 to 1900 had to be acquired without the equipment now at the caver's disposal.

The advance of the industrial age, bringing with it ever deeper penetration of the earth's surface in pursuit of coal and ores, opened up a wide field to geologists. Their interest extended to caves because of the information they provide as to the geological structure of our planet. The great naturalist Alexander von Humboldt himself utilized observations he had made in the Gailenreuth cave in his book, *Über Gruben-wetter und die Verbreitung des Kohlenstoffes in geognostischer Hinsicht*, published in 1795. This was the period during which the first shaft was sunk for coal in Germany, and when geologists began to inquire into the origin of caves. Besides von Humboldt, special mention must be made of the famous German geologists Leopold von Buch, C. W. von Guembel, and Major Adalbert Neischl, and the Bavarian topographer Adrian von Riedel, all of whom studied numerous cavities of Bavaria from a geological point of view. Von Guembel was the first, in 1879, to map and list the caverns of Franconian Switzerland, and to investigate karst phenomena—dolines (sinks, shake-holes or swallow-holes), uvalas (trough-line depressions), poljes (sunken fields), and limestone springs. Neischl, the topographer, was a strenuous advocate of surveying as an essential part of the scientific study of caves, thereby laying the foundations of modern speleology.

The first geological investigation of caverns in Germany went hand-in-hand with the first studies of cave fauna, initiated by a number of workers in the nineteenth century, and prehistorical research, which, as related to speleology, is linked with the names of Dr. K. Hörmann and Professor F. Birkner.

Amongst the most important pioneers of speleology in the nineteenth century was Dr. Heinrich von Dechen, after whom Dechen's Cave in Sauerland was named. He was one of the classical exponents of geognosy, as geology was once called; his activities centred round Bonn. He was born in 1800 at Berlin, where he was educated. After completing his training as a mining engineer he held various professional posts, travelled to broaden his outlook, and, in 1834, obtained a chair in mining technology at the University of Berlin, where he engaged in a wide range of fruitful activities. In particular, he was responsible for the drawing of exact geological maps. During this period he wrote *Geognostichen Umrisse der Rheinlande* and drew geognostic maps of the Rhineland, Germany, Britain, France and other neighbouring countries. Von Dechen remained at Berlin until 1841, after which he occupied a number of important official positions connected with mining, retiring in 1864. He published many valuable and comprehensive books. No worthier name than his could have been bestowed on the finest stalactite cave in Germany.

The number of German speleologists who worked during the twentieth century to complete and develop the achievements of their predecessors is very great. To name them all would go beyond the limits of this book. Many German geologists were in some degree speleologists. Most of them, however, kept to the well-worn traditional paths of their science and professed views that had been held by the earliest speleologists and whose validity was by then very questionable. Furthermore, speleology in the past was too local in character. Besides von Dechen the names of Dr. Julius Andree, Dr. Reichling, von Dücker, Fuhlrott, Schaafhausen, Wiegers, and Brand should be mentioned.

One speleologist of outstanding importance was the engineer Walter, Baron von Czoernig-Czernhausen, already referred to on several occasions, who was laid to rest by his friends during the last days of 1945, by the light of a miner's lamp and in sight of the legendary Untersberg, whose caverns he had explored during his lifetime. He lies in the same soil in which two other well-known speleologists— Hermann Rihl and Poldi Fuhrig—have their last resting-place. Unlike these two, or Alexander von Mörk, he was not cut off in his prime, but died at the age of sixty-two after an active and fruitful life. For thirty-three years he was a member of the Salzburg Speleological Society, which, under his leadership, achieved success and renown. The four hundred-odd cave surveys and innumerable literary publications he left behind him constitute an important body of speleological work.

Von Czoernig-Czernhausen, who was born in Trieste in 1883, was by profession a mechanical engineer. He came to Salzburg in 1913 and immediately joined the local section of the Austro-Hungarian Speleological Society, in which he was extremely active. He carried out a large number of explorations, of which he wrote very exact accounts. He himself said that he had made more than a thousand, without ever forgetting his measuring tape, his compass and his sketchbook. He was first and foremost, as already mentioned, the explorer of the Eisriesenwelt, into which he descended more than a hundred times. He explored many other caverns and produced a survey of all those in Salzburg and neighbouring districts. He visited caves in Hungary, Czechoslovakia, Istria, Belgium and Britain. In addition to his own literary activity, he collected all articles relating to speleology that appeared in newspapers and periodicals. His most important book was *Die Höhlen Salzburgs und seiner Grenzgebirge* (1926), which remains today the basis for all new speleological research and gained him widespread scientific renown.

'Czoernig,' wrote his friend Angermeyer, 'reverenced the mystery, the primeval forces of Mother Earth, the riddles of the depths which are revealed to the eye of the explorer in the everlasting darkness. Once he was under the spell of the underworld time ceased to exist for him; no matter how many hours, days and nights passed, he could not tear himself away. His life belonged to the subterranean world, with all its beauties and all its secrets.'

Another classic figure of speleology of equal stature to Czoernig-Czernhausen is the Frenchman Norbert Casteret, who has described the thrills and triumphs of his life of exploration in his two books, *Dix ans sous terre* (1933), which was honoured by the French Academy, and *Au fond des gouffres* (1936), selections from both of which were published in English under the title, *Ten Years Under the Earth* in 1939. His greatest achievement was the discovery of the prehistoric drawings and sculptures in the grotto of Montespan (Haute-Garonne).

'At Montespan,' writes Édouard-Alfred Martel in his introduction to *Ten Years Under the Earth*, 'he made his astonishing find by a piece of unparalleled daring: he plunged under a submerged ceiling into the shadows of an underground river, braving a tunnel whose length he could not know. As he neither drowned nor cracked his skull at the first attempt, the adventure whetted his appetite. This perilous feat is now one of his professional tools. It brought him to grips with the most difficult of scientific problems and with practical hydrogeology—the mysteries still surrounding abysses, caverns, subterranean reservoirs, and the like.'

18

Casteret's explorations were concerned less with the discovery of fine dripstone caves or the study of cave fauna and flora than with investigating the underground watercourses, which—as at Mas d'Azil (Ariège)—flow beneath the Pyrenees. Knowledge of these subterranean streams is of importance from the point of view of public health, and also in connexion with their possible utilization as sources of hydraulic energy. Casteret has succeeded in tracing a growing number of such rivers where only four were known at the beginning of the century. It was also he who explored the mighty ice-filled cavern in the Massif de Gavarnie, the highest in the world, which today bears his name. In addition, he discovered the vast Grotte de Gagire, the true sources of the Garonne, and the sacred grotto of Labastide, as well as that of Montespan. Casteret made all these discoveries during the years following the First World War, with relatively primitive equipment. He is one of those speleologists who has attained world renown.

Subterranean cavities are so abundant in France that many of her scientists have devoted themselves to speleology. Last century saw such outstanding explorers as Delarouzée, Linder and Lespès. They were succeeded by a large number of very active cavers like Abeille de Perrin, Piochard de la Brûlerie, Mestre, Marquet, Eugène, Simon, etc. To begin with, exploration was undertaken only by enthusiastic individuals working in isolation at various different places. In 1907, E. C. Racowitza and his collaborator Dr. René Jeannel created an organization for the purpose of surveying caves, collecting the animals that inhabited them, studying the material obtained, passing it on to experts, and publishing their findings.

This group, which called itself Biospeleologica, prospered, thanks to Racowitza's talent for organization and Dr. Jeannel's enthusiasm. Its first headquarters was the Arago Laboratory, Banyuls-sur-Mer. In 1920, it emigrated to Klausenburg in Rumania, where it became the Institute of

Speleology, which was founded on the initiative of Dr. Racowitza and directed by Dr. Jeannel until his departure from
Rumania, when his place was taken by Dr. Chapuis. This
Institute had the same aims as those of the Biospeleologica:
to survey caverns and collect specimens of their fauna. All
these efforts finally gave birth to the underground laboratory
at Moulis, of which we shall have more to say later.

At the present time speleology in France is going from
strength to strength, under the impetus imparted by Norbert
Casteret, Trombe, and Robert de Joly, president of the
Société Spéléologique de France, the Club Alpin Français
and many other scientific and sporting groups.

France offers the cavers every conceivable type of cavity,
from the humble rock-shelter under an overhang, in which
prehistoric man sheltered, to the great subterranean systems
whose galleries extend over several miles at a depth of hundreds of yards.

Recent, and sometimes dramatic, explorations have
drawn the attention of the public to these caverns. Among
them were the expeditions down the Henne Morte in the
Pyrenees, and those of 1952–4 down the Gouffre Pierre
Saint-Martin, likewise in the Pyrenees, on the Spanish side
of the Franco-Spanish frontier, which saw the death of
Loubens. Since it could not be raised immediately, his body
was left at the bottom of the chasm, from which it was only
recovered with great difficulty in the summer of 1954.

During this same year a group of French cavers exploring
the Puits Berger in the Vercors went down to 2,959 feet,
thereby breaking the world record for depth and demonstrating the vigour of French speleology.

The earliest reports of speleology in England date from the
seventeenth century, but Wookey Hole, near Wells in Somerset, seems to have been known to the Romans, and Kent's
Hole, Torquay, Devonshire, contains an inscription with
the date 1571 (cf. *The Literature of Kent's Hole*, 1868–78 by
William Pengelly). Lamb Lair in the Mendip Hills, near

Harptree, Somerset, was discovered by miners in 1660, but the entrance shaft was filled in again, forgotten, and not rediscovered till 1879. Ball Eye Cave, Stafford, was discovered by miners in 1663. The Derbyshire poet Charles Cotton mentions caves in his descriptive poem *The Wonder of the Peak* (1681). Bagshawe Cavern near Castleton, Derbyshire, was discovered 125 years later, in 1806, and ten years after this Mr. Whidbey began the first palaeontological investigation of caves at Oreston. Dr. Buckland explored Kirkdale Cave near Helmsley, Yorkshire, in 1821. Many other workers followed him, especially Sir William Boyd Dawkins, whose book *Cave Hunting* (1874) gives a survey of earlier research and of the physical structure of caves. This work has proved of great value to modern speleologists.

H. E. Balch first began work in Wookey Hole together with Sir William Boyd Dawkins in 1885, exploring the main cave from 1909 onwards, and especially during 1926–7. He recently conducted excavations in Badger Hole, which yielded important archaeological results.

In Yorkshire, potholing came to the fore round about 1850. Many of the caves and potholes (a vertical pitch open to the surface, or a cave system requiring the use of tackle) in which Yorkshire abounds had been entered before this date. But the real pioneers of cave and pothole exploration in this county were John Birkbeck of Settle and William Metcalfe of Chapel-le-Dale, who are known to have descended some forty potholes in all, amongst them Sell Ghyll and Alum Pot, the latter in 1870. The Yorkshire Ramblers' Club, which was founded in 1892 with climbing and fell walking as its aims, soon turned its attention to potholing and descended Gaping Gill in 1895, a year after E. A. Martel's historic descent. E. E. Roberts, who is still an active caver, was one of the pioneers in those far-off days.

The *Y.R.C. Journal*, Vol. I, 1900, contains a detailed account of the descent of Gaping Ghyll and subsequent descents into Yorkshire potholes. This may be regarded as the first account published in Britain of the systematic investigation of a pothole. As N. J. Dunnington writes in *British Caving*, however, 'The exploration of the horizontal caves must have been going on for countless years, as some of the old guide-books contain relatively accurate descriptions within their covers.'

ORGANIZED SPELEOLOGY

Speleology has received tremendous impetus during the last decade and no museum arouses such widespread interest or has so many visitors as an easily accessible cave, especially one with dripstones. The discovery and explanation of rare natural phenomena that resulted from cave exploration, and the information concerning dead and living fauna and flora and the past of the human race revealed through the excavation of caverns, raised speleology to the status of a science in its own right. Not only palaeontology, but also geology, botany, zoology, hydrology, medicine, biology, anthropology, archaeology, comparative ethnology and other branches of knowledge were in varying degrees stimulated and enriched by speleology. For here in the kingdom of eternal darkness completely virgin territory was opened up, full of surprises from many points of view.

The exploration of caves first developed in European countries; the more caves that were discovered and the more interest was caught by the objects found in them, the more active became associations catering for the explorer and scientist. Speleology has long ago advanced from the stage of inexpert amateurism. During the twentieth century, and especially after the First World War, it ceased to be the preserve of a few individual enthusiasts and became an organized scientific discipline with a codified body of knowledge and links with allied sciences. Today it is actively pursued all over the world by various clubs and societies and in small periodicals, for the most part without great publicity or sensational revelations, but with methodical diligence.

A number of new speleological organizations sprang up in Germany after the Second World War. In the nineteenth century there was the Schwäbische Höhlenverein, which published a few pamphlets and plans of caverns; while before the Second World War Berlin had a Deutscher Höhlenverband. In South Germany there is now a Verein für Höhlenkunde at Schellenberg, a Höhlenverein at Laichingen, a Verein für Höhlenforschung at Nuremberg, and a Verein der Schwäbischen Höhlenforscherfreunde. The numerous commercial caves in Sauerland and the Swabian Alps all have their own committees of administration, which are in more or less close contact with scientific institutions interested in the study of these caves.

In the Soviet Zone there is a special speleology section of the Friends of Nature, at Norhausen, which is particularly concerned with exploring the caves of the Harz. Speleology in Germany falls within the province of a series of Institutes, e.g. the Frobenius Institute, Frankfurt, the Geological Institute, Münster, and the Institute of Geology and Palaeontology of Tübingen University. The fact that Germany, unlike other European countries, has produced no speleological periodical since the war is due to the circumstances of the times. The *Mitteilungen der Deutschen Gesellschaft für Karstforschung* has ceased publication (the last number was 1942-3). But occasional articles on subjects closely related to speleology are to be met with from time to time in other scientific journals.

Austria has always been particularly active in the field of speleology. The scientific exploration of Alpine caverns was begun there in the nineteenth century. The Verein für Höhlenkunde, which was founded in Vienna in 1879 and published five issues of a bibliography of speleology, lasted only one year. It then combined with the Oesterreichischer Touristenklub, which had its own speleological section.

There were speleological societies in other parts of Austria during the nineteenth century, for example at Graz. This club was much talked about at the time as a result of the mishap suffered by seven of its members in the Lurloch. The Landesverein für Höhlenkunde, Salzburg, stands today in great esteem and is probably one of the largest and most active of all speleological societies. It possesses records of more than eight thousand caves in all parts of the world—arranged according to continents and countries, mountain ranges and individual groups of mountains—compiled by the speleologist Gustav Abel. The scientific aspect of speleology is taken care of in Austria by the Speleological Institute of Vienna University, founded by Professor G. Kyrle. Since 1950, the Verband Österreichischer Höhlenforscher has published a small quarterly periodical, *Die Höhle*; in addition, the periodicals *Natur und Land*, *Höhlenkundliche Mitteilungen*, the *Mitteilungsblatt*, the organ of the associated societies and the companies administrating commercial caves, *Verbandsnach-richten* and *Speläologische Mitteilungen* (the most recent edition of which came out in 1946) carry many articles on speleology.

The third German-speaking country to be named is Switzerland, where interest in its national caves has been growing during recent years. Since 1952, the Gesellschaft für Höhlenforschung or Société Suisse de Spéléologie of Geneva, has published the bi-monthly *Stalactite* and prints its club news and scientific reports in the fortnightly *L'Écho Mon-tagnard*. The periodicals, *Leben und Umwelt* (Aarau), and *Ur-Schweiz* also devote space to speleology.

In Italy, the Società delle Alpe Giulie, Trieste, whose year-books already contained valuable contributions on speleology in its early days, has been in existence since the eighteen-nineties. Today there are speleological societies at many places in Northern Italy. Italian speleologists also produce a number of important periodicals. The *Notiziario del Circolo Speleologico* is published in Rome. The *Bollettino della Società Adriatica di Scienze Naturali* (Trieste), deals with the karsts and grottoes of Istria. Speleology abroad is covered by the *Rassegna Speleologica Italiana*, published in Como. Greece produces the *Bulletin de la Société Spéléologique de Grèce*, published in Athens.

On October 24th, 1954, a union of Yugoslav speleological societies, an Institute of Speleology, etc., were founded after the first Yugoslavian speleological congress had been held in January, 1954, at Postojna.

Czechoslovakia brings out a number of publications entirely or largely devoted to speleology. A periodical for tourists, *Krasy Slovenska*, published in Bratislava, regularly prints articles on the Carpathian caves. The Speleologičky Kluv v Brné publishes ten issues annually of its periodical *Ceskoslovensky Kras*, which is primarily devoted to the study of the Moravian Karst areas.

In Western Europe, speleological activity is particularly intense in Belgium, France and Spain.

The Société Spéléologique de Belgique was founded in 1952 and publishes a periodical, *Les Troglodytes*, which, as the title indicates is principally devoted to cavernicolous fauna, a study to which Robert Leruth made a magnificent contribution with his monumental book.

France, the classical land of speleology, is particularly well served with speleological periodicals. The principal organ of French speleologists, *Annales de Spéléologie*, appears quarterly. A number of local clubs issue bulletins, e.g. the *Bulletin trimestriel de l'Association Spéléologique*, which has become, since 1952, *Les Cahiers de Spéléologie*. *Le Monde souterrain*, which deals with all problems relating to the world below ground, prints regular articles on speleological subjects. The society Les Chercheurs de la Wallonie publishes its *Bulletin illustré* at regular intervals, and the Muséum d'Histoire Naturelle, Paris, issues *Notes biospéléologiques*, edited by the celebrated speleologist Dr. Jeannel.

In Spain, the Institute of Geology of the University of Oviedo has published since 1950 the quarterly journal

Speleon, which deals mainly with cave speleology, biospeleology and the morphology of karst formations.

The Institute of Zoology of the University of Oporto, Portugal, issues the *Publicacoes*, which report biospeleological research.

Great Britain has at least sixty-five caving organizations, many of which are affiliated to the Cave Research Group, with a total membership of well over a thousand. The Cave Diving Group is a special organization devoted to the under-water exploration of caves. Many of the caving clubs and societies issue news-sheets and periodicals. The journal of the British Speleological Association, *Cave Science*, is copiously illustrated with maps and photographs, and also treats of caves in other countries; for the British Commonwealth—especially Australia, New Zealand, Tasmania, Burma, India and Ceylon—is particularly rich in caves, only a few of which have been explored.

The Cave Research Group is chiefly concerned with studying the cave fauna of the British Isles, which occupies a special position and is little known on the Continent. Wolf's *Animalium Cavernarum Catalogus* lists very few animals from the British Isles. The Cave Research Group publishes news and reviews in its *News Letter*, while longer contributions appear in the *Transactions of the C.R.G.* Other speleological publications are *Proceedings of the University of Bristol Speleological Society* and the *Stoke-on-Trent Pothole Club Journal*.

A number of individual Australian cavers are engaged in exploring the country's wealth of vertical and horizontal caverns. Since 1932, one of the keenest has been J. Maitland Thompson of Semaphore. Western Australia is particularly rich in caves, and there are also a large number in the 33,000 square miles of the Nullarbor Plain, South Australia, which are especially noteworthy for their fauna. Kangaroo Island, South Australia, has the large and beautiful Kelly's Cave and there are hundreds of impressive grottoes round Naracoorte and Mount Gambier, all in South Australia.

Apart from the Hobart Caverneering Club, the only speleological society in Australia and Tasmania, caving here is in the hands of individual enthusiasts like J. Maitland Thompson.

The United States have a number of local clubs, many of which publish periodicals. The National Speleological Society issues the monthly *N.S.S. News*, while longer reports appear in an annual *Bulletin*. The speleological journal *California Caver* is published in Altadena.

It can be seen that caving today has assumed world-wide significance. Cavers are cosmopolitans and their investigations are affected by those of their fellows all over the world. Speleology is a modest science, little known to the wide public. But its field of activity is a dark kingdom whose exploration calls for determination, courage and comradeship —qualities that have always been in demand when there were new worlds to be conquered.

Practical caving is neither simple nor safe. Many conditions have to be fulfilled, if the caver is not to risk his life. He must wear clothes that will protect him against cold and dirt. He requires considerable equipment: hammer, chisel, compass, thermometer, a plumbline and a level for surveying work, measuring instruments, rope ladders, ordinary ladders, ropes, a raft or rubber dinghy (in caves traversed by watercourses), digging implements, an ice-axe and crampons (in ice-filled caverns), acetylene lamp or candles, matches, pitons, telephone apparatus, a notebook and pencil, camping equipment and provisions, warm blankets, bandages, first-aid equipment, a spirit cooker, cooking utensils, etc., and equipment for preserving the cavernicolous fauna he may find—wrapping paper, spirit, collecting tubes, and so on.

An experienced caver never enters a cavern without at least two companions. Particular care is needed in negotiating underground rivers. The practised caver generally travels upstream first; if he goes downstream, he tests the speed of the current and keeps a lookout for treacherous waterfalls with the aid of a candle mounted on a small plank. The descent of shafts or potholes by rope is also a tricky business. In the 'nineties a simple but primitive method was employed: a horizontal beam attached to the rope, on which the caver sat as he was lowered by the unwinding of a wooden windlass. Today steel cable that can be run off steel winches is employed, but fatal accidents are still not unknown, as the death of Marcel Loubens in the Gouffre Pierre-Saint-Martin in 1952 shows. It is indispensable to take photographs and make drawings and sketches. Although much better photographs can now be obtained with the help of the electronic flash than used to be taken with magnesium powder, the caver still has to carry heavy photographic equipment. The first essential is to prepare a plan of the cave to be explored, so that the caver can find his way.

A great deal more could be written about the equipment of the scientific speleologist. Enough has been said, however, to show that in addition to courage, physical fitness and the determination to surmount obstacles, he needs—like the mountaineer—thoroughly efficient gear.

A LABORATORY IN THE DARK

Under the title of biospeleology a completely new science has sprung up, concerned with the study and breeding of cave fauna. Although it has now been practised for a number of years, biospeleology is still confronted by a good many unsolved problems. The multitude of creatures that live in the realm of darkness guarantees that this field of research is not only vast, but also full of interesting possibilities.

It was essential to go beyond merely catching and classifying cave-dwelling animals to a careful study of their physiology, embryology, ecology and ethnology. To this end, special laboratories were necessary. The merit of establishing the first underground laboratory belongs to the Frenchman Armand Viré, who, in 1897, set up the Laboratoire des

Catacombes, so-called because it was housed in part of the catacombs of Paris that extend beneath the Jardin des Plantes. The great Seine floods of 1910 inundated the catacombs and destroyed the laboratory. In 1930, G. A. Perco, director of the caves of Postojna, established a biospeleological station in a gallery of the latter. It had aquaria, terraria, and running water, and was lit by red light. Professor Dudich worked out an elaborate research programme, which was interrupted by the Second World War. As a result of frontier changes, the institute is now on Yugoslav soil.

In 1945, on the occasion of the congress of French societies for the advancement of science, Professor Jeannel proposed the establishment of a new underground laboratory in France. His proposal met with widespread approval and the project was rapidly put into execution, thanks to the support of Professors Fage and Teissier, the latter of whom was at that time director of the Centre National de la Recherche Scientifique.

Great care had to be exercised in choosing a site. A cave had to be found that possessed an abundant fauna, was easy of access, sufficiently large and with normal climatic conditions. It had also to have copious dripstone formations, clay, permanently flowing water, and be close to a station and a town, so that electric lighting could be installed without too great expense. The problem was not easy. It was decided at the outset that the laboratory should be in the Pyrenees, since the subterranean cavities of this range of mountains possess a richer fauna than those of any other region. The commission of the C.N.R.S. would certainly have had great difficulty in finding the right cavern, but for the valuable assistance of Henri Fourès, the municipal architect of Toulouse and a distinguished speleologist and entomologist well acquainted with Pyrenean caves and their fauna. Prolonged investigation showed that the Grotte de Moulis, three miles from Saint-Girons (Ariège) best conformed to the conditions required.

Professor Jeannel settled on this cavern, after visiting it on May 4th, 1947, largely because the surrounding countryside is exceptionally rich in subterranean cavities. The Salat basin contains a great many, some of which are well known, while hundreds of others, together with wells, springs and underground streams, have yet to be explored. The Arbas region, where the village of Moulis lies, has long been celebrated for its remarkable caves and potholes. Amongst them is the Henne-Morte chasm, one of the deepest in France. Finally, Moulis is in the heart of one of the classic zones, in which French speleology was born.

The caves of Moulis, Aubert, Liqué, Lestale, Peyort and Espuge are familiar to every entomologist. Moulis, in addition, conformed to the conditions laid down by Professor Jeannel. The cavern is three miles from Saint-Girons station and 300 yards from the village. It is big enough to house all the plant, it contains clay, calcareous concretions, and a subterranean stream. Its only disadvantage is an extremely narrow natural entrance. To reach the main gallery involves crawling several yards and then traversing a narrow passage. Professor Jeannel considered it important to leave the mouth of the cave as it was, so as not to disturb the life and development of its inhabitants in any way. A new entry was dug, 150 yards long. The cave, which was thought to consist of a single gallery, proved to comprise a whole network on several levels. It was large enough to receive all the installations required, and sufficiently ramified to keep the different sections separate from one another where necessary.

The laboratory was planned by Henri Fourès, who was exceptionally well qualified for the task, being simultaneously an architect, a speleologist and a biologist. Today, a road runs right up to the entrance of the cave, enabling cars and lorries to reach it. Two dry rooms, lit by electricity, contain the aquarium and the terrarium respectively. A cement tank divided by movable partitions is employed for raising cavernicoles: proteus, amphibians from the subterranean lakes met with particularly in Dalmatia, amblyopsidae, blind fish, cambarus, various types of crustacea, etc. A reservoir, fed by a motor pump, is arranged to receive water under pressure, and an air compressor ensures aeration. The underground installations are supplemented by a building on the banks of the Lez, 300 yards from the cave. This houses several laboratories, including a physics and chemistry laboratory, a photographic studio, a meteorological station, a library, the caretaker's quarters, living and office accommodation for the scientists, garages, etc.

In this laboratory the C.N.R.S. does not limit its activities to biospeleology. Its general title is the Laboratoire Souterrain du C.N.R.S. and it is concerned with everything relating to the subterranean world—measurement of the ionization of the atmosphere of caves, hydrometric and thermometric studies, the study of crystallization, dripstone formation, etc. Biospeleology is nevertheless its chief preoccupation. Cavernicoles are studied in their natural habitat and experiments on them are carried out under the most favourable conditions. Science at present knows little more about these creatures than their morphological description, being almost entirely ignorant of their habits, physiological needs, metabolism, diet, and mode of development. Professor Jeannel has laid down a very thorough research programme for the new laboratory.

I 2

CONCLUSION

✤

THE DISCOVERY OF THE 'SIXTH CONTINENT'

IN the preceding chapters an attempt has been made to acquaint the reader with the 'darkest of the sciences'—speleology—and with the results obtained from the exploration of caverns. This latter might be described as the 'discovery of the sixth continent', a continent that lives a secret life of its own amongst the shades. The magnitude of this subterranean world, which covers the whole of our planet, can scarcely be conveyed in a work of a few hundred pages. Hence this is no more than an outline of speleology, only touching upon the spheres of geography, archaeology, biology, geology, palaeontology and palaeontography which are involved. It has been necessary to confine discussion to a limited number of caves of special importance and the most outstanding discoveries and phenomena. At the same time, no conception of the subject could be formed without reference to its history and to finds made in the past. For the development of modern caving is inseparably bound up with the pioneer work of earlier generations. The almost fanatical zeal with which man sought to unveil the mysteries of the subterranean world, in order to acquire a knowledge of the origins of the human race, is unmistakably apparent.

The greatest minds have devoted themselves to the problems of caverns and countless intrepid cavers have wrested from them, at the cost of a stern struggle, the secrets they have held since the beginning of the world. Their feet trod soil that had never before felt the pressure of human foot, their eyes beheld a world that had lain till then in unbroken darkness. They have every right to the title of discoverers of a new continent, the entry and exploration of which was far more difficult than that of any territory on the surface.

The description of the most remarkable caves in all parts of the earth will have given the reader an overall picture of this mysterious underworld with its enigmatic traces of early human life, its hydrological conditions, its peculiar climate, and its marvellous fauna and flora, which are now studied by the new science of biospeleology, in the same way as its inert contents are investigated by the older sciences of geology, palaeontology and anthropology.

It will have become clear to him that speleology, with all its manifold subdivisions, is a science of tremendous potential value in extending the area of human knowledge in a great many different directions. Caverns provide the solution to any number of present problems—those connected with hydrology and the utilization of water power, for instance—and bygone ages live on here as nowhere else. Who knows what new and sensational facts concerning the past of mankind and his planet may emerge from the methodical study of caves and their contents?

INDEX